TEACHER'S ANNOTATED EDITION

Vocabulary Workshop

Level A

Jerome Shostak

Senior Series Consultant

Alex Cameron, Ph.D.
Department of English
University of Dayton
Dayton, Ohio

Series Consultants

Sylvia A. Rendón, Ph.D.
Coord., Secondary Language Arts
 and Reading
Cypress-Fairbanks I.S.D.
Houston, Texas

Mel H. Farberman
Supervisor of Instruction
Brooklyn High Schools
New York City Board of Education
Brooklyn, New York

John Heath, Ph.D.
Department of Classics
Santa Clara University
Santa Clara, California

Sadlier-Oxford
A Division of William H. Sadlier, Inc.

Reviewers

The publisher wishes to thank for their comments and suggestions the following teachers and administrators, who read portions of the series prior to publication.

Anne S. Crane
Clinician English Education
Georgia State University
Atlanta, GA

Susan W. Keogh
Curriculum Coordinator
Lake Highland Preparatory
Orlando, FL

Mary Louise Ellena-Wygonik
English Teacher
Hampton High School
Allison Park, PA

Lisa Anne Pomi
Language Arts Chairperson
Woodside High School
Woodside, CA

Arlene A. Oraby
Dept. Chair (Ret.), English 6–12
Briarcliff Public Schools
Briarcliff Manor, NY

Susan Cotter McDonough
English Department Chair
Wakefield High School
Wakefield, MA

Sr. M. Francis Regis Trojano
Sisters of St. Joseph (CSJ)
Educational Consultant
Boston, MA

Keith Yost
Director of Humanities
Tomball Ind. School District
Tomball, TX

Patricia M. Stack
English Teacher
South Park School District
South Park, PA

Joy Vander Vliet
English Teacher
Council Rock High School
Newtown, PA

Karen Christine Solheim
English Teacher
Jefferson High School
Jefferson, GA

Printed in the United States of America.
ISBN: 0-8215-7616-X
123456789/06 05 04 03 02

CONTENTS

INTRODUCTION

VOCABULARY WORKSHOP has for more than five decades been the leading program for systematic vocabulary development for grades 6–12. It has been proven a highly successful tool in helping students expand their vocabularies, improve their vocabulary skills, and prepare for the vocabulary strands of standardized tests.

This new edition of VOCABULARY WORKSHOP preserves and improves upon those key elements of the program that have made it so effective *and* introduces important new features that make the series more comprehensive in scope and current in approach to vocabulary instruction.

Key Elements

- At each Level, a **word list** of 300 main entries, plus hundreds of synonyms, antonyms, and other related words

- Proven and effective **five-step approach to instruction**, leading students to mastery of word meanings and usage

- Excellent **preparation for SAT I** and other standardized tests with strong correlations between word lists and words that frequently appear on the SAT, as well as practice in types and formats of exercises found on the SAT I

- Frequent **review and assessment** in both Student Text and in supplementary programs

New Features

- In each Unit and Review, **Vocabulary in Context**, a reading passage formatted to the SAT I reading comprehension sections that provides examples of how Unit words are used in context

- **Building with Classical Roots**, a Review exercise that acquaints students with Latin and Greek roots and provides a strategy for finding the meaning of words derived from these roots

- In each Review, **Writer's Challenge**, an exercise that helps students improve their writing skills by applying what they have learned about the meaning and proper usage of selected Unit words

- **Enriching Your Vocabulary**, a Cumulative Review feature designed to broaden and enhance the students' knowledge and understanding of the relationships, history, and origins of the words that make up our rich and dynamic language

- Instruction in and examples of key vocabulary **strategies**—using context and using word structure—for decoding word meaning

- In the Units, expanded **Definitions** sections, which now include synonyms, antonyms, and complete, illustrative sentences for each part of speech of every taught word

- **Synonyms** and **Antonyms** sections that offer more examples of range of contexts and distinctions of usage

- Stress marks in **Pronunciations** now reflect the system used in most leading dictionaries

- **Photographs** and color to engage student interest and illustrate reading and enrichment features

New Components

- For each Level, an **Annotated Teacher's Edition** that includes answers to all exercise items in the Student Text as well as valuable background information to help in lesson planning, instruction in vocabulary strategies, and assessment

- For each of Levels A–F, a **Test Generator CD-ROM** adds a new, secure assessment option to the program, eliminating the risk of "secondhand" tests that may distort assessment results

- For each of Levels A–F, an **Interactive Audio Pronunciation Program** now available in CD format as well as cassette—ideal for English Language Learners of all cultures and backgrounds and for use in ESL classrooms

In the following pages of this Teacher's Edition, you will learn more about the VOCABULARY WORKSHOP program, including these new features and components, as well as how to get the most out of the program in your classroom.

OVERVIEW

"Pure Vocabulary" Approach: Systematic Vocabulary Instruction

The VOCABULARY WORKSHOP program focuses on words themselves, their meanings (both literal and figurative), their ranges of application (or usage), and their relationships with other words.

The approach is systematic in the sense that it begins with and builds upon a word list compiled to provide students with vocabulary they will encounter in their reading both in and out of the classroom. It is designed to provide students with the vocabulary skills they will need in order to achieve higher-level reading proficiency and to succeed at standardized tests.

The VOCABULARY WORKSHOP systematic approach differs from a literature-based approach in that each Unit begins with a thorough consideration of the words themselves rather than with a reading selection featuring words to be studied. (This is not to say that VOCABULARY WORKSHOP cannot be profitably used as a complement to a literature-based approach. See pages T30–T31 for suggestions on how this might be done.)

Rather than in the circumstantial context of literature, VOCABULARY WORKSHOP introduces and exemplifies vocabulary usage in varied and controlled contexts. These range from short phrases to full sentences to the Vocabulary in Context reading passages that are new to this edition of the program.

For effective study, the "pure vocabulary" approach also offers these advantages:

- It provides unlimited flexibility in the choice and placement of grade-appropriate material.

- It avoids the problem of trying to deal with a literary passage both as literature and as a vehicle for vocabulary instruction.

- It focuses more directly and completely on the words themselves, their meanings, their usage, and their relationships with other words.

- By economizing space, it allows a greater range of practice, reinforcement, and enhancement.

- It allows maximum coverage to a maximum number of key words.

One of the cornerstones of the VOCABULARY WORKSHOP approach is intensive practice through varied and abundant "hands-on" exercises. This method ensures that students are provided with:

- maximum exposure to different meanings of the key words studied;

- maximum coverage of the range of each key word through its appearance in many different contexts;

• fullest understanding of the key words' relationships to other words.

The aim of the pattern of intensive practice is to include the words in the students' active, daily-use vocabulary. This implies the ability to use a given word not only in its literal, or narrow, sense but also in a figurative way. Furthermore, it means that students will be able to use the word with confidence both as speakers and as writers.

Grade-Level Placements

The chart below shows the suggested grade placement for each Level of VOCABULARY WORKSHOP, depending on the overall ability of the student population involved.

In determining "proper" placement of a particular Level of VOCABULARY WORKSHOP in a given situation, the following considerations should be taken into account:

• Grade placements are based on actual teacher experience and recommendations throughout the long course of VOCABULARY WORKSHOP'S history.

• Differences in grade are reflected not only in the "difficulty" of the words presented but also in the "maturity" of the sentences and other contexts in which those words are used.

• Grade levels indicated in the chart should not be taken in too literal or rigorous a sense. A certain amount of experimentation, as well as the use of the diagnostic materials provided in the program, will establish the "correct" placement of a particular Level in a given situation.

• The use of Level H with "above-average" students is designed to enhance preparation for the SAT I and other college-entrance examinations.

Grade Placements			
"Average" Students		"Above-Average" Students	
Level	Grade	Level	Grade
A	6	A	5
B	7	B	6
C	8	C	7
D	9	D	8
E	10	E	9
F	11	F	10
G	12	G	11
		H	12

Word Lists

Each Student Text in the VOCABULARY WORKSHOP program for Levels A–H contains 300 words organized in 15 Units.

Criteria for Selection

The selection of words for the VOCABULARY WORKSHOP program is based on four major criteria:

- currency in and usefulness for present-day American oral or written communication;
- frequency on recognized vocabulary lists;
- applicability to standardized tests, especially the SAT I;
- current grade-placement research.

General Sources

The lists of key words were developed from many sources:

- traditional, classic, and contemporary literature, including novels, short stories, essays, newspaper and magazine articles, plays, films, videos, TV programs;
- spelling and vocabulary lists recognized as valid bases for teaching language skills at the middle and secondary levels;
- current subject-area textbooks, glossaries, and ancillary materials (especially for general, nontechnical terms).

Dictionary and Reference Sources

The following were the primary dictionary resources used for word (and definition) selection:

- *Webster's Third International Dictionary of the English Language* (unabridged)
- *Merriam-Webster's Collegiate Dictionary* (ninth and tenth editions)

Other supplementary dictionaries consulted included:

- *The American Heritage Dictionary of the English Language* (all four editions)
- *The Random House Dictionary of the English Language* (unabridged; both editions)
- *The Compact Edition of the Oxford English Dictionary*

Standard Word-Frequency Sources

Standard word-frequency studies were employed to evaluate and revise the words on the tentative lists. These included:

- *Primary*
  Dale-O'Rourke: *The Living Word Vocabulary*
  Carroll-Davies-Richman: *Word Frequency Book*

- *Supplementary*
  Harris-Jacobsen: *Basic Reading Vocabularies*
  Thorndike-Lorge: *The Teacher's Word Book of 30,000 Words*
  Zeno-Ivens-Millard-Duvvuri: *The Educator's Word Frequency Guide*

"Sliding-Scale" Placement

Each word list works on a sliding scale based on these principles:

- No word that Dale-O'Rourke indicates as known in a given grade is presented in that grade. Instead, where possible, it is presented 2 or 3 grades earlier.

- Each grade level contains a preponderance of words not known (according to Dale-O'Rourke) 2 or 3 grades later, with an admixture (in decreasing numbers) of words not known 4 or more grades later.

- The higher the grade, the larger the percentage of more difficult words contained on the word list. This was done to accommodate as many "SAT-type" words as possible in the key word lists for Grades 10–12.

PROGRAM COMPONENTS

This new edition of VOCABULARY WORKSHOP, Levels A–H, consists of the following components:

Components of the VOCABULARY WORKSHOP Program*

- **Student Texts,** 8 Levels (A–H)

- **Teacher's Annotated Editions,** 8 Levels (A–H)

- **Test Booklets**
  - Form A, 8 Levels (A–H)
  - Form B, 8 Levels (A–H)
  - Combined Answer Keys, 8 Levels (A–H)

- **Test Generator CD-ROM,** 6 Levels (A–F only)

- SAT-Type **TEST PREP Blackline Masters** (answers included), 8 Levels (A–H)

- **Interactive Audio Pronunciation Program,** 6 Levels (A–F only)

The components have been designed for use in an integrated year-long vocabulary program, as suggested in the chart on pages T23–T25.

*Note that, in its entirety, the VOCABULARY WORKSHOP program now includes Student Texts, Teacher's Editions, and Supplementary Testing Programs for Grades 3–5 (Levels Green, Orange, and Blue).

The Student Texts

All eight Student Texts (Levels A–H) present 300 key words and are organized in the same way: 15 Units of 20 words each; 5 Reviews (following Units 3, 6, 9, 12, and 15); and 4 Cumulative Reviews. Preceding the first Unit is a section titled The Vocabulary of Vocabulary and a Diagnostic Test. Concluding each Student Text is a Final Mastery Test.

Vocabulary of Vocabulary (Student Text pages 7–17)

The purpose of this section is to familiarize students with some of the terms, concepts, and strategies that will be introduced and applied in the program. The practice exercises that accompany the discussions are meant to clarify and consolidate the concepts involved.

Some of these terms (for example, *synonyms* and *antonyms*) will already be familiar to most students. However, teachers should not hesitate to review these terms if doing so seems advisable, even at the upper levels of the program. Other, more complex concepts (such as analogies and context), however, may require more instruction and practice, both as preparation for related exercises and as review or reteaching for any students who have difficulty in successfully completing those exercises.

This is particularly true of analogies, which many students find especially challenging. Four pages of Vocabulary of Vocabulary are devoted to this important critical-thinking exercise so often found on standardized tests.

Diagnostic Test (Student Text pages 18–20)

A Diagnostic Test has been provided at the beginning of each Level as a means of assessing the students' overall vocabulary and test-taking skills. The Test covers a selection of key words introduced in the Level in question and is presented in the form of 50 synonym and antonym items.

Although the Diagnostic Test may be presented as a timed speed test, with the specific aim of determining how many items students can answer in 10 or 15 minutes, it is better used as an informal assessment and/or motivational device. Speed will come when confidence and vocabulary fluency have developed.

The Units

At the heart of the Student Texts—and of the VOCABULARY WORKSHOP program—are the 15 Units in which the 300 key words are introduced.

The work of each Unit is divided into a unique 5-part structure designed to give maximum coverage to each of the key words within the space available.

Structure of the Unit
(20 words)
1. Definitions
2. Completing the Sentence
3. Synonyms and Antonyms
4. Choosing the Right Word
5. Vocabulary in Context

The following descriptions of the individual exercises in a typical Unit of Levels A–H are designed to aid the teacher in using the text to maximum effect in the classroom.

1. Definitions

The first section of each Unit provides definitions, parts of speech, pronunciation, synonyms, antonyms, and illustrative sentences.

Definitions

The definitions provided are not of the dictionary type. They are, for the most part, relatively brief and simple. The intent is to give students a reasonably good "core" idea of what each word means, without extensive detail or secondary connotations.

Generally, only a single meaning of maximum usefulness is given the student. However, several meanings may be indicated if they are distinct, if they appear to be more or less equally useful, or if they will enable students to prepare for the vocabulary-in-context strand of the Critical Reading section of the new SAT I.

Part of Speech

The part of speech of each word is indicated at the beginning of the definition, using a simple set of abbreviations. When a word functions as several parts of speech, the appropriate abbreviation appears before the corresponding definition. (An explanation of the abbreviations used can be found on page 6 of each Student Text.)

Pronunciation

With each word listing, the pronunciation is indicated by means of a simple set of diacritical marks presented at the beginning of every Student Text (page 6).

The practice has been to indicate only one pronunciation, even where alternate pronunciations are sanctioned by the dictionary. There are only a few exceptions to this—for example, when a word changes its pronunciation in accordance with its use as different parts of speech (ob´ ject and ob ject´).

Note that once they have completed the first section of each Unit, students may utilize the **Interactive Audio Pronunciation Program** (Levels A–F only) for that Unit. This program provides about four hours of spoken material per Student Text, including pronunciations, parts of speech, definitions, and illustrative usages. For further details about the use of the Audio Program in this and other ways, see page T21.

Synonyms and Antonyms

A list of synonyms and/or antonyms is given for each key word for which there is one or more of either. Some of these synonyms and antonyms will reappear in the Synonyms and Antonyms section (see page T13). By studying the given synonyms and antonyms, students will better understand the denotational family of words of which each key word is part; and by comparing specific usages of key words and their synonyms, students can better appreciate appropriate contexts for, and nuances in meaning and connotation represented by, these words.

Note that the lists of synonyms and antonyms are not meant to be exhaustive. Grade-level parameters have been taken into account; and obscure, archaic, and slang synonyms and antonyms have generally been avoided.

ILLUSTRATIVE SENTENCE

Concluding each key entry is an illustrative sentence including a blank space in which students must write the taught word. These sentences, although necessarily brief, provide a context that clarifies the meaning of each word and points up its idiomatic usage. By writing the word in such contextual settings, students begin to see how it can be used effectively in their own writing. Furthermore, the act of writing is in itself a form of reinforcement; and by writing the word, the student must focus attention on its spelling as well.

2. COMPLETING THE SENTENCE

The next activity, Completing the Sentence, is a simple completion exercise in which students are asked to choose and write the word that logically and meaningfully fits into a blank in a given sentence.

When using this activity in the classroom, the teacher should bear in mind the following considerations:

- The sentences in this activity call for the literal or direct (as opposed to the metaphorical or extended) meaning of the words involved. This is an easier usage for students to grasp and provides a good foundation for the more sophisticated contexts that appear in Choosing the Right Word.

- The sentences are designed so that one and only one of the words fits in the given blank. Selection of the proper word has been facilitated by the introduction of context clues into each sentence.

- The words are to be used as the part of speech given in Definitions. The only exceptions are: Nouns given in the singular in Definitions may be plural in the sentences; verbs given in the base form in Definitions may be used in any tense or form (including participial) required by the sentence.

3. SYNONYMS AND ANTONYMS

In this section students are given phrases that include synonyms or antonyms as presented in the Definitions section, and must choose the appropriate key word for each phrase. Each of the 20 key Unit words is covered once in either the Synonyms or the Antonyms part of the section. Besides reinforcing meanings, this exercise provides students with further examples of usage and context.

4. Choosing the Right Word

The fourth activity in each Unit is called Choosing the Right Word. In it students are asked to choose the member of a pair of words that more satisfactorily completes the sentence. At first appearance this exercise may seem an easier activity than Completing the Sentence. In fact, however:

- sentences in this activity are more mature linguistically and in subject matter;

- in many cases the words covered are used in a more figurative, extended, or abstract meaning;

- the part of speech or form of the key word has been changed (for example, from an adjective to an adverb) whenever convenient.

Accordingly, this activity is in reality more difficult than Completing the Sentence and requires real effort and a thorough understanding of the range of a word to complete successfully.

5. Vocabulary in Context

The fifth, and last, section of each Unit is an activity titled Vocabulary in Context. The activity is presented in the form of a reading passage, approximating a standardized-test format, into which five or six of the key Unit words have been woven. Its purpose is threefold:

- to give further examples of usage for the selected words;

- to offer an opportunity to derive meaning from context;

- to provide practice in the sort of vocabulary exercises found on standardized tests.

With this activity, it may prove helpful to refer students, if necessary, to the section of Vocabulary of Vocabulary (see Student Text pages 7–17) that serves as an introduction to the strategies involved in studying vocabulary in context.

Follow-Up Activities

Once the work of the Unit is completed, you may find it useful to give a writing exercise in which students may apply and illustrate what they have learned about the words introduced in the Unit.

Writing Essays or Stories

Students might be invited to create their own brief essays or short stories and encouraged to use as many of the Unit's key words as is practical. (Students should, however, be discouraged from trying to "force" key words into their essays or stories indiscriminately, just for the sake of number alone. It is essential that students get in the habit of using these words correctly.) If they are to write essays, students might refer to the Vocabulary in Context passages as models.

WRITING SENTENCES

Depending on the ability level of individual students or of classes, you may prefer instead to administer a short writing exercise (5–10 items) such as the one shown below. This exercise is not so challenging as writing a story or essay but will give students an opportunity to "try out" some of the words they have learned and will provide the teacher with a means of assessing how well students have mastered the meaning and usage of these words.

Sample Writing Exercise (Level A)

Framing Sentences *On the lines provided, write an **original** sentence that illustrates the meaning and use of each of the following words. Do **not** merely copy one of the sentences given in the Student Text.*

1. barrage

_____

_____

_____

2. ravenous

_____

_____

_____

3. parody

_____

_____

_____

4. stupefy

_____

_____

_____

5. inflammatory

_____

_____

_____

The Reviews

A Review follows every three Units. Every effort has been made to include all of the 60 key words at least once in the Review for the three corresponding Units.

Structure of the Review
1. Analogies
2. Word Associations
3. Vocabulary in Context
4. Choosing the Right Meaning
5. Antonyms
6. Word Families
7. Two-Word Completions
8. Building with Classical Roots
9. Writer's Challenge

SAT I Sections

Four parts of each Review have been specially designed to meet the needs of students seriously preparing for the verbal part of the SAT I and similar standardized tests.

Analogies (Part 1)

The first of these special SAT sections involves analogies.

- Analogies are valuable and revealing, not merely as a kind of mental gymnastics, but also as a means of pinning down the exact meanings of words and of remedying misconceptions or uncertainties about how those words are used.

- Analogies provide an excellent means for testing and refining the critical-thinking skills used on the college level.

- Words that receive the attention necessary to complete an analogy successfully are much more likely to become part of the student's active daily-use vocabulary.

It is impossible, of course, to catalog all the relationships that may be embodied in analogy questions. They are as open-ended as the mental capacity to manipulate ideas and terms. However, the analogies illustrated and discussed on Student Text pages 13–16 will be helpful in reviewing with the students a few of the general "types" that occur in the Reviews and Cumulative Reviews.

Note: In the supplemental answer key on pages T38–T48, you will find explanations for the correct answers to all analogy exercises in the Student Text.

VOCABULARY IN CONTEXT (PART 3)

Like the Unit exercises that bear the same name, this activity is meant primarily as preparation for the vocabulary questions that appear in the SAT I and other standardized tests. Its format is changed in the Reviews, however, to more closely reflect the columnar format of standardized tests.

CHOOSING THE RIGHT MEANING (PART 4)

Focusing on usage-discrimination skills, this part of the Review challenges students to choose, from among two or more taught meanings of a word, the only one that the specific context will reasonably allow. This activity gives students useful practice in determining a word's meaning by careful attention to the context in which it appears, a skill assessed in the critical reading section of the SAT I.

Note: Explanations for the correct answers to the Choosing the Right Meaning exercises can be found in the supplemental answer key on pages T38–T48.

TWO-WORD COMPLETIONS (PART 7)

This part of the Review has been designed to familiarize students with the type of word-omission (cloze) exercise that appears on typical standardized tests, including the SAT I. Again the aim here is to refine students' critical-thinking skills. Context clues are embedded within the passages to guide students to the correct choice.

Note: Explanations for the correct answers to Two-Word Completions exercises can be found in the supplemental answer key on pages T38–T48.

OTHER SECTIONS OF THE REVIEW

WORD ASSOCIATIONS (PART 2)

The purpose of this activity is to reinforce and extend understanding of the meanings of key words with brief definitions or examples, situations, or allusions that in some way suggest key words.

ANTONYMS (PART 5)

As it requires of students that they recall the meaning of a key word in order to determine its opposite, this activity helps students "situate" a word within the cluster of words of related meanings.

WORD FAMILIES (PART 6)

This part extends the work of the Units by showing students that by learning one English word they often are acquiring a whole family of related words. It also provides practice in classifying words by part of speech.

Building on the foundation laid down in the Vocabulary of Vocabulary section titled Vocabulary Strategy: Word Structure (Student Text pages 11–12), this part of the Review introduces students to English words derived from common Latin and Greek stems and gives practice in the strategy of finding meaning by analyzing the parts of a word.

The concluding part of each Review provides an opportunity for students to apply to the writing and revising process what they have learned about word meanings and usage. Note that it is important that students understand that, apart from the conventions of Standard English (when applicable), there are no "rights" or "wrongs" in writing and that this activity is meant to make them more aware of ways in which the choice of words affects the tone, clarity, and coherence of their written work.

The Cumulative Reviews

Once students have completed the Reviews (and any follow-up activities), they may turn to the Cumulative Reviews.

Of the four parts of the Cumulative Reviews, three mirror activities presented in the Reviews: Analogies, Choosing the Right Meaning, and Two-Word Completions. These are presented in the same format and serve the same purpose as their counterparts in the Reviews, primarily to give students practice in types of questions they will encounter on the SAT I and other standardized tests.

The fourth part of the Cumulative Review, Enriching Your Vocabulary, is designed to broaden and enhance student knowledge of the interesting origins, history, and relationships of the words that make up the English language.

The Final Mastery Test

The Final Mastery Test in the Student Text of Levels A–H is designed as a practice test of 100 items that gives students and teachers reasonably good insight into how much progress has been made during the year and what kind of additional work is in order.

The purpose of the Final Mastery Test is fourfold.

- It can serve as a dry run in preparation for the more formal (and "secure") tests available as optional components of this program.

- It can serve as an informal evaluation of achievement to date.

- It can serve as a reinforcement activity.

- It can serve as a before-and-after comparison when used in conjunction with the Diagnostic Test.

For whichever purpose the test is used, it is both a testing and a teaching device, the culminating step in a process involving many class periods and, therefore, should be given careful attention.

Supplemental Assessment Components (Optional)

Test Generator CD-ROM (Levels A–F)

New to this edition, the VOCABULARY WORKSHOP Test Generator CD-ROM provides an array of secure student tests that support the Student Texts for Levels A–F. With the Test Generator, teachers may create countless unique vocabulary tests with a variety of question formats, all within seconds. With a database of more than 3,000 questions per Level, teachers never have to administer the same test twice.

The Test Generator CD-ROM provides:

- new and secure Unit Tests, Mastery Tests, Cumulative Tests, Diagnostic Tests, Mid-Year Tests, and Final Mastery Tests

- a wide assortment of question types to choose from: pronunciation, part of speech, spelling, definitions, synonyms and antonyms, sentence completions, sentence framing

- the ability to customize tests to include any number of questions and to assess any Unit in the Student Text

- a method of flagging questions so that they will not appear on other tests

- the option to save a test for future use

- an on-screen Help program

- a printed Teacher's Manual

- technical support

The Test Generator provides a convenient and secure source of assessment and/or extra practice. With the Test Generator CD-ROM, teachers may tailor tests to suit the specific needs of either individual students or an entire class.

The flexibility of the Test Generator makes it easy to use either as needed or more systematically, as an integral part of the VOCABULARY WORKSHOP series. See pages T22–29 for recommendations on how it may be used in conjunction with the Student Text and other components of the program.

Test Booklets (Levels A–H)

Two Test Booklets (Form A and Form B) are available for each of Levels A–H. These Test Booklets have been designed to be used in alternating years, thereby reducing the risk of answers being passed on. Each Test Booklet contains a full set of testing materials and is designed to cover the work of one entire Level of the Student Text. Though the formats of the Test Booklets are the same, the items tested in any given section are completely different. The contents of the Test Booklets have been organized to reflect that of the Student Text and include the following:

- preparatory test-taking tips for students

- a Warm-Up Test, corresponding to the Diagnostic Test in the Student Text)

- 15 Unit Tests each consisting of 25 items focusing on pronunciation, part of speech, spelling, definitions, synonyms, antonyms, and sentence completions

- 5 Cumulative Tests of 50 items each (plus 2 optional items)

The Warm-Up Test may serve either as an introduction to the Test Booklet as a whole or as an effective follow-up to the Diagnostic Test in the Student Text.

Each Unit Test has been designed for use as soon as the students have completed work on the Unit to which it corresponds or at any point thereafter.

Each Cumulative Test, including the Final Cumulative Test, covers all the work of the Student Text to the point at which it occurs and is designed to be used after the corresponding Review in the Student Text.

Note that these tests may also serve as effective "lead-ins" to the SAT-oriented Cumulative Reviews in the Student Texts and to the SAT-oriented PREP Worksheets in the corresponding TEST PREP Blackline Masters.

For recommendations on how to employ the Test Booklets as part of the complete VOCABULARY WORKSHOP program, see pages T22–T29.

TEST PREP Blackline Masters (Levels A-H)

For further assessment options, a booklet of reproducible TEST PREP Blackline Masters is available for each Level A–H. The TEST PREP component is designed to provide both practice in working with SAT I type test questions and formats *and* review tests covering the entire content of the corresponding Student Text.

- Prep Tests approximate as closely as possible, given the vocabulary that is to be covered, the analogy and word-omission sections of the SAT I and provide practice in the vocabulary-in-context strand with brief reading passages as well.

- Answer sheets provide an SAT I type test format to develop student ease and familiarity with standardized testing materials.

- Mastery Tests are meant to be used when students have completed the corresponding group of three Units in the Student Text. Each test covers basic meanings, synonyms, antonyms, sentence completions, and analogies.

- Answer keys, including selected answer rationales, are provided for all tests.

For recommendations on the implementation of the TEST PREP Blackline Masters as part of the complete VOCABULARY WORKSHOP program, see pages T22–T29.

Interactive Audio Pronunciation Program (Levels A–F)

Now available in CD format as well as cassette, the Interactive Audio Pronunciation Program provides teachers and students with a convenient and effective means of teaching and learning the recommended pronunciations of all key words introduced in the Student Texts for Levels A–F. It is designed to be used either by the teacher in a classroom setting or by the student (either individually or in small groups) in a language laboratory or at home.

- The audio program is ideal for English Language Learners of all cultures and backgrounds and for use in ESL classrooms.

- Students hear the recommended pronunciation of each word at least 6 times, both alone and in context.

- Full coverage is given to words with more than one recommended pronunciation.

- Students are provided with two opportunities to pronounce each word themselves.

- Pronunciations are followed by brief definitions based on those given in the Student Text.

- Usage examples in complete-sentence form extend student knowledge of how to use a word correctly in their speech and writing.

- Teacher's notes for the program are provided in Spanish as well as English.

For recommendations on when to use the program, see the chart on pages T22–27.

IMPLEMENTING THE PROGRAM

The format of the VOCABULARY WORKSHOP program allows for great flexibility. The teacher can easily adjust the activity assignments to conform to the special needs of an entire class, of groups within the class, or of individual students.

Schedule for the Year (28 Weeks)

The chart on pages T23–T25 shows how the various components of the VOCABULARY WORKSHOP program for Levels A–H can be scheduled effectively over an academic year lasting 28 weeks.

The following notes should prove helpful when adapting the chart to individual needs:

- Though the chart shows a disposition of material over 28 weeks, the time period can be extended to as many as 34 weeks simply by increasing to two weeks the time allotment for the items under weeks 6, 11, 16, 21, 26, and 28.

- It is not to be supposed that every item listed under Follow-Up Activities is meant to be covered during the week specified. The listings here are designed to offer teacher options from which to choose in order to tailor the VOCABULARY WORKSHOP program to the specific needs of a particular class. This is also true of the sections or subsections into which some of the Follow-Up components are divided.

KEY

IAPP = Interactive Audio Pronunciation
       Program, Levels A–F only

BLM = TEST PREP Blackline
       Masters

TB A/B = Test Booklet
       Form A/Form B

TG = Test Generator
       CD-ROM

Using the Program Over the Year (28 Weeks)

Note: "Framing Sentences" and "Story/Essay Writing" are to be supplied by the teacher.

Week	Student Text	Follow-Up Activities
1	Vocabulary of Vocabulary	
2	Diagnostic Test	Warm-Up Test (TB A/B) Warm-Up Prep Test (BLM)
3	Unit 1 IAPP	Framing Sentences Story/Essay Writing Unit Test 1 (TB A/B) Unit Test 1 (TG)
4	Unit 2 IAPP	Framing Sentences Story/Essay Writing Unit Test 2 (TB A/B) Unit Test 2 (TG)
5	Unit 3 IAPP	Framing Sentences Story/Essay Writing Unit Test 3 (TB A/B) Unit Test 3 (TG)
6	Review 1-3	Mastery Test 1–3 (BLM) Mastery Test (TG)
7	—	Cumulative Test 1–3 (TB A/B) Prep Worksheet 1–3 (BLM)
8	Unit 4 IAPP	Framing Sentences Story/Essay Writing Unit Test 4 (TB A/B) Unit Test 4 (TG)
9	Unit 5 IAPP	Framing Sentences Story/Essay Writing Unit Test 5 (TB A/B) Unit Test 5 (TG)

(Continued on pg. T24)

(Continued from pg. T23)

Week	Student Text	Follow-Up Activities
10	Unit 6 IAPP	Framing Sentences Story/Essay Writing Unit Test 6 (TB A/B) Unit Test 6 (TG)
11	Review 4–6	Mastery Test 4–6 (BLM) Mastery Test (TG)
12	Cumulative Review 1–6	Cumulative Test 1–6 (TB A/B) Prep Worksheet 4–6 (BLM)
13	Unit 7 IAPP	Framing Sentences Story/Essay Writing Unit Test 7 (TB A/B) Unit Test 7 (TG)
14	Unit 8 IAPP	Framing Sentences Story/Essay Writing Unit Test 8 (TB A/B) Unit Test 8 (TG)
15	Unit 9 IAPP	Framing Sentences Story/Essay Writing Unit Test 9 (TB A/B) Unit Test 9 (TG)
16	Review 7–9	Mastery Test 7–9 (BLM) Mastery Test (TG) Mid-Year Test (TG)
17	Cumulative Review 1–9	Cumulative Test 1–9 (TB A/B) Prep Worksheet 7–9 (BLM) Cumulative Test (TG)
18	Unit 10 IAPP	Framing Sentences Story/Essay Writing Unit Test 10 (TB A/B) Unit Test 10 (TG)
19	Unit 11 IAPP	Framing Sentences Story/Essay Writing Unit Test 11 (TB A/B) Unit Test 11 (TG)

Week	Student Text	Follow-Up Activities
20	Unit 12 IAPP	Framing Sentences Story/Essay Writing Unit Test 12 (TB A/B) Unit Test 12 (TG)
21	Review 10–12	Mastery Test 10–12 (BLM) Mastery Test (TG)
22	Cumulative Review 1–12	Cumulative Test 1–12 (TB A/B) Prep Worksheet 10–12 (BLM) Cumulative Test (TG)
23	Unit 13 IAPP	Framing Sentences Story/Essay Writing Unit Test 13 (TB A/B) Unit Test 13 (TG)
24	Unit Test 14 IAPP	Framing Sentences Story/Essay Writing Unit Test 14 (TB A/B) Unit Test 14 (TG)
25	Unit 15 IAPP	Framing Sentences Story/Essay Writing Unit Test 15 (TB A/B) Unit Test 15 (TG)
26	Review 13–15	Mastery Test 13–15 (BLM) Mastery Test (TG)
27	Cumulative Review 1–15	Cumulative Test 1–15 (TB A/B) Prep Worksheet 13–15 (BLM) Cumulative Test (TG)
28	Final Mastery Test	Cumulative Mastery Test (BLM) Cumulative Prep Test (BLM) Final Test (TG)

Using the Units

On the top of these 2 pages the teacher will find 2 models for using the Units effectively on a weekly basis. Though there is no single formula or plan that will be sure to yield optimum results all the time, the models presented here and on the next 2 pages are designed to get the teacher thinking about how best to adapt the program to the needs of individual classes.

KEY: IAPP = Interactive Audio Pronunciation Program

TB = Test Booklet Form A or B

TG = Test Generator CD-ROM

** Item to be supplied by teacher/student

Assignment
Classwork
Homework

MODEL B: 5 Sessions/Periods (20 Minutes)		
Assignment	**Day 1**	**Day 2**
Classwork	**1.** Collect Framing Sentences **2.** Review Unit Test **3.** Present Definitions	Review Completing the Sentences
Homework	**1.** Completing the Sentence **2.** IAPP	Synonyms and Antonyms

Using the Reviews

On the bottom of these 2 pages the teacher will find 2 models for using the Reviews effectively on a weekly basis.

Assignment
Classwork
Homework

MODEL B: 5 Sessions/Periods (20 Minutes)		
Assignment	**Day 1**	**Day 2**
Classwork	Present Analogies	**1.** Review homework **2.** Present Choosing the Right Meaning
Homework	**1.** Word Associations **2.** Antonyms	Vocabulary in Context

Weekly Lesson Plans

MODEL A: 3 Sessions/Periods (35–40 Minutes)

Day 1	Day 2	Day 3
1. Collect Framing Sentences** **2.** Present Definitions	**1.** Review Completing the Sentence, Synonyms and Antonyms **2.** Present Choosing the Right Word and Vocabulary in Context	**1.** Unit Test (TB or TG) **2.** Review last week's Framing Sentences**
1. Completing the Sentence, Synonyms and Antonyms **2.** IAPP	Test Study	Framing Sentences**

Day 3	Day 4	Day 5
Review Synonyms and Antonyms	**1.** Review Choosing the Right Word **2.** Present Vocabulary in Context	**1.** Unit Test (TB or TG) **2.** Review last week's Framing Sentences
Choosing the Right Word	Test Study	Framing Sentences**

MODEL A: 3 Sessions/Periods (35–40 Minutes)

Day 1	Day 2	Day 3
Present: Word Associations Vocabulary in Context Word Families	Review homework Present: Antonyms Choosing the Right Meaning Building with Classical Roots	**1.** Mastery Test (TB or TG) **2.** Review homework
1. Analogies **2.** Two-Word Completions	**1.** Test Study **2.** Writer's Challenge	Remedial work as required

Day 3	Day 4	Day 5
1. Review homework **2.** Present Two-Word Completions	Mastery Test (TB or TG)	**1.** Review Mastery Test **2.** Review homework
1. Test Study **2.** Word Families	**1.** Building with Classical Roots **2.** Writer's Challenge	Remedial work as required

Using the Cumulative Reviews

On the top of these 2 pages the teacher will find 2 models for using the Cumulative Reviews effectively on a weekly basis.

Assignment
Classwork
Homework

MODEL B: 5 Sessions/Periods (20 Minutes)		
Assignment	**Day 1**	**Day 2**
Classwork	Present Cumulative Review	Cumulative Test Parts 1–4 (TB)
Homework	Test Study	Test Study

Implementing the Weekly Schedules

The following may prove helpful when adapting the foregoing schedules to specific situations.

- The models shown are, as their designation suggests, purely models—that is, starting points. Accordingly, the teacher is expected to adapt them to the particular situation at hand.

- The models make only minimal use of the Follow-Up Activities suggested earlier and no use whatsoever of the Alternative Approaches to Using the Program suggested on the following pages. The teacher should in all cases feel free to introduce such alternative approaches as are convenient.

- Place assignments and timings are to some extent hypothetical. Teachers should switch items around and adjust timings as needed. Similarly, items may be modified or deleted and new items inserted as the teacher sees fit.

- Multiple listings in a Day's entry for either Classwork or Homework are to be seen as options from which the teacher should select appropriate material. It is unlikely that the teacher could cover all the suggested material in the indicated time allotment.

- With some adjustment, the allotments for each Day can accommodate a 2- or 4-day arrangement. There is usually too much material to cover in 1 day, and a 1-day approach is, therefore, not suggested.

MODEL A: 3 Sessions/Periods (35–40 Minutes)		
Day 1	**Day 2**	**Day 3**
Present Cumulative Review	Cumulative Test (TB or TG)	**1.** Review Cumulative Test **2.** Review Prep Worksheet
Test Study	Prep Worksheet	Remedial work as required

Day 3	**Day 4**	**Day 5**
Cumulative Test Parts 5–6 (TB)	Review Cumulative Test	Review Prep Worksheet
—	Prep Worksheet	Remedial work as required

Alternative Approaches to Using the Program

Writing Approach

Research has shown that vocabulary acquisition is maximized when learning is authentically contextualized—when learners have a "real-life" purpose for acquiring and using a new word. Activities such as the following can provide these authentic contexts.

- Students can create journals or logs in which they use the key words to express experiences, thoughts, or feelings that are personally meaningful. They are free to keep these entries for their eyes only or to share them with others.

- Students can use the key words in personal letters to friends and relatives or in letters to the editor of the school or local newspaper. Students should write about subjects of real interest and concern to them.

- Students can use the key words to write descriptions of people they know or characters they are interested in. These character sketches or personality profiles may be written for a class yearbook, for a book report, or as a reference for a friend.

Literature-Based Approach

The VOCABULARY WORKSHOP program can be combined with some of the items listed below to form a *literature-based* approach to vocabulary study. Each of the items listed has been surveyed for use of some of the key words presented in the specified level of VOCABULARY WORKSHOP. Seeing the words they are studying in classic world literature will reinforce student appreciation of the value of possessing a good active-use vocabulary.

Classic Literature To Use With The Program

Levels A–C

Lloyd Alexander
The Book of Three

Laurie Halse Anderson *Speak*

William H. Armstrong *Sounder*

Natalie Babbit *Tuck Everlasting*

Ray Bradbury *Dandelion Wine*

Pearl S. Buck
The Good Earth

Sheila Bumford
The Incredible Journey

Frances Hodgson Burnett
The Secret Garden

Sandra Cisneros
The House on Mango Street

Sook Nyul Choi
The Year of Impossible Good-byes

Robert Cornier
The Chocolate War

Karen Cushman
The Midwife's Apprentice

Daniel Defoe *Robinson Crusoe*

Elizabeth B. De Trevino
I, Juan de Pareja

Arthur Conan Doyle
The Hound of the Baskervilles

Esther Forbes *Johnny Tremain*

Paul Gallico
The Snow Goose

Jean Craighead George
Julie of the Wolves

William Goldman
The Princess Bride

Rosa Guy *The Friends*

Virginia Hamilton
The House of Dies Drear
M.C. Higgins, the Great

Jean Wakatrsuki Houston and James D. Houston
Farewell to Manzanar

Norton Juster
The Phantom Tollboth

Rudyard Kipling
Just So Stories

E.L. Konigsburg
The View from Saturday

Harper Lee
To Kill a Mockingbird

Madeline L'Engle
A Wrinkle in Time

Julius Lester
Long Journey Home

Lois Lowry
The Giver
Gathering Blue

Daniel P. Mannix
The Fox and the Hound

Nicholasa Mohr *Going Home*

Walter Dean Myers *Hoops*

Mary Norton *The Borrowers*

George Orwell *Animal Farm*

Katherine Paterson
Jacob Have I Loved

Anne Petry
*Harriet Tubman: Conductor on the
Underground Railroad*

Marjorie Kinnan Rawlings *The Yearling*

Jack Schaefer *Shane*

George Selden
The Cricket in Times Square

Antoine de Saint-Exupéry
The Little Prince

Elizabeth George Speare
The Sign of the Beaver

Rex Stout *Fer-de-Lance*
The Golden Spiders

Yoshido Uchida *Journey Home*

H.G. Wells
War of the Worlds

Laura Ingalls Wilder
Little House on the Prairie

Laurence Yep *Dragon's Gate*

Additional Titles and Enrichment

Louisa May Alcott *Little Women*

Lewis Carroll *Alice's Adventures in
Wonderland*

Willa Cather *My Antonia*

James Fenimore Cooper *The Deerslayer*

Charles Dickens
Oliver Twist
A Tale of Two Cities
A Christmas Carol

Carson McCullers
Member of the Wedding

To coordinate reading and vocabulary study, the following may prove helpful:

- Instruct students to devote a special notebook to vocabulary. As they come across key words in their reading, they should head a page of the notebook with the word; copy the title of the work; and then indicate (a) the definition of the word used in that sentence, (b) its part of speech, and (c) whether it is used in a literal or figurative sense.

- Students may then be instructed to check *Bartlett's Familiar Quotations* for other famous examples of the use of the key word in question. These may be copied into the notebook and shared with others in the class.

Content-Area Approach

VOCABULARY WORKSHOP can be used to enhance student understanding and use of vocabulary in subjects such as social studies and history, science and health, and other curriculum areas.

In the following list of nonfiction print and video titles you will find works that relate in content to Vocabulary in Context exercises appearing in specific Units and Reviews of the VOCABULARY WORKSHOP Student Texts for Levels A–C. Students may wish to read or view some of these works and report on the topics and issues that they treat. In their reports, whether oral or written, students should be encouraged to use words they have come to know through their Student Texts.

Literature and Media to Use with the Program

Middle Grades Nonfiction

Author	Title	Level & Unit
Alcott, Louisa May	*Hospital Sketches*	Level B, Unit 8
Asimov, Isaac	"Dial Versus Digital," from American Way magazine, (1985)	Level C, Unit 10
Ballard, Robert D.	*Exploring the Titanic*	Level C, Unit 15
Bean, Alan	*Apollo: An Eyewitness Account*	Level B, Unit 7
Chesnut, Mary	*Mary Chesnut's Civil War*	Level B, Unit 8
Dobie, J. Frank	*The Longhorns*	Level B, Unit 2
Freedman, Russell	*Lincoln: A Photography*	Level B, Unit 3
King, Martin Luther, Jr.	"I Have a Dream" speech (Aug. 28, 1963)	Level B, Review 10-12
Knight, Theodore	*The Olympic Games*	A, U 5; B, Rev. 13-15
Lauber, Patricia	*The News About Dinosaurs*	A, U 11; C, U8
Laycock, George	*Famous Caves Worldwide*	Level B, Unit 1
Levine, Ellen	*If Your Name Was Changed at Ellis Island*	Level A, Unit 3
Lindbergh, Anne Morrow	"Morning—'The Bird Perched for Flight'" from *Earth Shine*	Level B, Unit 7
McKissack, Frederick, Jr., and Patricia C. McKissack	*Black Diamond: The Story of the Negro Baseball Leagues*	Level C, Unit 2
Sandburg, Carl	*Abe Lincoln Grows Up*	Level B, Unit 3
Sills, Leslie	"Mary Cassatt" from *Visions About Women Artists*	Level A, Unit 13
Steger, Will, and Jon Bowermaster	*Over the Top of the World*	Level A, Review 10-12
Young, Donald	*Our National Parks*	Level B, Units 1, 6

Middle Grades Fiction

Author	Title	Genre	Level & Unit
Allen, Samuel	"To Satch"	Poem	Level C, Unit 2
Bradbury, Ray	"All Summer in a Day"	Short Story	Level B, Unit 7
Cisneros, Sandra	"Good Hot Dogs"	Poem	Level B, Unit 15
Sherwood, Robert	*Abe Lincoln in Illinois*	Play	Level B, Unit 3
Whitman, Walt	"O Captain! My Captain!"	Poem	Level B, Unit 3
Whittier, John Greenleaf	"Barbara Frietchie"	Poem	Level B, Unit 8

Middle Grades Videos

Title	Distributor	Level & Unit
America's Endangered Species	National Geographic Video	Level A, Review 7-9
The Bicycle Corps	PBS Home Video	Level C, Unit 4
Biographies of U.S. Presidents	Discovery Channel Video	Level B, Unit 13
The Gilbert & Sullivan Collection	PBS Home Video	Level C, Unit 1
Hoover Dam	PBS Home Video	Level C, Unit 13
The Incas	PBS Home Video	Level C, Review 13-15
Lewis and Clark	PBS Home Video	Level A, Unit 9
Lions of the African Night	National Geographic Video	Level B, Unit 4
River of Stone	Discovery Channel Video	Level B, Unit 6
Mary Cassatt from Artists' Specials	Discovery Channel Video	Level A, Unit 13
Mummies: Frozen in Time	Learning Channel Video	Level C, Review 13-15
Mysteries Underground	National Geographic Video	Level B, Unit 1
Rain Forest: Heroes of High Frontier	National Geographic Video	Level C, Unit 3

Other content-related activities to which students might apply vocabulary study are:

- Working in pairs or small groups, they can choose sentences from Completing the Sentence or Choosing the Right Word and discuss a larger context in which these sentences could have appeared, such as a history or mathematics textbook, a daily newspaper, a book review, a personal letter, or a scientific article.

- Students can work together to link individual vocabulary words to a particular content area. Then working in pairs, they can find "real-world" examples of the words used in context in that content area.

- Students can work cooperatively to create sentence and paragraph contexts that illustrate the meaning of the content-area words that they have identified.

Useful Classroom Techniques

Classroom experience and research have shown that some students learn more readily when they can exercise a great deal of personal choice and can interact with others. VOCABULARY WORKSHOP can be adapted in the following ways to accommodate such students.

Cooperative Activities

Working cooperatively does not just mean working in proximity to other students or dividing an assignment or project into discrete tasks. Rather it means that students take individual and collective responsibility for the learning of all members of the group and for the successful completion of the group goal. Students who cooperate to develop their vocabulary should maintain an ongoing dialog to monitor the comprehension of all group members.

Oral and Kinesthetic

- One student can write the key words in a given unit on the chalkboard while the rest of the class is divided into pairs or small groups. A member of each group will read a numbered item from the Unit aloud. The rest of the group will confer and then supply the required vocabulary word. The student reader will evaluate each answer and give reasons why it is correct or incorrect based on the word's definition and any context clues.

- Students in groups can discuss the shades of meaning or connotations among selected synonyms and antonyms for a given Unit and among the alternative answers in Choosing the Right Meaning.

- Students can work together to create puns, riddles, Tom Swifties, and limericks to illustrate the multiple meanings of appropriate vocabulary words. They may want to collect and publish their creations in illustrated books or an audio-anthology.

- Members of a group can work together to improvise stories, skits, or pantomimes that illustrate the meaning of a key word in a given Unit, while other group members guess the word being illustrated.

Written

- Students can work cooperatively to brainstorm their own vocabulary word lists based on their current reading and writing in all areas of the curriculum and on their personal reading and writing experiences.

- The class can collaborate to create their own Unit, covering vocabulary words they have chosen. Different groups can be assigned to develop each of the unit activities.

- Students may want to create their own minidictionaries, based on the word lists in VOCABULARY WORKSHOP or on categories of words that are especially meaningful or useful to them, such as sports, fashion, music, and career terms.

- Students can make use of semantic mapping and other graphic devices, such as flowcharts, to generate new vocabulary or to demonstrate understanding of word relationships. Semantic mapping, or webbing, can be used to illustrate word families, synonyms, and antonyms. Flowcharts can illustrate etymological and grammatical relationships.

Alternative Types of Assessment

The following types of assessment may be used in addition to or in lieu of the objective-scoring materials provided in the VOCABULARY WORKSHOP, Levels A–H. The emphasis here is on monitoring understanding rather than on ranking students.

Self-Evaluation

Students can use their journals to reflect on their own process of learning and use of new words. They may consider, for example, which words from VOCABULARY WORKSHOP they understood quickly and used frequently and why. They may want to use these insights to design their own vocabulary-acquisition strategies.

Teacher-Student Conferencing

Meetings take place at every stage of the vocabulary-acquisition process. Meeting over time allows teachers to assess students' developing understanding of words as used in specific contexts.

Observation

Using a checklist of 2 or 3 important criteria, the teacher can observe and evaluate students while they are interacting in groups or engaging in other oral activities. Teachers can also probe for deeper levels of comprehension by asking students to clarify or give reasons for their choice of word or context.

Peer Evaluation

Students meet in pairs or small groups to develop standards or criteria to evaluate their vocabulary acquisition. They then apply their standards to their peers' oral or written expression, giving positive feedback and concrete suggestions for improvement.

Portfolio Assessment

By having students collect and save self-selected samples of their writing over a period of time, teachers have an ongoing record of students' vocabulary development and of their facility in using words in context.

Multimodal Assessment

Students with strong nonverbal competencies can be given the opportunity to demonstrate in nonverbal media their understanding of new vocabulary. For example, they can draw, paint, model, dance, compose music, or construct objects to communicate their comprehension of a word and its definition.

TEACHER RESOURCES

The following lists have been compiled to assist the teacher in the effective presentation of the VOCABULARY WORKSHOP program, Levels A–H.

I. DICTIONARIES

Recommended

Merriam-Webster *Collegiate Dictionary* [Tenth Edition] (Springfield, MA: Merriam-Webster, 2000)

Webster's Third New International Dictionary (Springfield, MA: G. & C. Merriam, 1993)

American Heritage Dictionary (Boston: Houghton Mifflin, 2000)

Oxford English Dictionary [Compact Edition] (Oxford: Oxford University Press, 1971)

Skeat, W. W. *A Concise Etymological Dictionary of the English Language* (NY: G.P. Putnam, 1980)

Supplemental

12,000 Words [A Supplement to Webster's *Third International Dictionary*] (Springfield, MA: Merriam-Webster, 1993)

The Random House Dictionary of the English Language [Unabridged Edition] (NY: Random House, 1987)

II. THESAURI

Recommended

Roget's II The New Thesaurus (Boston: Houghton Mifflin, 1995)

Random House Roget's Thesaurus (NY: Random House, 2001)

Rodale, J. [Revised by Urdang, L. and La Roche, N.] *The Synonym Finder* (Emmaus, PA: Rodale Press, 1979)

Supplemental

Chapman, R.L. (Ed.). *Roget A to Z* (NY: Harper Perennial, 1994)

Laird, C. *Webster's New World Thesaurus* (NY: Warner Books, 1990)

Roget's International Thesaurus [Fifth Edition] (NY: HarperCollins, 1992)

Abate, F. *The Oxford Dictionary and Thesaurus: The Ultimate Language Reference for American Readers* (NY: Oxford University Press, 1996)

III. OTHER REFERENCE WORKS

Recommended

Carroll, J., Davies, P., and Richman, B. *Word Frequency Book* (Boston: Houghton Mifflin, 1971)

Dale, E. and O'Rourke, J. *The Living Word Vocabulary* (Chicago: Scott & Fetzer, 1981)

Supplemental

Harris, A. and Jackson, M. *Basic Reading Vocabularies* (NY: Macmillan, 1982)

Thorndike, E. and Lorge, I. *The Teacher's Book of 30,000 Words* (NY: Teachers College Press, Columbia University, 1968)

IV. HISTORY

General

Baugh, A.C. and Cable, T. *A History of the English Language* [Third Edition] (Englewood Cliffs, NJ: Prentice-Hall, 1992)

Carver, C. *A History of English in Its Own Words* (NY: HarperCollins, 1991)

Jespersen, O. *Growth and Structure of the English Language* (Chicago: University of ChicagoPress, 1982)

McCrum, R., Cran, W., and MacNeil, R. *The Story of English* (NY: Penguin, 1993)

Myers, L.M. *The Roots of Modern English* (Boston: Little, Brown, 1961)

Pyles, T. *The Origins and Development of the English Language* [Fourth Edition] (NY: Harcourt, Brace, Jovanovich, 1993)

Robinson, O. *Old English and Its Closest Relatives* (Stanford, CA: Stanford University Press, 1993)

American English

Dillard, J.L. *All-American English* (NY: Random House, 1975)

Dillard, J.L. *American Talk* (NY: Random House, 1976)

Flexner, S.B. *I Hear America Talking* (NY: Simon & Schuster, 1976)

Mencken, H.L. *The American Language* (NY: Alfred A. Knopf, 1979)

V. OTHER USEFUL RESOURCES

A Dictionary of American Idioms (Woodbury, NY: Barron's Educational Series, Inc., 1995)

Bryson, B. *A Dictionary of Troublesome Words* (NY: Viking Penguin, 1988)

Carroll, D. *Dictionary of Foreign Terms in the English Language* (NY: Hawthorn Books, 1973)

Dixson, R. *Essential Idioms in English* (Englewood Cliffs, NJ: Pearson ESL, 1993)

Evans, I.H. (Ed.) *Brewer's Dictionary of Phrase & Fable* (NY: Harper & Row, 2000)

Harrison, G. *Vocabulary Dynamics* (NY: Warner Books, 1992)

Hendrickson, R. *The Dictionary of Eponyms* (NY: Stein and Day, 1985)

Morris, W. and M. *Morris Dictionary of Word & Phrase Origins* (NY: Harper & Row, 1988)

Orgel, J.R. *Building an Enriched Vocabulary* (NY: William H. Sadlier, Inc., 1999)

Paxson, W. *New American Dictionary of Confusing Words* (NY: NAL-Dutton, 1990)

Room, A. *Dictionary of Contrasting Pairs* (NY: Routledge Educational Series Inc., 1988)

Room, A. *The Penguin Dictionary of Confusibles* (NY: Penguin Books, 1989)

Shipley, J. *Dictionary of Word Origins* (Glenville, IL: Greenwood Press, 1988)

Smith, R. *Dictionary of English Word-Roots* (Totowa, NJ: Littlefield, Adams & Co., 1980)

Spears, R. *Slang and Euphemisms* (NY: NAL-Dutton, 1991)

Webster's Word Histories (Springfield, MA: Merriam-Webster, 1989)

Answers To Exercises In Reviews
And Cumulative Reviews

Review Units 1–3

Analogies (page 42)

1. (c) Someone who is A would lack B.
2. (a) An A is a type of B.
3. (b) Something that is A would by definition bring a person B.
4. (a) An A is a topographical feature that is by definition B.
5. (b) An A is a person who would be noted for (or full of) B.
6. (d) If you were A, you would want something to B.
7. (b) Something that is A you cannot B.
8. (d) An A is much smaller than a B.
9. (c) B is the extreme of A.
10. (c) A runner in an A relies on B to win.
11. (a) To put out A, you must B it.
12. (a) You would A a fire with B.
13. (d) An A would cause a person to feel B.
14. (b) Someone who was A would by definition feel B.
15. (b) An A is a person who is by definition B.
16. (b) An A is opposed to B.
17. (d) You would use your A to B something.
18. (d) An A is someone who would by definition B things.

Choosing the Right Meaning (page 45)

1. (d) (Clue: What sort of beliefs would prevent one from "bearing arms"?) (a), (b), (c): irrelevant to meaning of word (ir).

2. (a) (Clue: What might be applied to a wound?) (b): ir; (c), (d): wrong sense of word (ws) (meanings derived from verb form).

3. (d) (Clue: What kind of command would affect the whole of something?) (a), (b), (c): ws.

4. (c) (Clue: Correct meaning indicated by "before they are confirmed.") (a), (b), (d): ir.

5. (b) (Clue: Context indicates a meaning having to do with clothing.) (a): ir; (c), (d): ws.

Two-Word Completions (page 47)

1. (d) arid (Situational clue: How would you describe the environment in the Sahara Desert?) . . . illusions (Situational clue: What kind of optical phenomena does a traveler often meet with in the desert?)

2. (c) stamina (Situational clue: What do you need to keep up with the pack in a cross-country race?) . . . terrain (Situational clue: Over what is a cross-country race run?)

3. (a) waylaid (Situational clue: What must the two ruffians have attempted to do if the traveler had to beat them off with his stout staff?) . . . assailants (Situational clue: What would you call people who had attempted to waylay you?)

4. (b) besieged (Situational clue: How would you describe an embattled fortress?) . . . queues (Situational clue: What would snake around the block from a box office?)

5. (b) ingenious (Situational clue: What kind of inventor was Edison?) . . . motivated (Restatement clue: "moved to action").

6. (d) barrage (Situational clue: What might you call a quantity of vigorous insults?) . . . denounce (Situational clue: If someone vigorously insulted you and you were tempted to retaliate, what might you do?)

REVIEW UNITS 4–6

Analogies (page 72)

1. (d) An A is a person whom others would B.
2. (d) If you A of something, you feel B for it; if you C of something, you take D in it.
3. (d) An A is someone who by definition Bs in a place.
4. (d) To A something is to leave it B.
5. (b) Something that is A is subject to B.
6. (a) If you are A, you are unable to B.
7. (b) An A is a person who would by definition be B.
8. (d) Something that is A lacks B.
9. (c) You would use an A to B a building.
10. (c) A is a person who would by definition B.
11. (c) Someone who is A displays B.
12. (b) You would A something with your B.
13. (b) Something that is A is filled with B.
14. (a) B is the extreme of A.
15. (a) A is a beverage that would B a person.
16. (c) Something that possesses A is B.
17. (a) An A is an animal that is proverbially considered B.
18. (b) If a jury were to A a defendant, it would be declaring his/her B.

Choosing the Right Meaning (page 75)

1. (b) (Clue: Context indicates a large number.) (a): ws; (c), (d): ir.

2. (a) (Clue: What must happen to a restraining order so that it is no longer in force?) (b), (c), (d): ws.

3. (b) (Clue: From what site would ships most likely "evacuate" troops?) (a): ws; (c): ws (meaning derived from verb form); (d): ir.

4. (c) (Clue: "Woeful ignorance" would probably result in what sort of opinion?) (a), (b), (d): ws.

5. (d) (Clue: Context indicates an architectural feature.) (a), (b), (c): ws.

Two-Word Completions (page 77)

1. (c) devastated (Situational clue: What would barbarians probably have done to the countryside they invaded?) . . . inhabitants (Situational clue: Whom would they have slain or carried off?)

2. (b) refute (Situational clue: What would the defense attempt to do to the prosecution's case?) . . . acquitted (Situational clue: If the defense refuted the prosecution's case convincingly, what would the jury do to the defendant?)

3. (b) plight (Situational clue: What would you call the situation of millions suffering the effects of a severe famine?) . . . generated (Restatement clue: "brought in")

4. (d) vagabonds (Situational clues: What kind of people were gypsies considered to be? What would you call people who roamed the countryside endlessly?) . . . tarrying (Situational clue: If you roam the countryside endlessly, what couldn't you be said to do for long? Contrast clue: "roamed")

5. (a) pacify (Situational clue: What would a new government try to do to a country that had been torn by revolution for 10 years?) . . . strife (Restatement clue: "and revolution")

6. (b) fidelity (Situational clue: What might a director want to maintain to a book in bringing the story to screen?) . . . leeway (Situational clue: What would a screenwriter need at least a little of when translating print to film?)

CUMULATIVE REVIEW I

Analogies (page 81)

1. (a) A story that was A would be likely to concern B.
2. (a) Something that is A is difficult to B.
3. (c) Something that As you causes you to feel B.
4. (b) An A is someone who would deliver a B.
5. (a) An A is something that would B you.
6. (a) If you A about something, you feel B in regard to it.
7. (c) A means the same as B.
8. (b) An A that is moving back may properly be said to B.
9. (d) An A is something that would by definition be B.
10. (c) An A is a home remedy for the treatment of B.

Choosing the Right Meaning (pages 81–82)

1. (d) (Clue: All beings that "dwell" upon earth are by definition what?) (a), (b), (c): ws.

2. (b) (Clue: What sort of entertainer adopts another's voice and mannerisms?) (a), (c), (d): ir.

3. (d) (Clue: What approach toward natural resources would a "naturalist" be likely to take?) (a), (b), (c): ir.

4. (a) (Clue: What sort of expression would be a symptom of "battle fatigue"?) (b), (c): ws; (d): ir. (N.B.: Though some may object to this usage of disinterested as a modern mistake, it is sanctioned by all recent dictionaries consulted, including

Webster's 3rd and Merriam-Webster's 10th, and has been included in the interest of showing students how the word is used in modern parlance, especially since this may affect SAT presentation.)

5. (a) (Clue: What sort of profit would management like to "wring" from a business?) (b), (c), (d): ir.

Two-Word Completions (page 82)

1. (b) blustery (Situational clue: What adjective would describe a windy November day?) . . . billowed (Situational clue: What happens to sheets on a clothesline on a windy day?)

2. (c) commentaries (Restatement clue: "accounts") . . . depicts (Restatement clue: "tell")

3. (b) reimbursed (Situational clue: What might you expect to receive for help you had given?) . . . gratitude (Situational clue: The lack of what might shock someone who had given others help?)

4. (d) inhabitants (Situational clue: Who would be affected when an area was devastated by a series of natural disasters?) . . . forsook (Situational clue: What might the inhabitants do in the face of such a catastrophe?)

5. (a) infuriated (Situational clue: How would an adverse call make a player in a championship match react?) . . . barrage (Situational clue: With how much verbal abuse might an incensed player shower the official who made an adverse call?)

REVIEW UNITS 7–9

Analogies (page 105)

1. (d) Something that is A would cause people to feel B.
2. (a) A applies to B.
3. (c) Someone who is A lacks B.
4. (c) An A is someone who would be likely to evidence a great deal of B.
5. (a) Something that is A is subject to B.
6. (c) If a person suffers an A, he or she is B, or A indicates that the person/thing involved is B.
7. (b) An A is a person who would be likely to try to B you.
8. (c) An A is a great deal smaller in quantity than a B.
9. (a) Something that is A can B easily.
10. (c) An A is a person who would be likely to wear a B, or a symbol of being an A is a B.
11. (a) If you set someone free from A, you B him/her.
12. (b) An A is a person who would by definition B.
13. (b) Something that is A a person cannot B.
14. (d) An A is an animal whose movements can be described by B.
15. (b) You would be likely to try to A something in B.
16. (d) If you are A, you are easy to B.
17. (a) Someone who is living in A can justly be described as B.
18. (c) A describes matters that relate to B.

Choosing the Right Meaning (page 108)

1. (a) (Clue: How would someone who has a "keen sense of humor" probably respond to a good story?) (b), (c), (d): ir.

2. (c) (Clue: Context indicates mathematics usage.) (a), (b); (d): ir.

3. (d) (Clue: What position would an officer occupy in relation to a "commander"?) (a), (b), (c): ir.

4. (b) (Clue: Context calls for adverb of degree, not time.) (a): ws; (c), (d): ir.

5. (d) (Clue: Context indicates an aesthetic quality.) (a), (b), (c): ws.

Two-Word Completions (page 110)

1. (b) liberated (Situational clue: What did the Emancipation Proclamation do?) . . . manacles (Situational clue: With what might a person be bound?)

2. (c) scoured (Situational clue: What might the police have done to the city when they carried out "Operation Dragnet"?) . . . culprits (Situational clue: What would you call the people who had pulled off a bank robbery?)

3. (d) retrieve (Situational clue: What did Joan of Arc attempt to do?) . . . cede (Situational clue: What were the French forced to do as the result of the English victories in the initial stages of the Hundred Years' War?)

4. (b) impact (Situational clue: With what do two things collide?) . . . writhing (Situational clue: How would you describe the movements of someone who was lying on the ground in agony?)

5. (a) intimidating (Situational clue: How might you describe a bully's general appearance or behavior?) . . . cringe (Situational clue: How might someone who was fearful react to a bully?)

6. (d) invested (Situational clue: What might one do with his or her "nest egg"?) . . . gullible (Situational clue: What might you call someone who was taken in by "an obviously crooked scheme"?)

CUMULATIVE REVIEW II

Analogies (page 114)

1. (a) Someone who is A possesses a great deal of B.
2. (b) If something is A, it allows for little or no B.
3. (a) An A is a kind of criminal who would by definition attempt to B you.
4. (d) A means the opposite of B.
5. (b) Someone who was A would be characterized by a general attitude of B.
6. (c) A is something that you B.
7. (c) In an A, you attempt to B something.
8. (a) An A is designed to B a person.
9. (a) A personal A would probably B you.
10. (a) A means the opposite of B.

Choosing the Right Meaning (pages 114–115)

1. (c) (Clue: What would an emperor be likely to seek for his enemies?) (a), (b): ws; (d): ir.

2. (c) (Clue: What is the fate most likely to fulfill a despot's bidding?) (a), (b), (d): ir.

3. (b) (Clue: What pace is most suitable for a tour of a famous boulevard?) (a), (c), (d): ir.

4. (b) (Clue: How would one check the lay of the land ahead?) (a), (c), (d): ir.

5. (a) (Clue: What quality would one expect to find in a tutor?) (b), (c): ws; (d): ir.

Two-Word Completions (page 115)

1. (d) besieged (Restatement clue: "surrounded . . . forces") . . barrage (Situational clue: What would you call a steady shower of missiles?)

2. (b) setbacks (Restatement clue: "problems and") . . . persevere (Situational clue: What must a person do to achieve a goal despite problems and setbacks?)

3. (b) withers (Situational clue: What happens to vegetation during a lengthy dry spell?) . . . terrain (Restatement clue: "landscape")

4. (a) cascaded (Situational clue: What happens to water going over a waterfall?) . . . devastating (Situational clue: What does an active volcano do to the surrounding countryside?)

5. (c) plight (Restatement clue: "hardships") . . . global (Contrast clue: "local")

REVIEW UNITS 10–12

Analogies (page 138)

1. (a) An A is used to hold B.
2. (d) An A is a kind of person who would B a lot.
3. (c) An A is a name that a B would use.
4. (c) One's A come B one.
5. (b) An A is a person who would by definition B a great deal.
6. (d) An A is a type of B.
7. (a) The A of something comes B it.
8. (b) An A is a person who would by definition be B.
9. (d) Something that is A is lacking in B.
10. (a) An A is a criminal who would by definition attempt to B a person.
11. (d) An A is one of the implements used in B.
12. (b) A means the same as B.
13. (b) Something that is A a person cannot B.
14. (d) Someone who is A possesses a great deal of B.
15. (c) If something is A, you would wish to B it.
16. (a) A indicates great B.
17. (c) An A would not be B.
18. (a) One indicates ownership of an A by using a B.

Choosing the Right Meaning (page 141)

1. (b) (Clue: How might someone end up doing that which he had hoped not to do?) (a), (c), (d): ir.

2. (c) (Clue: How would one describe a lot of people jammed together in a small space?) (a), (b), (d): ir.

3. (b) (Clue: What sort of deduction is likely to lead to the solution of a problem?) (a), (c), (d): ws.

4. (d) (Clue: How would one government respond to a foe's efforts to expand its influence?) (a), (c): ir; (b): ws.

5. (a) (Clue: How would one describe views that depart "from the mainstream"?) (b), (c), (d): ir.

Two-Word Completions (page 143)

1. (b) implement (Situational clue: After you have devised a plan, what must you then do?) . . . earmarked (Situational clue: What does the government do in regard to funds for future projects?)

2. (a) extinct (Situational clue: What kind of animals are the saber- toothed tiger and woolly mammoth examples of?) . . . fossilized (Situational clue: In what state do scientists usually find the remains of long-extinct animals?)

3. (b) panorama (Situational clue: What might you see that's breathtaking on a lovely autumn morning? (Restatement clue: "vista") . . . amble (Situational clue: If you didn't want to rush and miss the impact of a stunning vista, what might you do instead?)

4. (b) abduct (Situational clue: What would kidnappers do to an official if they planned to hold him for ransom?) . . . foil (Situational clue: If an informant tipped off the police about a kidnapping, what would they be able to do to such a scheme?)

5. (d) ambiguous (Situational clue: If you asked someone where something was, what type of reply might she give you to cause you to spend over an hour looking for that thing?) . . . rummaging (Situational clue: What might you spend over an hour doing in an attic if you were trying to find something?)

6. (c) maneuvered (Situational clue: What might a nimble quarterback be able to do easily? Restatement clue: "weaving") . . . burly (Situational clue: How would you describe the physique of the typical linebacker?)

7. (d) dumbfounded (Situational clue: What reaction would amazing powers of observation and deduction elicit from the ordinary person?) . . . sleuth (Situational clue: What profession is Sherlock Holmes a famous example of?)

Analogies (page 147)

1. (a) Someone who was A would feel B.
2. (b) A means the opposite of B.
3. (c) A by definition applies to B.
4. (b) An A is something that would B an area.
5. (d) If you were A, others would not be able to B you easily.
6. (d) An A is a person who would by definition B a crime.
7. (a) A refers to the whole B.
8. (d) An A is a person who would by definition B something.
9. (c) The purpose of A is to B.
10. (c) A means the same as B.

Choosing the Right Meaning (page 147–148)

1. (a) (Clue: restatement of "Emancipation.") (b), (c), (d): ir.

2. (c) (Clue: Where would a battle line most likely be arrayed?) (a), (b), (d): ir.

3. (d) (Clue: What would a rifleman clean from his weapon?) (a), (b), (c): ws.

4. (b) (Clue: How would one best describe the results of a powerful hurricane?) (a), (c), (d): ir.

5. (d) (Clue: "fencing matches.") (a): not sufficiently specific; (b), (c): ir.

Two-Word Completions (page 148)

1. (b) abominable (Situational clue: What type of snowman is a yeti?) elusive . . . (Situational clue: How would you describe a creature that few have seen and that may not really exist?)

2. (a) frigid (Situational clue: What type of temperatures would you expect in Antarctica? Restatement clue: "cold") . . . numb (Situational clue: What happens to a person's hands and feet after only a brief exposure to extreme cold?)

3. (b) rendezvous (Situational clue: What use might hoods and other disreputable characters make of a particular place?) . . . sinister (Situational clue: How would you describe the character of a hood or a pusher?)

4. (c) duration (Situational clue: What do you call the time during which something lasts?) . . . impassable (Situational clue: What happens to roads and highways during a severe snowfall?)

5. (d) implements (Situational clue: What are atomic bombs?) . . . enigmas (Situational clue: How would you describe a situation in which an implement of war acted as a guardian of the peace?)

Analogies (page 171)

1. (b) You would use an A to B something.
2. (c) An A is something that provides B.
3. (c) If you give your A to something, you B to/of it.
4. (a) As are designed to B a person.
5. (b) An A would make a person feel B.
6. (b) A is the emotion/mood indicated by B.
7. (b) You would A something with a B.
8. (a) The tone of A is B.
9. (d) An A is a person who is by definition B.
10. (c) A means "pertaining to B."
11. (d) You would put up an A to B something.
12. (d) An A is an animal that would B in its movements.
13. (a) At an A, you B someone/something new.
14. (c) A indicates that you have B of something than you had originally.
15. (a) An A is a kind of poem that relates B.
16. (c) Something that is A would by definition B a person.
17. (b) A means the opposite of B.
18. (d) An A is a person who would by definition be B.

Choosing the Right Meaning (page 174)

1. (c) (Clue: What sort of shield would an intruder be likely to display?) (a), (b), (d): ir.

2. (d) (Clue: What would men be likely to do if they were called to arms?) (a), (b), (c): ws.

3. (a) (Clue: Context indicates adversarial "debate.") (b), (d): ir; (c): ws.

4. (a) (Clue: On the occasion of a "historic event" what special feature might one find in a newspaper?) (b), (c), (d): ir.

5. (b) (Clue: Context indicates an adjective conferring dimension; contrast to "minor.") (a): ws; (c), (d): ir.

Two-Word Completions (page 176)

1. (a) prowler (Situational clue: What would you call someone who was lurking very suspiciously around the neighborhood?) . . . confiscated (Situational clue: What do the police do with illegal items such as burglar tools when they find them in the possession of a suspect?)

2. (b) enumerate (Situational clue: If you had many reasons for something, what might you do?) . . . traits (Situational clue: If you had many reasons to like someone, he might have excellent what?)

3. (d) taskmaster (Situational clue: What kind of person might work others very hard? . . . retaliate (Situational clue: What might someone do to respond to past wrongs done to her?)

4. (b) optimist (Situational clue: What kind of person would see a partially filled glass of water as half full?) . . . pessimist (Situational clue: What kind of person sees the same glass as half empty?)

5. (c) epic (Situational clue: What kind of poem is the Iliad an example of?) . . . sulking (Situational clues: What might Achilles be doing in his tent because he hasn't been rewarded properly? What, in fact, does the poem say Achilles is doing?)

6. (d) deter (Situational clue: What are stiff penalties on certain kinds of behavior designed to do?) . . . prosecute (Situational clue: If you are going to crack down successfully on drunk driving, what must you do to offenders?)

CUMULATIVE REVIEW IV

Analogies (pages 180)

1. (c) A indicates a B direction of movement.
2. (a) A indicates a state of B.
3. (d) Someone who As would produce a reaction that could be described as B.
4. (b) To be A is to lack B.
5. (b) An A is a device used to B material.
6. (d) Something that is A requires B to perform successfully.
7. (b) A indicates movement that is B.
8. (a) A means the opposite of B.
9. (c) Someone who gives his/her A to something is B to it.
10. (a) If you were A, you would by definition feel B.

Choosing the Right Meaning (page 180–181)

1. (d) (Clue: What found in a text would show it had been used?) (a), (b), (c): ir.

2. (a) (Clue: How much fame does "15 minutes' worth" amount to?) (b), (c): ws; (d): ir. Answer: Andy Warhol.

3. (b) (Clue: What is the purpose of a battlefield monument?) (a), (c): ws; (d): ir.

4. (c) (Clue: What would one find at water's edge ["skirt"]?) (a), (b), (d): ir.

5. (d) (Clue: What sort of thieves might one find in a seedy saloon?) (a), (b): ws; (c): ir.

Two-Word Completions (pages 181)

1. (a) prosecute (Situational clue: What would the district attorney decide not to do if the evidence against the accused were slight?) . . . acquittal (Situational clue: If the evidence against the accused is insubstantial, what is likely to be the outcome of the trial?)

2. (c) fatalities (Situational clue: What are there a great many of during a battle?) . . . goriest (Situational clue: How would you describe a battle in which a great many people died?)

3. (b) impact (Situational clue: With what would a large meteor be likely to crash into the Earth?) . . . extinction (Situational clue: What eventually happened to the dinosaurs?)

4. (d) oracle (Situational clue: What was someone who revealed the will of the gods to human beings called?) . . . sanctuary (Restatement clue: "temple")

5. (c) maze (Restatement clue: "Labyrinth") . . . strand (Situational clue: What is a ball of wool usually made up of?)

Vocabulary Workshop

Level A

Jerome Shostak

Senior Series Consultant

Alex Cameron, Ph.D.
Department of English
University of Dayton
Dayton, Ohio

Series Consultants

Sylvia A. Rendón, Ph.D.
Coord., Secondary Language Arts
  and Reading
Cypress-Fairbanks I.S.D.
Houston, Texas

Mel Farberman
Supervisor of Instruction
Brooklyn High Schools
New York City Board of Education
Brooklyn, New York

John Heath, Ph.D.
Department of Classics
Santa Clara University
Santa Clara, California

Sadlier-Oxford
A Division of William H. Sadlier, Inc.

Reviewers

The publisher wishes to thank for their comments and suggestions the following teachers and administrators, who read portions of the series prior to publication.

Anne S. Crane
Clinician English Education
Georgia State University
Atlanta, GA

Arlene A. Oraby
Dept. Chair (Ret.), English 6–12
Briarcliff Public Schools
Briarcliff Manor, NY

Patricia M. Stack
English Teacher
South Park School District
South Park, PA

Susan W. Keogh
Curriculum Coordinator
Lake Highland Preparatory
Orlando, FL

Susan Cotter McDonough
English Department Chair
Wakefield High School
Wakefield, MA

Joy Vander Vliet
English Teacher
Council Rock High School
Newtown, PA

Mary Louise Ellena-Wygonik
English Teacher
Hampton High School
Allison Park, PA

Sr. M. Francis Regis Trojano
Sisters of St. Joseph (CSJ)
Educational Consultant
Boston, MA

Karen Christine Solheim
English Teacher
Jefferson High School
Jefferson, GA

Lisa Anne Pomi
Language Arts Chairperson
Woodside High School
Woodside, CA

Keith Yost
Director of Humanities
Tomball Ind. School District
Tomball, TX

Photo Credits

Adventure Photo & Film/Thomas Ulrich: 123. *Corbis*: 34, 137, 149; Bettmann: 27, 90; The Philadelphia Musum of Art: 156; Philip Gould: 163. *Neal Farris*: 97. *Getty*: 41, 64, 71, 83, 104, 170. *The Image Works*/Capital Features: 57. *Index Stock Imagery*/Sandra Baker: 116. *The Natural History Museum of London*: 130.

PREFACE

For over five decades, VOCABULARY WORKSHOP has proven a highly successful tool for guiding systematic vocabulary growth. It has also been a valuable help to students preparing for the vocabulary-related parts of standardized tests. In this, the latest edition of the series, many new features have been added to make VOCABULARY WORKSHOP even more effective in increasing vocabulary and improving vocabulary skills.

The **Definitions** sections in the fifteen Units, for example, have been expanded to include synonyms and antonyms and for each taught word an illustrative sentence for each part of speech.

In the **Synonyms** and **Antonyms** sections, exercise items are now presented in the form of phrases, the better to familiarize you with the range of contexts and distinctions of usage for the Unit words.

New to this edition is **Vocabulary in Context**, an exercise that appears at the end of each Unit and in the Reviews. In this exercise, you will read an expository passage containing a selection of Unit words. In addition to furnishing you with further examples of how and in what contexts Unit words are used, this exercise will also provide you with practice with vocabulary questions in standardized-test formats.

In the five Reviews, you will find two important new features, in addition to Analogies, Two-Word Completions, and other exercises designed to help you prepare for standardized tests. One of these new features, **Building with Classical Roots**, will acquaint you with Latin and Greek roots from which many English words stem and will provide you with a strategy that may help you find the meaning of an unknown or unfamiliar word.

Another new feature, **Writer's Challenge**, is designed to do just that—challenge you to improve your writing skills by applying what you have learned about meanings and proper usage of selected Unit words.

Finally, another new feature has been introduced in the four Cumulative Reviews. **Enriching Your Vocabulary** is meant to broaden and enhance your knowledge and understanding of the relationships, history, and origins of the words that make up our rich and dynamic language.

In this Level of VOCABULARY WORKSHOP, you will study three hundred key words, and you will be introduced to hundreds of other words in the form of synonyms, antonyms, and other relatives. Mastery of these words will make you a better reader, a better writer and speaker, and better prepared for the vocabulary parts of standardized tests.

CONTENTS

PRONUNCIATION KEY

The pronunciation is indicated for every basic word introduced in this book. The symbols used for this purpose, as listed below, are similar to those appearing in most standard dictionaries of recent vintage. The author has consulted a large number of dictionaries for this purpose but has relied primarily on *Webster's Third New International Dictionary* and *The Random House Dictionary of the English Language (Unabridged)*.

There are, of course, many English words for which two (or more) pronunciations are commonly accepted. In virtually all cases where such words occur in this book, the author has sought to make things easier for the student by giving just one pronunciation. The only significant exception occurs when the pronunciation changes in accordance with a shift in the part of speech. Thus we would indicate that *project* in the verb form is pronounced prə jekt', and in the noun form, präj' ekt.

It is believed that these relatively simple pronunciation guides will be readily usable by the student. It should be emphasized, however, that the *best* way to learn the pronunciation of a word is to listen to and imitate an educated speaker.

Vowels	ā	lake	e	stress	ü	loot, new
	a	mat	ī	knife	ù	foot, pull
	â	care	i	sit	ə	rug, broken
	ä	bark, bottle	ō	flow	ər	bird, better
	aù	doubt	ô	all, cord		
	ē	beat, wordy	oi	oil		

Consonants	ch	child, lecture	s	cellar	wh	what
	g	give	sh	shun	y	yearn
	j	gentle, bridge	th	thank	z	is
	ŋ	sing	th	those	zh	measure

All other consonants are sounded as in the alphabet.

Stress	The accent mark *follows* the syllable receiving the major stress: en rich'

Abbreviations	*adj.* adjective	*n.* noun	*prep.* preposition
	adv. adverb	*part.* participle	*v.* verb
	int. interjection	*pl.* plural	

THE VOCABULARY OF VOCABULARY

There are some interesting and useful words that are employed to describe and identify words. The exercises that follow will help you to check and strengthen your knowledge of this "vocabulary of vocabulary."

Denotation and Connotation

The **denotation** of a word is its specific dictionary meaning. Here are a few examples:

Word	Denotation
peerless	without equal
lethal	deadly
specimen	a sample

The **connotation** of a word is its **tone**—that is, the emotions or associations it normally arouses in people using, hearing, or reading it. Depending on what these feelings are, the connotation of a word may be *favorable* (*positive*) or *unfavorable* (*negative, pejorative*). A word that does not normally arouse strong feelings of any kind has a *neutral* connotation. Here are some examples of words with different connotations:

Word	Connotation
peerless	favorable
lethal	unfavorable
specimen	neutral

Exercises *In the space provided, label the connotation of each of the following words F for "favorable," U for "unfavorable," or N for "neutral."*

_N_ **1.** fork   _N_ **3.** quote   _F_ **5.** gallant

_U_ **2.** snobbish   _U_ **4.** ruthless   _F_ **6.** gracious

Literal and Figurative Usage

When a word is used in a **literal** sense, it is being employed in its strict (or primary) dictionary meaning in a situation (or context) that "makes sense" from a purely logical or realistic point of view. For example:

> When we *cross that bridge*, we will be in New York.

In this sentence, *crossing that bridge* is employed literally. We will cross over that roadway to get into New York.

Sometimes words are used in a symbolic or nonliteral way in situations that do not "make sense" from a purely logical or realistic point of view. We call this nonliteral application of a word a **figurative** or **metaphorical** usage. For example:

> I realize that this decision may mean trouble for us down the road," said the senator, "but we'll *cross that bridge* when we come to it."

In this sentence, *crossing that bridge* is not being used in a literal sense. That is, the senator was not suggesting to cross an actual bridge. Rather, the expression is intended to convey dealing with a particular obstacle.

Exercises   *In the space provided, write **L** for "literal" or **F** for "figurative" next to each of the following sentences to show how the italicized expression is being used.*

___F___ **1.** The new press secretary *fielded* the reporters' questions like a seasoned pro.

___L___ **2.** When I was a boy, one of my favorite dishes was the savory hunter's *stew* that Grandmother used to make.

___F___ **3.** When our luggage failed to appear at the airport baggage terminal, we really began to *stew*.

Synonyms

A **synonym** is a word that has *the same* or *almost the same* meaning as another word. Here are some examples:

under—beneath   rough—coarse
entire—complete   final—last
silent—quiet   pile—heap

Exercises   *In each of the following groups, circle the word that is most nearly the **synonym** of the word in **boldface** type.*

1. rule	**2. spring**	**3. tidy**	**4. craving**
a. cover	a. walk	(a. neat)	a. feast
b. leave	b. ride	b. sloppy	(b. hunger)
c. change	(c. jump)	c. poor	c. fullness
(d. govern)	d. drive	d. helpful	d. anger

Antonyms

An **antonym** is a word that means *the opposite* of or *almost the opposite* of another word. Here are some examples:

fail—succeed   crowded—empty
hire—fire   grief—joy
bend—straighten   beneath—above

Exercises   *In each of the following groups, circle the word that is most nearly the **antonym** of the word in **boldface** type.*

1. guilt	**2. definite**	**3. healthy**	**4. create**
(a. innocence)	a. tardy	a. sturdy	a. make
b. sentence	b. unusual	b. messy	b. suggest
c. freedom	(c. vague)	c. bossy	(c. destroy)
d. judgment	d. certain	(d. sickly)	d. reveal

VOCABULARY STRATEGY: USING CONTEXT

How do you go about finding the meaning of an unknown or unfamiliar word that you come across in your reading? You might look the word up in a dictionary, of course, provided one is at hand. But there are two other useful strategies that you might employ to find the meaning of a word that you do not know at all or that is used in a way that you do not recognize. One strategy is to analyze the **structure** or parts of the word. (See pages 11 and 12 for more on this strategy.) The other strategy is to try to figure out the meaning of the word by reference to context.

When we speak of the **context** of a word, we mean the words that are near to or modify that word. By studying the context, we may find **clues** that lead us to its meaning. We might find a clue in the immediate sentence or phrase in which the word appears (and sometimes in adjoining sentences or phrases, too); or we might find a clue in the topic or subject matter of the passage in which the word appears; or we might even find a clue in the physical features of a page itself. (Photographs, illustrations, charts, graphs, captions, and headings are some examples of such features.)

One way to use context as a strategy is to ask yourself what you know already about the topic or subject matter in question. By applying what you have learned before about deserts, for example, you would probably be able to figure out that the word *arid* in the phrase "the arid climate of the desert" means "dry."

The **Vocabulary in Context** exercises that appear in the Units and Reviews and the **Choosing the Right Meaning** exercises that appear in the Reviews and Cumulative Reviews both provide practice in using subject matter or topic to determine the meaning of given words.

When you do the various word-omission exercises in this book, look for **context clues** built into the sentence or passage to guide you to the correct answer. Three types of context clues appear in the exercises in this book.

A **restatement clue** consists of a *synonym* for, or a *definition* of, the missing word. For example:

The <u>noise and commotion</u> in the crowded gymnasium were so great that we could barely make ourselves heard above the

_____ .

a. score   b. referees   (c. din)   d. bleachers

In this sentence *noise and commotion* are synonyms of the missing word, *din*, and act as a restatement clue for it.

A **contrast clue** consists of an *antonym* for, or a phrase that means the *opposite* of, the missing word. For example:

When bad weather prevented the bomber from striking the ((**primary,** **secret**) target, the pilot guided the plane to the <u>secondary</u> objective.

In this sentence, *secondary* is an antonym of the missing word, *primary.* Since bad weather prevented the bomber from accomplishing his main objective, he had to resort to his second choice.

An **inference clue** implies but does not directly state the meaning of the missing word or words. For example:

> Those in the audience who <u>agreed</u> with the speaker _____
> their _____ by cheering, while those who
> <u>disagreed booed.</u>
> a. registered . . . boredom   c. indicated . . . horror
> b. expressed . . . approval   d. showed . . . dislike

In this sentence, there are several inference clues: (a) The word *cheering* has a favorable connotation. *Approval* is the only word in any of the answer choices that also has a favorable connotation; (b) Just as booing is an *expression* of disagreement, cheering is an *expression* of approval. Accordingly, these words are inference clues because they suggest or imply, but do not directly state, the missing word or words.

Exercises   *Use context clues to choose the word or words that complete each of the following sentences or sets of sentences.*

1. The climbers inched their way to the top of the peak until at last they stood upon the very _____ of the mountain.
a. bottom   b. slope   c. range   d. summit

2. There were a few moments of excitement in the first set, but on the whole it was an extremely (**thrilling, monotonous**) tennis match.

3. After we measured out the _____ that the recipe called for, we used a mixer to _____ them in a bowl.
a. amounts . . . separate   c. ingredients . . . combine
b. directions . . . shred   d. temperature . . . bake

VOCABULARY STRATEGY: WORD STRUCTURE

One important way to build your vocabulary is to learn the meaning of word parts that make up many English words. These word parts consist of **prefixes**, **suffixes**, and **roots**, or **bases**. A useful strategy for determining the meaning of an unknown word is to "take apart" the word and think about the parts. For example, when you look at the word parts in the word *invisible,* you find the prefix *in-* ("not") + the root *-vis-* ("see") + the suffix *-ible* ("capable of"). From knowing the meanings of the parts of this word, you can figure out that *invisible* means "not capable of being seen."

Following is a list of common prefixes. Knowing the meaning of a prefix can help you determine the meaning of a word in which the prefix appears.

Prefix	Meaning	Sample Words
bi-	two	bicycle, biannual
com-, con-	together, with	compatriot, contact
de-, dis-	lower, opposite	devalue, disloyal
fore-, pre-	before, ahead of time	forewarn, preplan
il-, im-, in-, ir, non-, un-	not	illegal, impossible, inactive, irregular, nonsense, unable
in-, im-	in, into	inhale, import
mid-	middle	midway, midday, midterm
mis-	wrongly, badly	mistake, misbehave
re-	again, back	redo, repay
sub-	under, less than	submarine, subzero
super-	above, greater than	superimpose, superstar
tri-	three	triangle

Following is a list of common suffixes. Knowing the meaning and grammatical function of a suffix can help you determine the meaning of a word.

Noun Suffix	Meaning	Sample Nouns
-acy, -ance, -ence, -hood, -ity, -ment, -ness, -ship	state, quality, or condition of, act or process of	adequacy, attendance, persistence, neighborhood, activity, judgment, brightness, friendship
-ant, -eer, -ent, -er, -ian, -ier, -ist, -or	one who does or makes something	contestant, auctioneer, resident, banker, comedian, financier, dentist, doctor
-ation, -ition, -ion	act or result of	organization, imposition, election

Verb Suffix	Meaning	Sample Verbs
-ate	to become, produce, or treat	validate, salivate, chlorinate
-en	to make, cause to be	weaken, shorten, lengthen
-fy, -ify, -ize	to cause, make	liquefy, glorify, legalize

Adjective Suffix	Meaning	Sample Adjectives
-able, -ible	able, capable of	believable, incredible
-al, -ic,	relating to, characteristic of	natural, romantic
-ful, -ive, -ous	full of, given to, marked by	beautiful, protective, poisonous
-ish, -like	like, resembling	foolish, childlike
-less	lacking, without	careless

A **base** or **root** is the main part of a word to which prefixes and suffixes may be added. Many roots come to English from Latin, such as *-socio-,* meaning "society," or from Greek, such as *-logy-,* meaning "the study of." Knowing Greek and Latin roots can help you determine the meaning of a word such as *sociology,* which means "the study of society."

In the **Building with Classical Roots** sections of this book, you will learn more about some of these Latin and Greek roots and about English words that derive from them. The lists that follow may help you figure out the meaning of new or unfamiliar words that you encounter in your reading.

Greek Root	Meaning	Sample Word
-astr-, -aster-, -astro-	star	astral, asteroid, astronaut
-auto-	self	autograph
-bio-	life	biography
-chron-, chrono-	time	chronic, chronological
-cosm-, -cosmo-	universe, order	microcosm, cosmopolitan
-cryph-, -crypt-	hidden, secret	apocryphal, cryptographer
-dem-, -demo-	people	epidemic, democracy
-dia-	through, across, between	diameter
-dog-, -dox-	opinion, teaching	dogmatic, orthodox
-gen-	race, kind, origin, birth	generation
-gnos-	know	diagnostic
-graph-, -graphy-, -gram-	write	graphite, autobiography, telegram
-log-, -logue-	speech, word, reasoning	logic, dialogue
-lys-	break down	analysis
-metr-, -meter-	measure	metric, kilometer
-micro-	small	microchip
-morph-	form, shape	amorphous
-naut-	sailor	cosmonaut
-phon-, -phone-, -phono-	sound, voice	phonics, telephone, phonograph
-pol-, -polis-	city, state	police, metropolis
-scop-, -scope-	watch, look at	microscopic, telescope
-tele-	far off, distant	television
-the-	put or place	parentheses

Latin Root	Meaning	Sample Word
-cap-, -capt-, -cept-, -cip-	take	capitulate, captive, concept, recipient
-cede-, -ceed-, -ceas-, -cess-	happen, yield, go	precede, proceed, decease, cessation
-cred-	believe	incredible
-dic-, -dict-	speak, say, tell	indicate, diction
-duc-, -duct-, -duit-	lead, conduct, draw	educate, conduct, conduit
-fac-, -fact-, -fect-, -fic-, -fy-	make	faculty, artifact, defect, beneficial, clarify
-ject-	throw	eject
-mis-, -miss-, -mit-, -mitt-	send	promise, missile, transmit, intermittent
-note-, -not-	know, recognize	denote, notion
-pel-, -puls-	drive	expel, compulsive
-pend-, -pens-	hang, weight, set aside	pendulum, pension
-pon-, -pos-	put, place	component, position
-port-	carry	portable
-rupt-	break	bankrupt
-scrib-, -scribe-, -script-	write	scribble, describe, inscription
-spec-, -spic-	look, see	spectator, conspicuous
-tac-, -tag-, -tang-, -teg-	touch	contact, contagious, tangible, integral
-tain-, -ten-, -tin-	hold, keep	contain, tenure, retinue
-temp-	time	tempo, temporary
-ven-, -vent-	come	intervene, convention
-vers-, -vert-	turn	reverse, invert
-voc-, -vok-	call	vocal, invoke

WORKING WITH ANALOGIES

Today practically every standardized examination involving vocabulary, especially the SAT-I, employs the **analogy** as a testing device. For that reason, it is an excellent idea to learn how to read, understand, and solve such verbal puzzles.

What Is an Analogy?

An analogy is a kind of equation using words rather than numbers or mathematical symbols and quantities. Normally, an analogy contains two pairs of words linked by a word or symbol that stands for an equal sign (=). A complete analogy compares the two pairs of words and makes a statement about them. It asserts that the logical relationship between the members of the first pair of words is *the same as* the logical relationship between the members of the second pair of words. This is the only statement a valid analogy ever makes.

Here is an example of a complete analogy. It is presented in two different formats.

Format 1
maple is to tree as rose is to flower

Format 2
maple : tree :: rose : flower

Reading and Interpreting Analogies

As our sample indicates, analogies are customarily presented in formats that need some deciphering in order to be read and understood correctly. There are a number of these formats, but you need concern yourself with only the two shown.

Format 1: Let's begin with the format that uses all words:

maple is to tree as rose is to flower

Because this is the simplest format to read and understand, it is the one used in the student texts of Vocabulary Workshop. It is to be read exactly as printed. Allowing for the fact that the word pairs change from analogy to analogy, this is how to read every analogy, no matter what the format is.

Now you know how to read an analogy. Still, it is not clear exactly what the somewhat cryptic statement "maple is to tree as rose is to flower" means. To discover this, you must understand what the two linking expressions *as* and *is to* signify.

- The word *as* links the two word pairs in the complete analogy. It stands for an equal sign (=) and means "is the same as."

- The expression *is to* links the two members of each word pair, so it appears twice in a complete analogy. In our sample, *is to* links *maple* and *tree* (the two words in the first pair) and also *rose* and *flower* (the two words in the second word pair). Accordingly, the expression *is to* means "has the same logical relationship to" the two words it links.

Putting all this information together, we can say that our sample analogy means:

> The logical relationship between a *maple* and a *tree* is *the same as* (=) the logical relationship between a *rose* and a *flower*.

Now you know what our sample analogy means. This is what every analogy means, allowing for the fact that the word pairs will vary from one analogy to another.

Format 2: Our second format uses symbols, rather than words, to link its four members.

> maple : tree :: rose : flower

This is the format used on the SAT-I and in the *TEST PREP Blackline Masters* that accompany each Level of Vocabulary Workshop. In this format, a single colon (:) replaces the expression *is to*, and a double colon (::) replaces the word *as*. Otherwise, format 2 is the same as format 1; that is, it is read in exactly the same way ("maple is to tree as rose is to flower"), and it means exactly the same thing ("the logical relationship between a *maple* and a *tree* is the same as the logical relationship between a *rose* and a *flower*").

Completing Analogies

So far we've looked at complete analogies. However, standardized examinations do not provide the test taker with a complete analogy. Instead, the test taker is given the first, or key, pair of words and then asked to *complete* the analogy by selecting the second pair from a given group of four or five choices, usually lettered *a* through *d* or *e*.

Here's how our sample analogy would look on such a test:

1. maple is to tree as
a. acorn is to oak
b. hen is to rooster
c. rose is to flower
d. shrub is to lilac

or

1. maple : tree ::
a. acorn : oak
b. hen : rooster
c. rose : flower
d. shrub : lilac

It is up to the test taker to complete the analogy correctly.

Here's how to do that in just four easy steps!

Step 1: *Look at the two words in the key (given) pair, and determine the logical relationship between them.*

In our sample analogy, *maple* and *tree* form the key (given) pair of words. They indicate the key (given) relationship. Think about these two words for a moment. What is the relationship of a maple to a tree? Well, a maple is a particular kind, or type, of tree.

Step 2: *Make up a short sentence stating the relationship that you have discovered for the first pair of words.*

For our model analogy, we can use this sentence: "A maple is a particular kind (type) of tree."

Step 3: *Extend the sentence you have written to cover the rest of the analogy, even though you haven't completed it yet.*

The easiest way to do this is to repeat the key relationship after the words *just as*, leaving blanks for the two words you don't yet have. The sentence will now read something like this:

A maple is a kind (type) of tree, just as a _?_ is a kind of _?_.

Step 4: *Look at each of the lettered pairs of words from which you are to choose your answer. Determine which lettered pair illustrates the same relationship as the key pair.*

The easiest and most effective way to carry out step 4 is to substitute each pair of words into the blanks in the sentence you made up to see which sentence makes sense. Only one will.

Doing this for our sample analogy, we get:

a. A maple is a kind of tree, just as an acorn is a kind of oak.
b. A maple is a kind of tree, just as a hen is a kind of rooster.
c. A maple is a kind of tree, just as a rose is a kind of flower.
d. A maple is a kind of tree, just as a shrub is a kind of lilac.

Look at these sentences. Only *one* of them makes any sense. Choice *a* is clearly wrong because an acorn is *not* a kind of oak. Choice *b* is also wrong because a hen is *not* a kind of rooster. Similarly, choice *d* is incorrect because a shrub is *not* a kind of lilac, though a *lilac* is a kind of shrub. In other words, the two words are in the wrong order. That leaves us with choice *c*, which says that a rose is a kind of flower. Well, that makes sense; a rose is indeed a kind of flower. So, choice *c* must be the pair of words that completes the analogy correctly.

Determining the Key Relationship

Clearly, determining the nature of the key relationship is the most important and the most difficult part of completing an analogy. Since there are literally thousands of key relationships possible, you cannot simply memorize a list of them. The table on page 16, however, outlines some of the most common key relationships. Study the table carefully.

Complete Analogy	Key Relationship
big is to **large** as **little** is to **small**	**Big** means the same thing as **large**, just as **little** means the same thing as **small**.
tall is to **short** as **thin** is to **fat**	**Tall** means the opposite of **short**, just as **thin** means the opposite of **fat**.
brave is to **favorable** as **cowardly** is to **unfavorable**	The tone of **brave** is **favorable**, just as the tone of **cowardly** is **unfavorable**.
busybody is to **nosy** as **klutz** is to **clumsy**	A **busybody** is by definition someone who is **nosy**, just as a **klutz** is by definition someone who is **clumsy**.
cowardly is to **courage** as **awkward** is to **grace**	Someone who is **cowardly** lacks **courage**, just as someone who is **awkward** lacks **grace**.
visible is to **see** as **audible** is to **hear**	If something is **visible**, you can by definition **see** it, just as if something is **audible**, you can by definition **hear** it.
invisible is to **see** as **inaudible** is to **hear**	If something is **invisible**, you cannot **see** it, just as if something is **inaudible**, you cannot **hear** it.
frigid is to **cold** as **blistering** is to **hot**	**Frigid** is the extreme of **cold**, just as **blistering** is the extreme of **hot**.
chef is to **cooking** as **tailor** is to **clothing**	A **chef** is concerned with **cooking**, just as a **tailor** is concerned with **clothing**.
liar is to **truthful** as **bigot** is to **fair-minded**	A **liar** is by definition not likely to be **truthful**, just as a **bigot** is by definition not likely to be **fair-minded**.
starvation is to **thinness** as **overindulgence** is to **fatness**	**Starvation** will lead to **thinness**, just as **overindulgence** will lead to **fatness**.
practice is to **proficient** as **study** is to **knowledgeable**	**Practice** will make a person **proficient**, just as **study** will make a person **knowledgeable**.
eyes are to **see** as **ears** are to **hear**	You use your **eyes** to **see** with, just as you use your **ears** to **hear** with.
sloppy is to **appearance** as **rude** is to **manner**	The word **sloppy** can refer to one's **appearance**, just as the word **rude** can refer to one's **manner**.
learned is to **knowledge** as **wealthy** is to **money**	Someone who is **learned** has a great deal of **knowledge**, just as someone who is **wealthy** has a great deal of **money**.

Exercises   *In each of the following, circle the item that best completes the analogy. Then explain the key relationship involved.*

1. fox is to **clever** as
a. chicken is to brave
b. snake is to honest
c. owl is to foolish
d. mule is to stubborn

2. page is to **book** as
a. baseball is to football
b. leaf is to tree
c. cover is to magazine
d. letter is to note

3. groan is to **pain** as
a. laugh is to sorrow
b. yawn is to weariness
c. wink is to fear
d. frown is to happiness

4. mean is to **kindness** as
a. brave is to courage
b. faithful is to loyalty
c. foolish is to wisdom
d. sincere is to honesty

VOCABULARY AND WRITING

When you study vocabulary, you make yourself not only a better reader but also a better writer. The greater the number of words at your disposal, the better you will be able to express your thoughts. Good writers are always adding new words to their personal vocabularies, the pool of words that they understand *and* know how to use properly. They use these words both when they write and when they revise.

There are several factors to consider when choosing words and setting the tone of your writing. First, your choice of words should suit your purpose and your audience. If you are writing an essay for your social studies teacher, you will probably want to choose words that are formal in tone and precise in meaning. If you are writing a letter to a friend, however, you will probably choose words that are more informal in tone and freer in meaning. Your **audience** is the person or people who will be reading what you write, and your **purpose** is the reason why you are writing. Your purpose, for example, might be to explain; or it might be to describe, inform, or entertain.

Almost any kind of writing—whether a school essay, a story, or a letter to a friend—can be improved by careful attention to vocabulary. Sometimes you will find, for example, that one word can be used to replace a phrase of five or six words. This is not to say that a shorter sentence is always better. However, readers usually prefer and appreciate **economy** of expression. They grow impatient with sentences that plod along with vague, unnecessary words rather than race along with fewer, carefully chosen ones. Writing can also be improved by attention to **diction** (word choice). Many writers use words that might make sense in terms of *general* meaning but that are not precise enough to convey *nuances* of meaning. In the **Writer's Challenge** sections of this book, you will have an opportunity to make word choices that will more clearly and precisely convey the meaning you intend.

Exercises   *Read the following sentences, paying special attention to the words and phrases underlined. From the words in the box, find better choices for the underlined words and phrases.*

1. When President John F. Kennedy was killed by an assassin's bullet on November 22, 1963, the very unfortunate event shocked the nation.

frightening	surprising	predictable	tragic

2. Dutch painter Vincent van Gogh felt great delight at the completion of each new painting, but he despaired that his work never sold.

relaxed	rejoiced	collapsed	splurged

3. What an amazing act that shows daring, skill, or strength it was that the skier qualified for the Olympics only a year after shattering her leg!

feat	plan	reaction	surprise

4. The hikers were almost buried by the sudden large mass of rocks falling swiftly down the mountainside.

tornado	hurricane	avalanche	earthquake

5. Medical schools did not accept women in the mid-1800s because it was thought that they would not make fit or skilled doctors.

informed	sympathetic	relaxed	capable

This test contains a sampling of the words that are to be found in the exercises in this Level of VOCABULARY WORKSHOP. It will give you an idea of the types of words to be studied and their level of difficulty. When you have completed all the units, the Final Mastery Test at the end of this book will assess what you have learned. By comparing your results on the Final Mastery Test with your results on the Diagnostic Test below, you will be able to judge your progress.

Synonyms

*In each of the following groups, circle the word or phrase that **most nearly** expresses the meaning of the word in **boldface** type in the given phrase.*

1. a **synopsis** of the play
   a. performance   b. review   (c. summary)   d. defense

2. the **plight** of the homeless
   (a. misfortune)   b. plans   c. hopes   d. hunger

3. **mimic** my way of speaking
   a. notice   b. study   c. improve   (d. imitate)

4. an **ingenious** scheme
   (a. clever)   b. wicked   c. clumsy   d. childish

5. plan to **rendezvous** at a certain place
   a. eat   (b. meet)   c. dance   d. sleep

6. **relish** the idea
   a. hate   b. ignore   (c. delight in)   d. examine

7. an **inflammatory** speech
   (a. fiery)   b. boring   c. long-winded   d. informal

8. the **indisputable** leader
   (a. unquestioned)   b. powerful   c. experienced   d. cruel

9. a **strapping** fellow
   a. timid   (b. husky)   c. hardworking   d. dependable

10. a **gory** horror movie
    a. successful   (b. bloody)   c. new   d. long

11. **designate** her successor
    a. dislike   (b. name)   c. criticize   d. fire

12. **rummaged** in the attic
    a. hid   b. cleaned up   (c. searched)   d. played

13. **pacify** the angry customers
    a. arrest   (b. calm)   c. scold   d. ignore

14. **dissect** the report
    a. accept   b. reject   c. make fun of   (d. analyze)

15. **foil** the plot
    a. cover up   (b. defeat)   c. join   d. help

16. an **acute** attack
    a. unpleasant   b. fatal   (c. severe)   d. mild

17. adhere to his promise
    a. break   b. explain   (c. stick to)   d. listen to

18. vie for the championship
    (a. compete)   b. travel   c. rehearse   d. cheat

19. abduct the official
    a. introduce   (b. kidnap)   c. fire   d. elect

20. as his troubles **receded**
    a. grew worse   b. remained   (c. retreated)   d. grew larger

21. made **rigorous** demands
    a. expected   (b. tough)   c. fair   d. easy

22. stored the **data** in the computer
    a. surplus   (b. information)   c. supplies   d. equipment

23. forsake their comrades
    a. call together   (b. desert)   c. protect   d. arm

24. topple the government
    a. join   b. strengthen   c. threaten   (d. overthrow)

25. confiscated the weapon
    a. sold   (b. seized)   c. hid   d. displayed

26. quash a rebellion
    a. lead   (b. crush)   c. explain   d. start

27. sage advice
    (a. wise)   b. odd   c. old-fashioned   d. foolish

28. a **pathetic** sight
    a. vivid   b. humorous   (c. moving)   d. unexplained

29. enumerate the rules
    (a. list)   b. enforce   c. break   d. change

30. an **unerring** aim
    a. noble   b. uncertain   (c. unfailing)   d. hurried

31. an **extinct** animal
    (a. vanished)   b. tame   c. common   d. local

32. traffic **fatalities**
    a. lights   b. expenditures   c. regulations   (d. deaths)

33. show **scant** concern
    a. great   b. false   (c. very little)   d. sincere

34. verging on insanity
    a. curing   (b. approaching)   c. preventing   d. discussing

35. taut nerves
    a. strong   (b. tense)   c. weak   d. damaged

36. a useful **implement**
    a. suggestion   b. idea   c. move   (d. tool)

37. built a **replica** of the ship
    a. side   (b. copy)   c. deck   d. mast

38. with a **serene** expression on her face
a. worried   b. cruel   (c. peaceful)   d. surprised

39. share our **reveries**
a. profits   (b. dreams)   c. troubles   d. possessions

40. a **wholesome** development
a. bad   b. popular   (c. healthy)   d. strange

41. show remarkable **discretion**
(a. judgment)   b. courage   c. pride   d. carelessness

42. a **far-fetched** excuse
a. convincing   (b. unlikely)   c. written   d. overused

43. a **sluggish** economy
a. competitive   (b. slow-moving)   c. free   d. growing

44. a **self-seeking** attitude
(a. selfish)   b. noble   c. intelligent   d. effective

45. **disquieting** news
(a. upsetting)   b. sensational   c. funny   d. encouraging

46. **blighted** the neighborhood
a. beautified   b. rebuilt   c. lived in   (d. ruined)

47. broke his **vow**
a. sword   b. arm   c. habit   (d. promise)

48. **amalgamated** their forces
a. disbanded   b. weakened   c. led   (d. combined)

49. took **optional** courses
a. easy   b. advanced   (c. not required)   d. time-consuming

50. having **global** significance
a. little   b. unexpected   (c. worldwide)   d. personal

Definitions

Note carefully the spelling, pronunciation, part(s) of speech, and definition(s) of each of the following words. Then write the word in the blank space(s) in the illustrative sentence(s) following. Finally, study the lists of synonyms and antonyms given at the end of each entry.

1. apparel
(ə par' əl)

(*n.*) clothing, that which serves as dress or decoration; (*v.*) to put clothes on, dress up

Winter _____ apparel _____ should be warm and cozy.

Let's _____ apparel _____ our cats for the party.

SYNONYMS: (*n.*) attire, garments; (*v.*) deck out
ANTONYMS: (*v.*) undress, unclothe, strip, denude

2. besiege
(bi sēj')

(*v.*) to attack by surrounding with military forces; to cause worry or trouble

If troops _____ besiege _____ their stronghold, the rebel forces may be forced to surrender.

SYNONYMS: blockade, encircle, pressure, hound

3. compress
(*v.*, kəm pres',
n., käm' pres)

(*v.*) to press together; to reduce in size or volume; (*n.*) a folded cloth or pad applied to an injury

The editor helped to _____ compress _____ my rambling 25-page mystery into an 8-page thriller.

A cold _____ compress _____ may soothe headache pain.

SYNONYMS: (*v.*) condense, shrink, shorten
ANTONYMS: (*v.*) expand, enlarge

4. denounce
(di naůns')

(*v.*) to condemn openly; to accuse formally

The United Nations decided to publicly _____ denounce _____ the tyrant's crimes against his people.

SYNONYMS: criticize, censure
ANTONYMS: hail, acclaim

5. dispatch
(dis pach')

(*v.*) to send off or out for a purpose; to kill; (*n.*) an official message; promptness, speed; the act of killing

We'll _____ dispatch _____ a repair crew right away.

He approved the request with _____ dispatch _____.

SYNONYMS: (*v.*) slay; (*n.*) report, communication
ANTONYMS: (*v.*) recall, withhold

6. douse
(daůs)

(*v.*) to plunge into a liquid, drench; to put out quickly, extinguish

I'll _____ douse _____ the flames with the hose.

SYNONYMS: submerge, soak, dunk, immerse
ANTONYMS: dry out, dehydrate, kindle, ignite

7. expressly
(ek spres' lē)

(*adv.*) plainly, in so many words; for a particular purpose

At the meeting, parents _____ **expressly** _____ stated their approval of students wearing school uniforms.

SYNONYMS: clearly, pointedly, explicitly
ANTONYMS: implicitly, accidentally

8. famished
(fam' isht)

(*adj., part.*) suffering severely from hunger or from lack of something

The Vietnamese immigrants, new to a strange American city, were _____ **famished** _____ for news of home.

SYNONYMS: hungry, starving, ravenous
ANTONYMS: well fed, full, satisfied, satiated

9. forsake
(fôr sāk')

(*v.*) to give up, renounce; to leave, abandon

I will never _____ **forsake** _____ my children, no matter what they do or say.

SYNONYMS: desert, disown
ANTONYMS: keep, hold on to, stand by

10. gainful
(gān' fəl)

(*adj.*) profitable; bringing in money or some special advantage

I hope to find _____ **gainful** _____ employment that is pleasing to me.

SYNONYMS: moneymaking, paying
ANTONYMS: unprofitable, unrewarding, nonpaying

11. immense
(i mens')

(*adj.*) very large or great; beyond ordinary means of measurement

Alaska enjoys _____ **immense** _____ natural resources, but its severe climate makes those resources difficult to use.

SYNONYMS: vast, enormous, immeasurable, gigantic
ANTONYMS: small, tiny, minute, infinitesimal

12. inept
(in ept')

(*adj.*) totally without skill or appropriateness

The scientist is brilliant in the research laboratory but is _____ **inept** _____ at dealing with people.

SYNONYMS: clumsy, unskilled, bungling, incompetent
ANTONYMS: skillful, accomplished, adroit

13. ingenious
(in jēn yəs)

(*adj.*) showing remarkable originality, inventiveness, or resourcefulness; clever

The students found an _____ **ingenious** _____ solution to the math problem.

SYNONYMS: imaginative, inventive, resourceful
ANTONYMS: unimaginative, unoriginal, uninventive

14. instantaneous
(in stən tā′ nē əs)

(*adj.*) done in an instant; immediate

Most computer software is designed so that users can obtain nearly _____ instantaneous _____ responses.

SYNONYMS: prompt, quick, speedy
ANTONYMS: delayed, slow, gradual

15. irk
(ərk)

(*v.*) to annoy, trouble, make weary

Questions that show a student's lack of attention _____ irk _____ the teacher.

SYNONYMS: bother, irritate, vex
ANTONYMS: please, delight, cheer, gladden

16. libel
(lī′ bəl)

(*n.*) a statement that unfairly or falsely harms the reputation of the person about whom it is made; (*v.*) to write or publish such a statement

The celebrity accused her biographer of _____ libel _____.

It is a crime to _____ libel _____ others, no matter how you feel about them.

SYNONYMS: (*n.*) ~~slander,~~ slur; (*v.*) smear, bad-mouth defame

17. misgiving
(mis giv′ iŋ)

(*n.*) a feeling of fear, doubt, or uncertainty

They had _____ misgivings _____ about joining the chorus because of its demanding schedule.

SYNONYMS: worry, qualm, hesitation
ANTONYMS: feeling of confidence, assurance

18. oaf
(ōf)

(*n.*) a stupid person; a big, clumsy, slow individual

He generally moved like an _____ oaf _____, so I was surprised to see how graceful he was on the dance floor.

SYNONYMS: bonehead, dunce, clod, lout

19. recede
(ri sēd′)

(*v.*) to go or move backward; to become more distant

The town residents must wait for the flood waters to _____ recede _____ before they can deal with the terrible mess left behind.

SYNONYMS: retreat, go back, back up, ebb
ANTONYMS: advance, come closer

20. repast
(ri past′)

(*n.*) a meal, food

Let's get together after the show at Callie's Café for a late-night _____ repast _____.

SYNONYM: victuals

Completing the Sentence

From the words for this unit, choose the one that best completes each of the following sentences. Write the word in the space provided.

1. Some people hailed the man as a genius; others _____ denounced _____ him as a quack.

2. While all true vegetarians _____ forsake _____ animal meats, some do eat dairy products.

3. Your _____ apparel _____ can be neat and attractive without being expensive.

4. The terms of our agreement _____ expressly _____ forbade us to take any of the goods for our own use.

5. When you are really hungry, even the simplest foods will be a delicious _____ repast _____.

6. Since it was well past their lunchtime by the time we arrived home, the children were _____ famished _____.

7. You had no right to call me a clumsy _____ oaf _____ just because I spilled some water on you.

8. The laws of this land do not shield public figures from just criticism, but they do protect them against _____ libel _____.

9. Far away on the horizon, we saw the tiny figures of a lonely traveler and his mule _____ recede _____ into the sunset.

10. On my first baby-sitting job, I found that one must have _____ immense _____ patience to take care of young children.

11. Let's make certain to _____ douse _____ the fire before leaving camp.

12. When you play tennis for the first time, you are going to find that your attempts to hit the ball are very _____ inept _____.

13. If you _____ compress _____ all the items as much as possible, you will be able to get everything into a single suitcase.

14. As an inexperienced sailor, I had more than a few _____ misgivings _____ about taking out the small boat in such rough weather.

15. Don't allow yourself to be _____ irked _____ by every small trouble that may arise during the day.

16. Because I have reached an age at which I am unwilling to depend on my parents, I am out to find a _____ gainful _____ occupation.

17. None of us could figure out how the _____ ingenious _____ magician had managed to escape from the trunk submerged in the tank of water.

18. How can we hope to _____ besiege _____ a city that is surrounded by such strong walls and has ample supplies of everything it needs?

19. A(n) _____ dispatch _____ will be sent to all our representatives in Latin America advising them how to handle the problem.

20. Some of life's rewards are _____ instantaneous _____; others are a long time in coming.

Synonyms

*Choose the word from this unit that is **the same** or **most nearly the same** in meaning as the **boldface** word or expression in the given phrase. Write the word on the line provided.*

1. enjoyed the **meal** served to them — repast
2. had to fire the **bungling** carpenter — inept
3. thought the article **smeared** her reputation — libeled
4. **resourceful** use for lumber scraps — ingenious
5. refused to invite the **lout** — oaf
6. fashionable hand-me-down **garments** — apparel
7. waiting until the crowds **ebb** — recede
8. **qualms** about the leading candidate — misgivings
9. is **clearly** forbidden for use by minors — expressly
10. sent them a top-secret **communication** — dispatch
11. compelled to **desert** the leaky boat — forsake
12. were far too **hungry** to wait politely — famished
13. can provide **speedy** results at home — instantaneous
14. chose a **profitable** career in advertising — gainful
15. **pressure** us with repeated phone calls — besiege

Antonyms

*Choose the word from this unit that is **most nearly opposite** in meaning to the **boldface** word or expression in the given phrase. Write the word on the line provided.*

16. sailing across the **tiny** ocean — immense
17. knew when to **kindle** the torch — douse
18. **expand** the bundle to fit — compress
19. was certain to **gladden** the passengers — irk
20. reasons to **acclaim** the winner — denounce

Choosing the Right Word

*Circle the **boldface** word that more satisfactorily completes each of the following sentences.*

1. Which job would you take—one that is more (**ingenious, gainful**) right now or one that pays a small salary but offers a chance for valuable training?

2. We were pleasantly surprised to see that she completed the difficult task we had given her with neatness and (**irk, dispatch**).

3. As soon as she took over the office of Mayor, she was (**besieged, dispatched**) by dozens of people eager to get city jobs.

4. I will never (**recede, forsake**) the people who helped me in my hour of need!

5. (**Famished, Compressed**) for a chance to see her work in print, the young writer begged the magazine editor to publish her story.

6. After all the bad things he has done, I feel no (**dispatches, misgivings**) about telling him that I don't want him to be my "friend" anymore.

7. As soon as he began his long, boring speech, our excitement died down, as though we had been (**denounced, doused**) with cold water.

8. Each day, after she finishes her homework, she enjoys a light (**repast, misgiving**) of the detective stories she loves so well.

9. Her conscience forced her to (**denounce, libel**) the conspirators to the authorities.

10. His notebooks show that Leonardo da Vinci was not only a masterful artist but an (**inept, ingenious**) inventor as well.

11. Tom may not be as polished and clever as some of the other boys, but I think it is unfair of you to call him an (**apparel, oaf**).

12. We can (**compress, besiege**) the message of the sermon into one short sentence: "Do unto others as you would have others do unto you."

13. His conceit is so (**immense, gainful**) that he cannot imagine anyone voting against him in the election for class president.

14. Instead of feeling (**forsaken, irked**) because you did poorly on the exam, why don't you make up your mind to study harder in the future?

15. We are working hard to improve conditions in our community, but we cannot expect (**famished, instantaneous**) results.

16. He may claim that we have (**libeled, doused**) him, but we have facts to back up every statement made in the column about him.

17. You may criticize the roads and the lights, but the fact is that most car accidents are caused by (**inept, immense**) drivers.

18. When I realized that I was thoroughly prepared for the final exams, my fears quickly (**receded, irked**).

19. Where did he ever get the curious idea that we set up this volleyball court (**expressly, instantaneously**) for him and his friends?

20. I always feel sad at the end of the autumn, when the trees lose their beautiful (**repast, apparel**) of leaves.

 **Vocabulary in Context**

Read the following passage, in which some of the words you have studied in this unit appear in **boldface** type. Then complete each statement given below the passage by circling the letter of the item that is **the same** or **almost the same** in meaning as the highlighted word.

Clothing Fads of the 1960s

(Line)

The 1960s left a definite mark on American **apparel**. This influence began when First Lady Jacqueline Kennedy moved into the White House in 1961 with her husband, President John Kennedy. Her sophisticated sense of style appealed to many. Fashion designers, department stores, and boutiques could barely satisfy the
(5) **immense** demand for pillbox hats, two-piece suits, A-line skirts, wraparound sunglasses, and low-heeled pumps.

After the tragic Kennedy assassination in 1963, fashion looked elsewhere for inspiration. The Nehru jacket, named for
(10) India's first Prime Minister, had no lapels and a small stand-up collar. The Beatles promoted this style, which became an **instantaneous** hit.

What about everyday attire? Enter bell-
(15) bottoms. These wide-legged pants, which flared out at the bottom, were modeled after traditional sailor pants. In an effort to distance bell-bottoms from their military origins, **ingenious** designers widened the
(20) bells and added broad belts, a hip-hugging line, fancy cuffs or pleats, and outrageous patterns and fabrics.

Even accessories had a distinctly sixties air. Opticians were **besieged** by people

Raffia pillbox hat with attached pigtails, wraparound sunglasses, matching bag

(25) begging for Ben Franklins—delicate, wire-rimmed glasses whose lenses came in many colors. Long hair parted down the middle completed the look.

Don't forget mini-skirts. These super-short skirts were **denounced** as being shameless, unhealthy, and totally ridiculous. But negative opinion didn't stop fad-conscious teens.
(30) Do these styles seem to be more than just a part of history? That is because some of them have made a comeback and are very much a part of today's fashions.

---

1. The meaning of **apparel** (line 1) is
  a. promptness   (c.) clothing
  b. victuals   d. slander

2. Immense (line 5) most nearly means
  (a.) enormous   c. accidental
  b. clumsy   d. gradual

3. Instantaneous (line 13) is best defined as
  a. particular   c. profitable
  b. gradual   (d.) immediate

4. The meaning of **ingenious** (line 19) is
  a. unskilled   c. starving
  (b.) clever   d. explicit

5. Besieged (line 24) most nearly means
  a. criticized   (c.) hounded
  b. soaked   d. abandoned

6. Denounced (line 27) is best defined as
  a. acclaimed   c. shortened
  b. recalled   (d.) condemned

Definitions

Note carefully the spelling, pronunciation, part(s) of speech, and definition(s) of each of the following words. Then write the word in the blank space(s) in the illustrative sentence(s) following. Finally, study the lists of synonyms and antonyms given at the end of each entry.

1. adverse
(ad vərs′)

(*adj.*) unfavorable, negative; working against, hostile

Some people suffer an _____adverse_____ reaction if they eat peanut butter or anything with peanuts.

SYNONYMS: difficult, trying
ANTONYMS: favorable, positive, helpful, beneficial

2. arid
(ar′ id)

(*adj.*) extremely dry; uninteresting, dull

Although California leads the nation in farming, crops won't grow in its most _____arid_____ regions.

SYNONYMS: waterless, parched, boring, unimaginative
ANTONYMS: waterlogged, soggy, fertile, lush

3. assailant
(ə sa′ lənt)

(*n.*) a person who attacks violently (with blows or words)

The jogger was injured by an unknown _____assailant_____, who left him immobile at the side of the road.

SYNONYMS: assaulter, attacker, mugger
ANTONYMS: victim, prey, injured party

4. billow
(bil′ o)

(*n.*) a large wave; (*v.*) to rise or swell like a wave

The ocean _____billows_____ rose and fell, attracting the most daring surfers.

Fans cheered enthusiastically when they saw their team's flags _____billow_____ over the stadium.

SYNONYMS: (*n.*) breaker; (*v.*) surge, bulge, balloon
ANTONYMS: (*n.*) trough; (*v.*) deflate, collapse

5. confront
(kən frənt′)

(*v.*) to meet face-to-face, especially as a challenge; come to grips with

In court, defendants can _____confront_____ their accusers in a controlled setting.

SYNONYMS: face, encounter
ANTONYMS: avoid, evade, sidestep

6. constrain
(kən strān′)

(*v.*) to force, compel; to restrain, hold back

You can't _____constrain_____ me against my will.

SYNONYMS: pressure, restrict, confine, limit
ANTONYMS: loosen, liberate, unfetter, relax

7. contemporary
(kən tem′ pə rer ē)

(*adj.*) belonging to the same period of time as oneself; (*n.*) a person of the same time

His novel used a _____ contemporary _____ style but had a historical setting.

Rather than ask parents for help, teens often turn to a _____ contemporary _____ for advice.

SYNONYMS: (*adj.*) present-day, modern, current; (*n.*) peer
ANTONYMS: (*adj.*) ancient, prehistoric, antique, antiquated

8. depict
(di pikt')

(*v.*) to portray; to represent or show in the form of a picture

The painter chose to _____ depict _____ a plain prairie landscape using bold colors and shadows.

SYNONYMS: sketch, draw, picture, illustrate

9. disinterested
(dis in' trəst id)

(*adj.*) fair-minded, free from selfish motives; indifferent

A judge must remain _____ disinterested _____ in order to render an evenhanded and logical decision.

SYNONYMS: neutral, impartial, unbiased, apathetic
ANTONYMS: partial, biased, prejudiced

10. encompass
(en kəm' pəs)

(*v.*) to encircle, go or reach around; to enclose; to include with a certain group or class

Oceans _____ encompass _____ about three-fourths of the surface of our planet.

SYNONYMS: surround, envelop, comprise
ANTONYMS: leave out, omit, exclude

11. groundless
(graünd' ləs)

(*adj.*) without any good reason or cause, unjustified

Kate's _____ groundless _____ fear of hurting herself during exercise has left her weak and out of shape.

SYNONYMS: baseless, unsupported
ANTONYMS: well-founded, reasonable, justified

12. hypocrite
(hip' ə krit)

(*n.*) a person who pretends to be what he or she is not or better than he or she really is; a two-faced person

The speaker who said one thing but did something else entirely was regarded as a _____ hypocrite _____ .

SYNONYMS: phony, charlatan, fraud

13. incomprehensible
(in käm pri hen' sə bəl)

(*adj.*) impossible to understand

Our school's intercom system is so old that this morning's announcements were almost _____ incomprehensible _____ .

SYNONYMS: baffling, confusing, bewildering
ANTONYMS: understandable, clear, plain, intelligible

14. manipulate
(mə nip' yə lāt)

(*v.*) to handle or use skillfully; to manage or control for personal gain or advantage

Scientists should not _____ manipulate _____ data.

SYNONYMS: work, maneuver, exploit, influence

15. maximum
(mak' sə məm)

(*n.*) the greatest possible amount or degree; (*adj.*) reaching the greatest possible amount or degree

This postage scale can weigh a _____ maximum _____ of only five pounds.

To ease the patient's suffering, the doctor prescribed the _____ maximum _____ dosage of painkillers.

SYNONYMS: largest, highest, utmost
ANTONYMS: least, lowest, minimum, smallest

16. mimic
(mim' ik)

(*n.*) a person who does imitations; (*v.*) to imitate; to make fun of

The comedy troupe has many talented members, but it still needs to hire a good _____ mimic _____.

Troy continually entertains his friends because he can _____ mimic _____ any accent he hears.

SYNONYMS: (*n.*) copycat, impersonator; (*v.*) parrot, impersonate

17. ruffle
(rəf' əl)

(*v.*) to wrinkle, make uneven; to annoy, upset; to flip through; (*n.*) a gathered strip of material used for trimming edges; a ripple; a low drumbeat

Try not to let wisecracks _____ ruffle _____ your feelings.

My favorite pillow is soft and fluffy to the touch and has a velvet _____ ruffle _____.

SYNONYMS: (*v.*) disturb; (*n.*) frill
ANTONYMS: (*v.*) smooth out, soothe

18. serene
(sə rēn')

(*adj.*) peaceful, calm; free of emotional upset; clear and free of storm; majestic, grand

How does she manage to stay so _____ serene _____ in the face of such chaos?

SYNONYMS: tranquil, composed, fair, august
ANTONYMS: agitated, troubled, stormy, inclement

19. sheepish
(shēp' ish)

(*adj.*) embarrassed; resembling a sheep in meekness, timid

His _____ sheepish _____ grin made the crowds cheer all the more for his unlikely victory.

SYNONYMS: shamefaced, meek
ANTONYMS: bold, saucy, brazen, confident

20. stamina
(stam' ə nə)

(*n.*) the strength needed to keep going or overcome physical or mental strain; staying power

Marathon runners need a great deal of _____ stamina _____.

SYNONYM: endurance

Completing the Sentence

From the words for this unit, choose the one that best completes each of the following sentences. Write the word in the space provided.

1. The brisk breeze caused the sheets on the line to _____ **billow** _____ like the sails on a yacht that is running with the wind.

2. The hot, _____ **arid** _____ climate of Arizona is favorable for many people suffering from various diseases, such as arthritis.

3. The skyscraper is one of the best-known forms of _____ **contemporary** _____ architecture.

4. Although I may hurt your feelings, my conscience _____ **constrained** _____ me to tell you exactly what is on my mind.

5. Since Tom is both smart and _____ **disinterested** _____, I think he is just the person to decide which of us is right in this long and bitter quarrel.

6. Fortunately, I was able to fight off my _____ **assailant** _____, even though his attack took me by complete surprise.

7. You talk so fast and in such a low tone of voice that you are going to be completely _____ **incomprehensible** _____ to most people.

8. Held back by _____ **adverse** _____ winds, the plane arrived at the airport two hours late.

9. Parrots and a few other kinds of birds can _____ **mimic** _____ sounds, particularly human speech.

10. Under the law, the _____ **maximum** _____ number of people who may ride in this bus is seventy-five.

11. For a long time, I thought that he was a good and sincere person, but I finally saw that he was no more than a(n) _____ **hypocrite** _____.

12. The _____ **serene** _____ expression on her face showed that she was totally undisturbed by the confusion and turmoil around her.

13. This basic textbook _____ **encompasses** _____ all the information you will have to master for the entrance examination.

14. Using the entire east wall of the new Post Office building, the painter tried to _____ **depict** _____ the founding of our city.

15. The jury found the defendant "not guilty" because they were convinced that the charges against her were _____ **groundless** _____.

16. I was so embarrassed by my blunder that I could do nothing but grin in a(n) _____ **sheepish** _____ and self-conscious way.

17. You and Lucy will never settle your quarrel unless you _____ **confront** _____ each other directly and listen to what the other person has to say.

18. Very few starting pitchers have the _____ stamina _____ to pitch well for nine innings.

19. A breeze sprang up and began to _____ ruffle _____ the smooth and tranquil surface of the water.

20. As you become a more skillful driver, you will be able to _____ manipulate _____ all the controls of the car while keeping your eyes on the road.

Synonyms

*Choose the word from this unit that is **the same** or **most nearly the same** in meaning as the **boldface** word or expression in the given phrase. Write the word on the line provided.*

1. enough **endurance** for the walk-a-thon — stamina

2. the **largest** quantity available — maximum

3. **maneuver** the dial to the exact position — manipulate

4. that she can **parrot** my every action — mimic

5. could not mask that **shamefaced** look — sheepish

6. confused by the child's **bewildering** behavior — incomprehensible

7. mistrustful of that **phony** — hypocrite

8. a **tranquil** expanse of clear blue sky — serene

9. tried to **restrict** the patient — constrain

10. to serve as a **neutral** witness — disinterested

11. as colorful parachutes **surge** open — billow

12. difficult to iron those lace **frills** — ruffles

13. will never forget the **attacker**'s voice — assailant

14. used pastels to **illustrate** the scene — depict

15. a fence to **surround** the whole backyard — encompass

Antonyms

*Choose the word from this unit that is **most nearly opposite** in meaning to the **boldface** word or expression in the given phrase. Write the word on the line provided.*

16. has a very **fertile** imagination — arid

17. with a collection of **antique** chairs — contemporary

18. **reasonable** concerns about our safety — groundless

19. due to **favorable** experiences in the past — adverse

20. to continually **evade** problems — confront

Choosing the Right Word

*Circle the **boldface** word that more satisfactorily completes each of the following sentences.*

1. If you (**billow, confront**) your problems honestly and openly, instead of trying to hide them, you will have a better chance of solving them.

2. The big-league shortstop (**manipulates, constrains**) his glove like a magician, snaring every ball hit within reach.

3. A good scientist must have a keen mind, an unquenchable curiosity, and a (**groundless, disinterested**) desire to discover the truth.

4. She has many interesting ideas, but she seems to lack the physical and mental (**stamina, assailant**) to make good use of them.

5. The (**adverse, sheepish**) publicity that he received during the investigation was probably the cause of his defeat in the next election.

6. Do you think it would be a good idea to set a (**maximum, contemporary**) figure for the amount of homework any teacher is allowed to assign?

7. After giving a few (**sheepish, serene**) excuses, the swimmers packed up and left the private beach.

8. Anyone who has ever sailed a small boat knows how thrilling it is to feel the spray in your face while the sails (**billow, encompass**) overhead.

9. After many stormy years in the service of his country, George Washington retired to the (**serene, adverse**) life of his beloved Mount Vernon.

10. After living for many years in that roomy old farmhouse, I felt awfully (**arid, constrained**) in that small apartment.

11. My idea of a(n) (**assailant, hypocrite**) is a person who gives advice that he or she is not willing to follow.

12. His decision not to accept our sincere offer of assistance is completely (**disinterested, incomprehensible**) to me.

13. I didn't want to (**ruffle, manipulate**) the feelings of the hotel manager, but I felt that I had to complain about the miserable service.

14. Martin Luther King, Jr. and Robert F. Kennedy were (**contemporaries, mimics**), born within a few years of each other.

15. We expected the lecture on the energy crisis to be exciting, but it turned out to be a(n) (**ruffled, arid**) rundown of well-known facts and figures.

16. Despite the fact that she was in shock, the victim gave a clear description of her (**hypocrite, assailant**).

17. The science program in our school (**depicts, encompasses**) biology, chemistry, physics, earth science, and other related courses.

18. What a relief to learn that my parents had been delayed by a storm, and that all my fears about an accident were (**groundless, maximum**)!

19. She has gained success as a writer who knows how to (**confront, depict**) in a lifelike way the hopes, fears, and problems of young people today.

20. Instead of working so hard to (**mimic, ruffle**) popular TV stars, why don't you try to develop an acting style of your own?

*Read the following passage, in which some of the words you have studied in this unit appear in **boldface** type. Then complete each statement given below the passage by circling the letter of the item that is **the same** or **almost the same** in meaning as the highlighted word.*

"A Pageant of Fatigue"

(Line)

One of the most **incomprehensible** public competitions ever conceived was the dance marathon. The object of this crazy contest, first held in 1923, was to see which couple could dance for longer than any other. Grace and style didn't matter. **Stamina** was the only thing that counted.

Dance marathons were wildly popular in the 1920s and 1930s. Young couples (5) staggered around dance floors, moving to the **contemporary** tunes of the day. The music was played by live bands or on records. The last couple to remain standing won. Winners might be rewarded up to a **maximum** of $1000, which was a vast sum at that time. But they faced (10) highly **adverse** conditions in their efforts to win.

Rules varied slightly from contest to contest, but the main idea was always the same. Dancers could never leave the dance floor, except to use the rest room. They were (15) **constrained** to eat, drink, and sleep on their feet. They always had to move, at least a little. Partners took turns supporting each other as best they could.

Critics claimed that the dance marathons (20) were simply physical cruelty. Lawmakers tried to get the contests banned. However, curious onlookers packed the dance halls. To them, it was entertaining to watch weary dancers.

A woman struggles to hold up her fast-fading dance partner.

Why did people put themselves through this? (25) Of course, there was prize money at stake. But the major reason seemed to be the power of the fad itself. Marathon dancers became overnight celebrities. Morning papers ran ongoing stories on them. People couldn't resist tales of wacky, risk-taking heroism, and juicy gossip about the dancers, whose relationships suffered as much as their bodies did during those grueling hours. (30)

---

1. The meaning of **incomprehensible** (line 1) is
   a. understandable
   c. baffling
   b. famous
   d. tiring

2. The meaning of **stamina** (line 4) is
   a. endurance
   c. rhythm
   b. weakness
   d. intelligence

3. Contemporary (line 6) most nearly means
   a. ancient
   c. popular
   b. jazzy
   d. current

4. Maximum (line 9) is best defined as
   a. money reward
   c. lowest amount
   b. special prize
   d. greatest amount

5. Adverse (line 11) most nearly means
   a. helpful
   c. musical
   b. difficult
   d. competitive

6. Constrained (line 16) is best defined as
   a. liberated
   c. portrayed
   b. compelled
   d. exploited

Definitions

Note carefully the spelling, pronunciation, part(s) of speech, and definition(s) of each of the following words. Then write the word in the blank space(s) in the illustrative sentence(s) following. Finally, study the lists of synonyms and antonyms given at the end of each entry.

1. barrage
(bə räzh')

(*n.*) a rapid, large-scale outpouring of something
The audience asked the governor a ____**barrage**____ of questions about possible budget cuts.
SYNONYMS: bombardment, shelling, volley, blast

2. bigot
(big' ət)

(*n.*) an intolerant, prejudiced, or biased person
When you speak in that narrow-minded way, you sound like a ____**bigot**____.
SYNONYM: racist

3. designate
(dez' ig nāt)

(*v.*) to indicate, point out; to appoint; (*adj.*) selected but not yet installed
Will you please tell me when the coach will ____**designate**____ a team leader?
The new student council ____**designate**____ is looking forward to making many changes to the student government.
SYNONYMS: (*v.*) name, signify, denote, nominate, choose

4. diversity
(di vər' sə tē)

(*n.*) difference, variety; a condition of having many different types or forms
Our science teacher has a ____**diversity**____ of interests, including an appreciation of Russian literature.
SYNONYM: dissimilarity
ANTONYMS: similarity, sameness, uniformity

5. enigma
(i nig' mə)

(*n.*) someone or something that is extremely puzzling; that which cannot be understood or explained
Critics complained that the plot twists in the new mystery movie make it an ____**enigma**____.
SYNONYMS: riddle, mystery, puzzle, conundrum

6. gloat
(glōt)

(*v.*) to look at or think about with great intensity and satisfaction; to take great personal joy in
I will try not to ____**gloat**____ about winning a scholarship to music camp.
SYNONYMS: relish, revel in, crow over
ANTONYMS: regret, bemoan, mourn, feel chagrined

7. global
(glō′ bəl)

(*adj.*) of, relating to, or involving the entire world; comprehensive

E-mail and the Internet have linked the entire world into a
_____ **global** _____ village.

SYNONYMS: worldwide, universal, widespread
ANTONYMS: local, regional, provincial

8. illusion
(i lü′ zhən)

(*n.*) a false idea; something that one seems to see or to be aware
of that really does not exist

Artist M. C. Escher often used optical _____ **illusions** _____.

SYNONYMS: delusion, fantasy, deception
ANTONYMS: reality, truth, actuality

9. infuriate
(in fyür′ ē āt)

(*v.*) to make very angry, enrage

It _____ **infuriates** _____ most parents when their
children refuse to listen to them and treat them with disrespect.

SYNONYMS: provoke, incense, madden
ANTONYMS: calm, soothe, pacify, please

10. motivate
(mō′ tə vāt)

(*v.*) to provide with a reason for doing; to push on to some goal or
course of action

What is the best way to _____ **motivate** _____
students to undertake challenging work?

SYNONYMS: spur on, encourage, prompt, goad
ANTONYMS: discourage, dissuade, disincline

11. pacifist
(pas′ ə fist)

(*n.*) one who is against war or the use of violence; (*adj.*) opposing
war or violence

Martin Luther King, Jr. was a famous _____ **pacifist** _____
who had a very strong influence on the civil rights movement.

_____ **Pacifist** _____ students protested the war.

SYNONYMS:(*n.*) peacemaker, dove
ANTONYM: (*n.*) warmonger

12. queue
(kyü)

(*n.*) a line of people waiting for something (such as a bus or the
opening of a store); (*v.*) to form such a line

The long _____ **queue** _____ at the bus stop
indicated that a bus had not come for a while.

Eager fans _____ **queue** _____ up hours before
the box office opens, hoping to get the best tickets.

SYNONYMS: (*n.*) column, file, row, line
ANTONYM: (*n.*) disorganized crowd

13. restrict
(ri strikt′)

(*v.*) to keep within set limits; to confine

Doctors often advise patients to _____ **restrict** _____
their intake of fatty or salty foods.

SYNONYMS: hold back, limit
ANTONYMS: open up, enlarge, expand

14. sage
(sāj)

(*adj.*) wise; (*n.*) a very wise person

My aunt always gives me _____ **sage** _____ advice when I'm struggling with a decision.

Let's ask the _____ **sage** _____ for his opinion on how to handle this problem.

SYNONYMS: (*adj.*) sagacious; (*n.*) philosopher, Solomon
ANTONYMS: (*adj.*) foolish, unwise; (*n.*) fool, dunce

15. slake
(slāk)

(*v.*) to satisfy, relieve, or bring to an end

Nothing can _____ **slake** _____ my thirst better than a tall glass of ice water.

SYNONYMS: quench, gratify, sate, ease, assuage
ANTONYMS: increase, intensify, aggravate

16. terrain
(tə rān′)

(*n.*) the landscape, especially considered with regard to its physical features or fitness for some use; a field of knowledge

Mountain bikes are designed to stand up to even the most rugged _____ **terrain** _____ .

SYNONYMS: ground, topography, territory

17. vocation
(vō kā′ shən)

(*n.*) any trade, profession, or occupation; a sense of fitness or special calling for one's work

After many years of searching, she found her true _____ **vocation** _____ as a horse trainer.

SYNONYMS: career, pursuit
ANTONYMS: hobby, pastime, avocation

18. vow
(vau̇)

(*n.*) a solemn or sacred promise or pledge; (*v.*) to declare or promise in a solemn way

Prince Hamlet made a solemn _____ **vow** _____ to avenge his father's murder.

A bride and groom _____ **vow** _____ to love, honor, and respect each other throughout their marriage.

SYNONYMS: (*n.*) word of honor; (*v.*) pledge

19. waylay
(wā′ lā)

(*v.*) to lie in wait for and attack, ambush

Thugs often choose to _____ **waylay** _____ travelers as they wearily make their way back home.

SYNONYMS: entrap, ensnare

20. wither
(with′ ər)

(*v.*) to dry up, wilt, sag; to cause someone to feel ashamed, humiliated, or very small

Despite people's best efforts to remain young looking, skin will eventually _____ **wither** _____ with age.

SYNONYMS: shrivel, droop, shame, abash
ANTONYMS: bloom, flower, flourish, burgeon

Completing the Sentence

From the words for this unit, choose the one that best completes each of the following sentences. Write the word in the space provided.

1. Since he greatly enjoys woodworking and also makes a living from it, his hobby and his _____**vocation**_____ are one and the same.

2. I came to regard my grandmother as a(n) _____**sage**_____ whose wisdom helped to solve many family problems.

3. Even before the new president took office, he _____**designated**_____ the men and women who were to serve in his cabinet.

4. No decent person will _____**gloat**_____ over someone else's failures or misfortunes.

5. How sad it is to see such beautiful flowers _____**wither**_____ and die!

6. Is it possible to be a(n) _____**pacifist**_____ in a world where so many people are using force to take unfair advantage of others?

7. The animals in the drought area traveled for many miles to reach a body of water where they could _____**slake**_____ their thirst.

8. A person can usually tell how popular a new movie is by the length of the _____**queue**_____ in front of the box office.

9. The desire to be the world's top tennis player _____**motivated**_____ the young woman to spend hours every day improving her game.

10. Our hike was not very long, but the _____**terrain**_____ was so rocky and hilly that we were exhausted by the time we reached our goal.

11. The rich _____**diversity**_____ of plant and animal life in a tropical rain forest never ceases to amaze me.

12. I don't understand what he is aiming at or why he behaves as he does; in fact, his whole personality is a(n) _____**enigma**_____ to me.

13. Because the show is scheduled to end after midnight, the management will _____**restrict**_____ admission to people over sixteen.

14. As she was sworn in, she made a(n) _____**vow**_____ that she would never use the powers of her office for selfish or unworthy purposes.

15. Like a typical _____**bigot**_____, he believes that any customs different from his own are "wrong" and "uncivilized."

16. For better or for worse, as you become older and more experienced, you will lose many of the comforting _____**illusions**_____ of youth.

17. The deadly _____**barrage**_____ of shells from our guns pinned down the enemy troops on the narrow beach where they had landed.

18. The pollution problem, far from being limited to the United States, is truly _____ global _____ in scope.

19. Nothing _____ infuriates _____ my boss more than an employee who is late for work and then offers a foolish excuse for not arriving on time.

20. The police now believe that the mugger _____ waylaid _____ the elderly woman as she entered the elevator of her apartment house.

Synonyms

*Choose the word from this unit that is **the same** or **most nearly the same** in meaning as the **boldface** word or expression in the given phrase. Write the word on the line provided.*

1. a dirty look that made me **droop** _____ wither _____

2. **quench** their cravings for a refreshing drink _____ slake _____

3. a plot to **ensnare** unsuspecting victims _____ waylay _____

4. the most respected **philosopher** of them all _____ sage _____

5. must **pledge** to tell the truth _____ vow _____

6. ignored the ravings of that **biased person** _____ bigot _____

7. the magician's most unique **deception** _____ illusion _____

8. to **revel in** our team's victory _____ gloat about _____

9. trying to **incense** the manager _____ infuriate _____

10. the rewarding **career** of being a chef _____ vocation _____

11. ending with a **volley** of fireworks _____ barrage _____

12. close-ups of the **topography** of Mars _____ terrain _____

13. **choose** it as the team's new logo _____ designate _____

14. **mystery** to anyone who stumbled upon it _____ enigma _____

15. the last in the **row** of guests _____ queue _____

Antonyms

*Choose the word from this unit that is **most nearly opposite** in meaning to the **boldface** word or expression in the given phrase. Write the word on the line provided.*

16. appreciated the **uniformity** of the activities _____ diversity _____

17. to **expand** their options _____ restrict _____

18. might **discourage** people who aren't sure _____ motivate _____

19. in speeches given by a notable **warmonger** _____ pacifist _____

20. part of a **local** manufacturing company _____ global _____

Choosing the Right Word

*Circle the **boldface** word that more satisfactorily completes each of the following sentences.*

1. The United States has laws that (**restrict,** waylay) the numbers and kinds of immigrants allowed to enter this country.

2. By the time you are old enough to enter the workforce, many (**vocations,** sages) that are important today may not even exist anymore.

3. As the defense attorney left the courtroom, he was (**waylaid,** designated) by a group of eager reporters trying to get a statement from him.

4. With the other team ten points ahead and only a few minutes left to play, our hopes of victory began to (**wither,** gloat).

5. Since I am convinced that violence always creates more problems than it solves, I have become a (**pacifist,** bigot).

6. The children who are admitted free to the ball game will be allowed to sit only in certain (**designated,** motivated) parts of the stands.

7. To (**slake,** restrict) our curiosity, you will have to tell us everything that happened during that strange trip.

8. No matter what it may cost me to carry out, I will never break my sacred (**vow,** illusion).

9. Before we begin our backpacking trip, we should have a good idea of the (**terrain,** vocation) we are going to cover.

10. Has it ever occurred to you that your belief that you are a superior person and a natural leader may be no more than a(n) (illusion, **barrage**)?

11. Just how and why two people fall in love is a(n) (queue, **enigma**) that no scientist has ever been able to explain.

12. A good loser doesn't sulk over defeat; a good winner doesn't (**gloat,** vow) after victory.

13. Since you have so many prejudices of your own, you should think twice before you accuse other people of being (enigmas, **bigots**).

14. A great teacher not only makes the material of the course understandable but also (infuriates, **motivates**) the students to want to learn more.

15. World War II was a truly (**global,** pacifist) struggle, fought in all parts of the world by people of every race and background.

16. She is never bored because she has a great (enigma, **diversity**) of interests, ranging from folk dancing to mathematics.

17. The applicants for the job will have to (**queue,** slake) up in an orderly way and wait their turns to be interviewed.

18. Entangled in the trapper's net, the (**infuriated,** withered) lion roared in helpless anger.

19. When the speaker asked for opinions from the audience, he was greeted with a (**barrage,** terrain) of critical remarks and angry questions.

20. Her analysis of what is wrong with our city government seems to me remarkably (**sage,** global) and helpful.

Vocabulary in Context

*Read the following passage, in which some of the words you have studied in this unit appear in **boldface** type. Then complete each statement given below the passage by circling the letter of the item that is **the same** or **almost the same** in meaning as the highlighted word.*

Welcome to Ellis Island

(Line)

A range of factors **motivated** immigrants to leave their homelands to come to America. Many sought to escape poverty or prejudice. Some wanted to follow dreams, such as promises of jobs, safe homes, or their own farms. Others clung to exciting **illusions** about how grand life in America would be. Whatever the

(5) reasons, between 1892 and 1954, more than twelve million immigrants passed through the Federal Immigration Center on Ellis Island in New York Harbor. There, beneath the welcoming arms of the Statue of Liberty, a

(10) **diversity** of hopeful newcomers took their first steps on American soil.

Many immigrants had spent as long as two miserable, seasick weeks on the harsh ocean crossing. What a joy it must have been for

(15) these weary newcomers to step onto land. At Ellis Island, they were greeted by a **barrage** of languages, sights, and smells.

Not all immigrants arriving in New York entered through Ellis Island. Those rich enough

Dreamlike, the towers of Ellis Island rise beyond a welcoming Lady Liberty.

(20) to travel as first- or second-class passengers did not have to wait and worry on the endless **queues** of the inspection process. These lucky ones had brief shipboard inspections and could exit right into the hustle and bustle of New York City.

The third-class passengers had to endure many medical and legal inspections. Lucky ones might complete the Ellis Island process in about five hours. Inspectors

(25) checked legal papers and asked questions about the immigrant's family and **vocation**. The process was nerve-racking, but nearly 98% of new arrivals were let into the United States when it was over.

Visitors to the Ellis Island Immigration Museum today can retrace the footsteps of those immigrants. They can pass through the original Great Hall, which was restored in

(30) the 1980s. They can see photographs, documents, and precious possessions and hear recordings of immigrants sharing their experiences.

1. The meaning of **motivated** (line 1) is
  a. prompted   c. angered
  b. dissuaded   d. confined

2. Illusions (line 4) is best defined as
  a. realities   c. stories
  b. fantasies   d. notes

3. Diversity (line 10) most nearly means
  a. college   c. uniformity
  b. swarm   d. variety

4. The meaning of **barrage** (line 16) is
  a. landscape   c. bombardment
  b. scarcity   d. scene

5. Queues (line 21) most nearly means
  a. crowds   c. questions
  b. lines   d. process

6. Vocation (line 26) is best defined as
  a. friends   c. background
  b. hobbies   d. occupation

Analogies

In each of the following, circle the item that best completes the comparison.

See pages T38–T48 for explanations of answers.

1. inept is to **skill** as
a. serene is to calmness
b. immense is to size
c. ignorant is to knowledge ✓
d. ingenious is to cleverness

2. jacket is to **apparel** as
a. chair is to furniture ✓
b. ruffle is to equipment
c. horse is to utensil
d. rope is to machine

3. gainful is to **profit** as
a. groundless is to substance
b. informative is to knowledge ✓
c. penniless is to money
d. uniform is to diversity

4. desert is to **arid** as
a. plateau is to flat ✓
b. valley is to high
c. stream is to broad
d. mountain is to low

5. sage is to **wisdom** as
a. assailant is to skill
b. bigot is to prejudice ✓
c. pacifist is to fear
d. mimic is to wealth

6. famished is to **eat** as
a. sleepy is to write
b. fatigued is to wear
c. exhausted is to play
d. thirsty is to drink ✓

7. invisible is to **see** as
a. inaccurate is to correct
b. incomprehensible is to understand ✓
c. inclined is to do
d. intelligent is to know

8. nosh is to **repast** as
a. blizzard is to tornado
b. thunderstorm is to breeze
c. flood is to heat wave
d. shower is to hurricane ✓

9. big is to **immense** as
a. high is to wide
b. black is to green
c. small is to tiny ✓
d. smooth is to rough

10. marathon is to **stamina** as
a. award is to money
b. election is to manipulation
c. sprint is to speed ✓
d. prize is to strength

11. thirst is to **slake** as
a. fire is to extinguish ✓
b. city is to besiege
c. family is to forsake
d. pest is to irk

12. douse is to **liquid** as
a. kindle is to flame ✓
b. dispatch is to air
c. freeze is to heat
d. thaw is to snow

13. enigma is to **puzzlement** as
a. illusion is to satisfaction
b. vow is to horror
c. libel is to pleasure
d. misgiving is to uncertainty ✓

14. sheepish is to **embarrassment** as
a. delighted is to disgust
b. infuriated is to anger ✓
c. puzzled is to contentment
d. bored is to enthusiasm

15. hypocrite is to **insincere** as
a. fool is to sage
b. oaf is to clumsy ✓
c. assailant is to sheepish
d. dunce is to ingenious

16. pacifist is to **war** as
a. glutton is to food
b. vegetarian is to meat ✓
c. drunkard is to liquor
d. piper is to smoking

17. hand is to **manipulate** as
a. foot is to denounce
b. head is to compress
c. nose is to designate
d. eye is to observe ✓

18. painter is to **depict** as
a. dancer is to compose
b. sculptor is to suggest
c. author is to hide
d. mimic is to imitate ✓

Word Associations

In each of the following groups, circle the word that is best defined or suggested by the given phrase.

1. living at the same time
a. gainful
b. maximum
c. global
d. contemporary

2. to hold someone back
a. constrain
b. vow
c. wither
d. slake

3. totally lacking skill or appropriateness
a. instantaneous
b. inept
c. immense
d. arid

4. something that is deeply puzzling
a. dispatch
b. illusion
c. bigot
d. enigma

5. to enrage
a. billow
b. infuriate
c. recede
d. ruffle

6. to provide a reason or purpose for doing something
a. motivate
b. restrict
c. forsake
d. designate

7. a feeling of doubt or uneasiness
a. libel
b. diversity
c. misgiving
d. stamina

8. having no substance or foundation
a. ingenious
b. disinterested
c. groundless
d. sheepish

9. a heavy outpouring (as of questions)
a. barrage
b. queue
c. compress
d. terrain

10. one who pretends to be better than he or she really is
a. hypocrite
b. assailant
c. contemporary
d. pacifist

11. to quench
a. slake
b. constrain
c. gloat
d. dispatch

12. an idea not based on reality
a. billow
b. hypocrite
c. illusion
d. sage

13. calm and composed
a. sheepish
b. gainful
c. instantaneous
d. serene

14. a person's lifework or career
a. terrain
b. libel
c. stamina
d. vocation

15. a solemn promise
a. vow
b. repast
c. apparel
d. misgiving

16. to include or enclose within certain boundaries
a. depict
b. encompass
c. manipulate
d. denounce

17. a person whose prejudices are always showing
a. pacifist
b. oaf
c. bigot
d. mimic

18. the swelling waters
a. dispatching
b. dousing
c. billowing
d. receding

19. to brag about their victory
a. encompass
b. gloat
c. confront
d. motivate

20. writing that can harm someone's reputation
a. dispatch
b. libel
c. ruffle
d. diversity

Vocabulary in Context

*Read the following passage, in which some of the words you have studied in Units 1–3 appear in **boldface** type. Then complete each statement given below the passage by circling the item that is **the same** or **almost the same** in meaning as the highlighted word.*

Wintry Wonder

(Line)

Picture a vast castle or imagine an oversized cartoon figure. Now, try to imagine each of them made of snow and ice. This is what you would see if
(5) you attend the Sapporo Snow Festival, a weeklong event held each year in northern Japan, on the island of Hokkaido.

Unlike other cities in Japan,
(10) Sapporo is fairly young. It has no ancient temples. Its streets are unusually wide and straight. The city is a popular destination for those who enjoy winter sports. In fact, the 1972
(15) Winter Olympic Games were held in Sapporo.

The Sapporo Snow Festival draws both young and old into its wintry wonderland fantasies. Most people
(20) familiar with winter festivals **designate** the Sapporo Snow Festival as the most famous of its kind. The city plans ahead for months. It is impossible for visitors to
(25) get hotel rooms without **expressly** reserving them far in advance.

The Sapporo Snow Festival had modest beginnings. In 1950, high school students made six snow
(30) sculptures in a **serene** park in the center of town. What began as fun for creative teenagers has grown into a **global** event. Odori Park, the location of those first snow sculptures,
(35) continues to be one of the three main festival sites.

Since the early days, much of the work to mount the festival has been done by the Self-Defense Forces.
(40) This branch of the Japanese military **dispatches** hundreds of soldiers in army trucks to haul snow from nearby mountains into the city. This peacetime work serves the public
(45) and keeps costs down.

Visitors to the Snow Festival today might see gigantic sculptures that **depict** prehistoric animals, Viking warriors, famous people, and even
(50) cartoon characters! Bands play music from atop huge sound stages built of snow. Daredevils can zoom down elaborate ice slides. Nightly fireworks, colored lights, and other
(55) special sound and lighting effects add extra excitement.

Make your reservations now!

---

1. The meaning of **designate** (line 21) is
  a. avoid
  (b. name)
  c. deny
  d. design

2. Expressly (line 25) most nearly means
  a. quickly
  (b. explicitly)
  c. casually
  d. accidentally

3. Serene (line 30) is best defined as
  a. enormous
  b. municipal
  (c. tranquil)
  d. pretty

4. The meaning of **global** (line 33) is
  a. festive
  b. regional
  c. mysterious
  (d. universal)

5. Dispatches (line 41) most nearly means
  (a. sends out)
  b. rewards
  c. joins with
  d. repairs

6. Depict (line 48) is best defined as
  a. encircle
  b. analyze
  c. surround
  (d. represent)

Choosing the Right Meaning

Read each sentence carefully. Then circle the item that best completes the statement below the sentence.

See pages T38–T48 for explanations of answers.

In keeping with his strong pacifist beliefs, the poet Robert Lowell served a prison term for refusing to bear arms during World War II. (2)

1. In line 1 the word **pacifist** most nearly means

a. militant   b. criminal   c. old-fashioned   (d. antiwar)

When compresses failed to slow the bleeding, medics applied a tourniquet above the soldier's wound. (2)

2. The word **compresses** in line 1 is used to mean

(a. bandage pads)   b. medicines   c. condensations   d. reductions

In computer terminology a global command is one that applies to an entire file, document, or program. (2)

3. The word **global** in line 1 is best defined as

a. worldwide   b. widespread   c. random   (d. comprehensive)

Before they are confirmed by the Senate, those whom the president selects for cabinet posts are termed "secretaries designate." (2)

4. The word **designate** in line 2 is used to mean

a. veteran   b. resigned   (c. nominated)   d. experienced

The well-dressed gentleman of the late eighteenth century wore ruffles of sheer linen or lace at his throat and wrists. (2)

5. In line 1 the word **ruffles** most nearly means

a. wrinkles   c. ripples
(b. gathered trimmings)   d. irritations

Antonyms

*In each of the following groups, circle the word or expression that is most nearly the **opposite** of the word in **boldface** type.*

1. immense
a. illegal
b. vast
c. useless
(d. small)

2. adverse
a. fatal
b. harmful
(c. positive)
d. puzzling

3. maximum
(a. lowest)
b. highest
c. biggest
d. average

4. sheepish
a. unfriendly
(b. bold)
c. timid
d. silly

5. sage
(a. foolish)
b. wise
c. strange
d. unexpected

6. expressly
a. purposely
(b. accidentally)
c. quickly
d. cleverly

7. infuriate
a. anger
b. cheat
(c. please)
d. ignore

8. wither
(a. flourish)
b. ensnare
c. discourage
d. pressure

9. famished
a. frozen
b. confident
c. satiated
d. hungry

10. disinterested
a. wise
b. prejudiced
c. bored
d. foreign

11. global
a. local
b. worldwide
c. vast
d. unmeasured

12. vocation
a. job
b. house
c. family
d. hobby

13. contemporary
a. intelligent
b. puzzling
c. ancient
d. famous

14. irk
a. smear
b. delight
c. punish
d. hurt

15. forsake
a. stall
b. stand by
c. hire
d. leave

16. incomprehensible
a. puzzling
b. understandable
c. interesting
d. boring

Word Families

A. *On the line provided, write the word you have learned in Units 1–3 that is related to each of the following nouns.*

EXAMPLE: compression—**compress**

1. manipulator, manipulation — manipulate
2. restriction — restrict
3. motivation, motivator — motivate
4. confrontation, confrontationist — confront
5. designation, designator — designate
6. denouncement, denunciation — denounce
7. adversity, adverseness — adverse
8. recession — recede
9. ingeniousness — ingenious
10. depicter, depiction — depict
11. immenseness, immensity — immense
12. ineptitude — inept
13. encompassment — encompass
14. aridity, aridness — arid
15. fury — infuriate
16 instant — instantaneous

B. *On the line provided, write the word you have learned in Units 1–3 that is related to each of the following verbs.*

EXAMPLE: pacify—**pacifist**

17. maximize — maximum
18. divert — diversity
19. assail — assailant
20. comprehend — incomprehensible

Two-Word Completions

Circle the pair of words that best complete the meaning of each of the following passages.

See pages T38–T48 for explanations of answers.

1. As the travelers crossed the hot and _____ wasteland known as the Sahara Desert, their eyes were deceived more than once by mirages and other optical _____ .

a. adverse . . . mimics
b. immense . . . vocations
c. groundless . . . enigmas
d. arid . . . illusions

2. It took a great deal of _____ to keep up with the rest of the pack as they sped across the broken and hilly _____ that separated them from the finish line in the cross-country race.

a. dispatch . . . apparel
b. misgiving . . . repast
c. stamina . . . terrain
d. diversity . . . barrage

3. Two ruffians _____ the weary traveler on a lonely stretch of road, but the man was able to beat off his _____ with the help of his stout staff.

a. waylaid . . . assailants
b. dispatched . . . oafs
c. confronted . . . hypocrites
d. constrained . . . pacifists

4. The demand for tickets to the play-offs was so heavy that for days the box office was _____ like some embattled fortress by mobs of people waiting more or less impatiently in long _____ that snaked endlessly around the whole block.

a. denounced . . . enigmas
b. besieged . . . queues
c. confronted . . . ruffles
d. encompassed . . . billows

5. Though other people have been moved to action by high ideals, Thomas Alva Edison, one of the most _____ inventors ever to be produced by this country, seems in part to have been _____ simply by the love of a challenge.

a. disinterested . . . manipulated
b. ingenious . . . motivated
c. inept . . . infuriated
d. immense . . . dispatched

6. Despite the _____ of vigorous insults coming from the other gubernatorial candidate, she refused to retaliate and _____ her competition.

a. illusion . . . libel
b. billow . . . infuriate
c. apparel . . . besiege
d. barrage . . . denounce

de—down; away from; completely; not

Building with Classical Roots

Many words in English are made up of a root and/or a prefix and suffix. In order to determine the meanings of many words, you have to know the meaning of the root, prefix, and/or suffix. The prefix *de*, for example, appears in **denounce** (page 21), **depict** (page 29), and **designate** (page 35). Some other words in which this prefix appears are listed below.

debunk	default	demerit	desperate
decapitate	defraud	depression	devolve

From the list of words above, choose the one that corresponds to each of the brief definitions below. Write the word in the blank space in the illustrative sentence below the definition.

1. a mark against, usually involving the loss of some privilege or right; a fault, defect

Unacceptable behavior earned him so many _____**demerits**_____ that he was not allowed to go on the class trip.

2. to fail to perform a task or fulfill an obligation; the failure to do something required by law or duty

The challenger failed to show up, so the defender won by _____**default**_____.

3. to cut off the head, behead

Experienced chefs know how to gut, scale, and _____**decapitate**_____ a fish before cooking it.

4. driven to take any risk; hopeless; extreme

Lack of water led homesteaders to take _____**desperate**_____ measures to save their families.

5. an area that is sunk below its surroundings; a period of severe economic decline; a mood of dejection or sadness.

Slapstick comedy films were popular during the Great _____**Depression**_____ of the 1930s.

6. to pass on (a duty, task, or the like) to someone else; to be passed on to; to be conferred on

Little will change when the mayor's powers _____**devolve**_____ onto her successor.

7. to cheat, take away from, or deprive of by deceit or trickery

The corrupt attorney tried to _____**defraud**_____ her of her rightful inheritance.

8. to expose the falseness of unsound or exaggerated claims

New evidence has emerged that allows us to _____**debunk**_____ a time-honored legend.

From the list of words on page 48, choose the one that best completes each of the following sentences. Write the word in the space provided.

1. The rescue team made one last, _____ desperate _____ attempt to save the people still trapped in the sinking ship.

2. On the whole, I'd say that the new program's good points far outweigh its _____ demerits _____.

3. When my boss became ill, many of the duties and responsibilities of his job suddenly _____ devolved _____ onto me.

4. When the debtor failed to repay the loan in a timely manner, the bank was forced to declare him in _____ default _____.

5. Scores of those condemned to death by the French revolutionary tribunals were _____ decapitated _____ by the guillotine.

6. Over the years, historians have _____ debunked _____ many of the famous stories associated with George Washington because they have no basis in fact.

7. After we had lost the championship game by one point, we returned to the locker room in a profound state of _____ depression _____.

8. Posing as investment counselors, the wily swindlers managed to _____ defraud _____ the elderly couple of most of their savings.

---

*Circle the **boldface** word that more satisfactorily completes each of the following sentences.*

1. Most working parents who would share their personal stories could easily (**debunk,** **devolve**) the myth that it's easy to have it all.

2. After spending hours customizing my computer display to fit my exacting standards, I accidentally engaged the (**desperate,** **default**) settings and wound up back where I started.

3. Although the brilliant student was full of potential, the major (**depression,** **demerit**) for failing to complete her senior project blocked her graduation.

4. After all conventional approaches to curing her illness failed, she felt (**desperate,** **defrauded**) and decided to take part in experimental clinical trials of new medications.

5. In 1536, King Henry VIII ordered his wife Anne Boleyn to be (**decapitated,** **defaulted**) as the ultimate punishment for treason.

6. The corrupt official attempted to (**defraud,** **debunk**) the city when she claimed certain personal expenses were business expenses.

7. Meteor Crater is a deep (**demerit,** **depression**) in Northern Arizona formed about 50,000 years ago when a meteorite crashed into the earth's surface.

8. During flu season, the job of music teacher (**devolved,** **decapitated**) to the janitor, who was able to reveal his rich talent for singing.

Writer's Challenge

Read the following sentences, paying special attention to the words and phrases underlined. From the words in the box below, find better choices for these underlined words and phrases. Then use these choices to rewrite the sentences.

WORD BANK				
adverse	barrage	diversity	instantaneous	motivate
apparel	designate	douse	irk	repast
arid	disinterested	immense	imanipulate	slake
assailant	dispatch	incomprehensible	mimic	terrain

Rattlesnakes

1. The difference of rattlesnake varieties allows them to exist in 46 of the 50 United States (excluding Alaska, Hawaii, Delaware, and Maine), but most live in deserts.

diversity

2. Most rattlesnakes prefer waterless climates, although some rattlers can exist in cold conditions and at high elevations.

arid

3. Emerging only at night to hunt, rattlesnakes may find quiet places to hide in the rocky ground—in holes, caves, crevices, or overhangs.

terrain

4. To a rattlesnake, a fine food would consist of a tasty young rodent—a mouse, a chipmunk, or a squirrel, for instance.

repast

5. Many people mistakenly believe that if they are ever bitten by a rattlesnake, they will face prompt death.

instantaneous

6. Rattlesnakes' venom is poisonous, but for most human victims, the unfavorable reactions to a bite include pain, disorientation, and fever, all of which can be treated with specific medicines.

adverse

Definitions

Note carefully the spelling, pronunciation, part(s) of speech, and definition(s) of each of the following words. Then write the word in the blank space(s) in the illustrative sentence(s) following. Finally, study the lists of synonyms and antonyms given at the end of each entry.

1. acquit
(ə kwit′)

(*v.*) to declare not guilty, free from blame, discharge completely; to conduct or behave oneself

Now that we have proof of their innocence, we can _____**acquit**_____ them of all charges.

SYNONYMS: exonerate, dismiss
ANTONYMS: convict, declare guilty

2. deem
(dēm)

(*v.*) to think, believe; to consider, have an opinion

Most people _____**deem**_____ it a wise plan to set aside savings for the future.

SYNONYMS: judge, regard

3. devastate
(dev′ ə stāt)

(*v.*) to destroy, lay waste, leave in ruins

Failure or harsh criticism can _____**devastate**_____ a person who has shaky self-esteem.

SYNONYMS: wreck, desolate
ANTONYMS: develop, improve

4. discredit
(dis kred′ it)

(*v.*) to throw doubt upon, cause to be distrusted; to damage in reputation; (*n.*) a loss or lack of belief, confidence, or reputation

We have gathered a considerable amount of evidence to _____**discredit**_____ her story.

Both parents and students felt strongly that the cheating scandal was a _____**discredit**_____ to the school.

SYNONYM: (*v.*) disparage
ANTONYMS: (*v.*) confirm, corroborate, bolster

5. elusive
(ē lü′ siv)

(*adj.*) difficult to catch or to hold; hard to explain or understand

According to legend, Zorro, the heroic Mexican character, was too _____**elusive**_____ for local police to capture.

SYNONYMS: slippery, wily, fleeting, puzzling, baffling

6. generate
(jen′ ə rāt)

(*v.*) to bring into existence; to be the cause of

Solar power uses the energy of the sun to _____**generate**_____ electricity.

SYNONYMS: create, produce, beget, cause
ANTONYMS: end, terminate, extinguish, stifle

7. idolize
(ī' dəl īz)

(v.) to worship as an idol, make an idol of; to love very much

Teens who _____idolize_____ a movie star may repeatedly see the same movie featuring that actor or actress.

SYNONYMS: adore, revere
ANTONYMS: despise, scorn, disdain, detest

8. ingratitude
(in grat' ə tüd)

(n.) a lack of thankfulness

Hosts who make every effort to please their guests are apt to be hurt by _____ingratitude_____.

SYNONYMS: thanklessness, ungratefulness
ANTONYMS: thankfulness, gratefulness, recognition

9. keepsake
(kēp' sāk)

(n.) something kept in memory of the giver; a souvenir

Before my grandmother died, she made me a special quilt as a _____keepsake_____ of her love.

SYNONYMS: reminder, memento

10. mortal
(môr' təl)

(n.) a being that must eventually die; (adj.) of or relating to such a being; causing death, fatal; possible, conceivable

In the mythology of many cultures, a heavenly god can come down to Earth and act as a _____mortal_____.

The soldier was the only one in her battalion to suffer a _____mortal_____ injury.

SYNONYMS: (n.) human; (adj.) fleeting, extreme
ANTONYMS: (n.) a god; (adj.) undying, everlasting, eternal, divine

11. ovation
(ō vā' shən)

(n.) an enthusiastic public welcome, an outburst of applause

The audience gave the dancer a standing _____ovation_____ after his impressive performance.

SYNONYMS: cheers, bravos, hurrahs
ANTONYMS: boos, jeers

12. petty
(pet' ē)

(adj.) unimportant, trivial; narrow-minded; secondary in rank, minor

You say my complaint is _____petty_____, but to me it is an issue of great importance.

SYNONYMS: insignificant, piddling
ANTONYMS: important, major, significant, weighty

13. plight
(plīt)

(n.) a sorry condition or state; (v.) to pledge, promise solemnly

The _____plight_____ of the homeless upsets many concerned citizens.

The bride and groom vowed to _____plight_____ their love for the rest of their lives.

Wedding guests watch the bride y groom plight their undying love.

14. repent
(ri pent′)

(v.) to feel sorry for what one has done or has failed to do

As people grow older and gain more maturity, some of them come to _____ repent _____ their youthful mistakes.

SYNONYM: regret
ANTONYMS: rejoice over

15. reverie
(rev′ ə rē)

(n.) a daydream; the condition of being lost in thought

My boss interrupted my deep and pleasant _____ reverie _____ by reminding me about our deadline.

SYNONYMS: fantasy, meditation

16. revocation
(rev ə kā′ shən)

(n.) an act or instance of calling back, an annulment, cancellation

His failure to complete the job according to schedule led to a _____ revocation _____ of his contract.

SYNONYMS: repeal, withdrawal
ANTONYMS: ratification, confirmation

17. scan
(skan)

(v.) to examine closely; to look over quickly but thoroughly; to analyze the rhythm of a poem; *(n.)* an examination

Let's _____ scan _____ the list to see the finishing times of each marathon runner.

The doctor did a bone _____ scan _____ to discover the location of each fracture.

SYNONYMS: *(v.)* study, glance at, skim; *(v., n.)* survey

18. strand
(strand)

(n.) a beach or shore; a string of wire, hair, etc.; *(v.)* to drive or run aground; to leave in a hopeless position

We asked the waiter to take back the soup when we discovered that a _____ strand _____ of hair in it.

I don't want to be the one to get the third out in the inning and _____ strand _____ the two base runners.

SYNONYMS: *(n.)* fiber, thread; *(v.)* abandon, maroon
ANTONYMS: *(v.)* rescue, save

19. strife
(strīf)

(n.) bitter disagreement; fighting, struggle

The experienced senator from South Carolina was a veteran of political _____ strife _____ .

SYNONYMS: conflict, discord, turmoil
ANTONYMS: peace, calm, harmony, agreement

20. topple
(täp′ əl)

(v.) to fall forward; to overturn, bring about the downfall of

The trains that rumble past our apartment often cause books to _____ topple _____ from the shelves.

SYNONYMS: unseat, upset, tumble
ANTONYMS: remain upright, establish, set up

Completing the Sentence

From the words for this unit, choose the one that best completes each of the following sentences. Write the word in the space provided.

1. Though that actress's name and face are all but forgotten today, she used to be _____**idolized**_____ by adoring fans all over the world.

2. The hurricane so _____**devastated**_____ a large section of the coast that the president declared it a disaster area.

3. I plan to save this old notebook as a(n) _____**keepsake**_____ of one of the best and most enjoyable classes I have ever had.

4. Since I sincerely appreciate all my parents have done for me, how can you accuse me of _____**ingratitude**_____?

5. Because the members of my family disagree on so many matters, the dinner table is often the scene of much verbal _____**strife**_____.

6. The evidence against the accused man proved to be so weak that the jury had no choice but to _____**acquit**_____ him.

7. I don't have the time to read every word of that long newspaper article, but I'll _____**scan**_____ it quickly to get the main idea.

8. Since it is clear that his only interest is to make money for himself, his plan for building a new highway has been completely _____**discredited**_____.

9. The wound at first did not appear to be too serious, but to our great grief it proved to be _____**mortal**_____.

10. Instead of telling us how much you _____**repent**_____ for your outrageous conduct, why don't you sincerely try to reform?

11. Regardless of what you may think proper, I do not _____**deem**_____ it necessary for someone of your age to wear an evening gown to the dance.

12. The TV program made us keenly aware of the _____**plight**_____ of elderly people trying to live on Social Security payments.

13. Tom is not a very fast runner, but he is so _____**elusive**_____ that he is extremely hard to tackle on the football field.

14. Why argue about such _____**petty**_____ matters when there are so many important problems to deal with?

15. The rope is made of many _____**strands**_____ of fiber woven together.

16. We learned that even unfavorable reviews of a new book may help to _____**generate**_____ a certain amount of public interest in it.

17. The defendant was warned that another speeding ticket would result in the _____**revocation**_____ of her driver's license.

18. The sudden racket produced by a noisy car radio jolted me out of my peaceful ___reverie___ .

19. The famous Leaning Tower of Pisa looks as though it were going to ___topple___ over any minute.

20. She richly deserved the audience's ___ovation___ for her brilliant performance.

Synonyms

*Choose the word from this unit that is **the same** or **most nearly the same** in meaning as the **boldface** word or expression in the given phrase. Write the word on the line provided.*

1. argued for a **repeal** of the law — revocation

2. **pledge** to leave them all my worldly goods — plight

3. too much **discord** to remain partners — strife

4. to **maroon** them on a deserted island — strand

5. may never **regret** his evil deeds — repent

6. power to **wreck** an entire community — devastate

7. waved his cap to acknowledge the **cheers** — ovation

8. **study** the night sky for shooting stars — scan

9. dim lights and soft music during my **meditation** — reverie

10. expect **thanklessness** from so selfish a person — ingratitude

11. for the computer to **produce** a list of dates — generate

12. so **baffling** an idea to explain to children — elusive

13. to **regard** this as my best work so far — deem

14. a **memento** of our trip to Canada — keepsake

15. **damage** his standing within the group — discredit

Antonyms

*Choose the word from this unit that is **most nearly opposite** in meaning to the **boldface** word or expression in the given phrase. Write the word on the line provided.*

16. no choice but to **convict** the defendant — acquit

17. accused of a **major** offense — petty

18. how they **disdain** their coach — idolize

19. **divine** beings, according to the legend — mortal

20. may **establish** the championship team — topple

Choosing the Right Word

*Circle the **boldface** word that more satisfactorily completes each of the following sentences.*

1. Imagine his (**plight,** ingratitude)—penniless, unemployed, and with a large family to support!

2. After so many years of (**strife,** strand)—in business, politics, and the family—he wants only to retire to the peace and quiet of his ranch.

3. I knew that she was wrapped up in herself, but I never dreamed that even she could be guilty of such (revocation, **ingratitude**).

4. We should respect our national leaders, but we should not (**idolize,** discredit) them and assume that they can do no wrong.

5. A special edition of poems by the noted writer was presented as a (**keepsake,** strife) to all who attended her 80th birthday party.

6. What an (**ovation,** reverie) he received when he trotted back to the bench after scoring the winning touchdown!

7. In my composition, I tried to give a definition of "humor," but I found the idea too (petty, **elusive**) to pin down.

8. In Shakespeare's *A Midsummer Night's Dream*, which character speaks the line, "Lord, what fools these (**mortals,** keepsakes) be"?

9. Many diseases that have disappeared in the United States continue to (**devastate,** idolize) countries in other parts of the world.

10. Since you are the only one of us who has had experience with this kind of problem, we shall do whatever you (**deem,** scan) necessary.

11. Our business is barely managing to pay its bills; one bad break will be enough to (acquit, **topple**) it into bankruptcy.

12. Are we going to allow (elusive, **petty**) quarrels to destroy a friendship that has been built up for so many years?

13. We will never allow vicious rumors to (deem, **generate**) racial hatred in our school!

14. At times we all enjoy a(n) (ovation, **reverie**) about "what might have been," but before long we must return to "the way things are."

15. Once order had been restored, the leaders of the opposition called for the (**revocation,** keepsake) of martial law.

16. At times it is quite natural to feel afraid, and it is certainly no (**discredit,** mortal) to anyone to admit it.

17. While the actors were busy rehearsing, the manager ran away with all the money and left them (**stranded,** plighted) in a strange town.

18. By reelecting him to Congress, the court of public opinion has forever (generated, **acquitted**) him of the charges of neglecting his duties.

19. Father often says that he has never stopped (**repenting,** devastating) the decision he made many years ago to give up the study of medicine.

20. Our supervisor (topples, **scans**) the newspaper each morning for items that may serve as leads for the sales force.

Vocabulary in Context

*Read the following passage, in which some of the words you have studied in this unit appear in **boldface** type. Then complete each statement given below the passage by circling the letter of the item that is **the same** or **almost the same** in meaning as the highlighted word.*

Quimby's Quest

(Line)

In May of 1911, a young pilot from Long Island's Moisant Avenue Aviation School was practicing flying. When a gust of wind blew back the person's veil, onlookers realized that the pilot was *not* a man! It was journalist Harriet Quimby. How could a woman **acquit herself** so fearlessly to such a daring endeavor?

(5)   Flying was risky for anyone at that time. Just eight years earlier, the success of the Wright Brothers' flight at Kitty Hawk, North Carolina, **generated** new goals for adventurers. Pioneering pilots **deemed** flying as the greatest challenge of the day. Determined not to let her gender hold her back, Harriet

(10) Quimby started to take flying lessons.

Quimby earned her pilot's license on August 1, 1911, making her the world's second woman—and the first American woman—to do so. Dressed in a flight suit of

(15) purple satin, she gave flying demonstrations around the United States and Mexico.

Pilot Barbara Harmer is the first and only woman to fly the Concorde SST.

Quimby was the first pilot ever to cross the English Channel. Nowadays, it may be easy to **discredit** this accomplishment since some

(20) people actually swim the 32 miles of water that separates England from France. Yet, in Quimby's time, people had little knowledge of flying or of predicting weather. She was lucky to get through the clouds that day to land safely, though way off course. Imagine the

(25) shock French fishermen must have felt when they **scanned** the horizon to see a flying machine headed for their beach!

Less than a year after Harriet Quimby became a pilot, she ~~had a~~ suffered **mortal** ~~accident.~~ injuries when She and a passenger were suddenly thrown from their seats and fell nearly a mile to their deaths in the waters near Boston. The world lost a pilot but

(30) gained a legendary pioneer.

---

1. The meaning of **acquit herself** (line 4) is
- a. behave
- b. steer
- c. react
- d. gamble

2. The meaning of **generated** (line 6) is
- a. stifled
- b. described
- c. created
- d. promised

3. Deemed (line 7) most nearly means
- a. feared
- b. ignored
- c. chose
- d. considered

4. Discredit (line 19) most nearly means
- a. explain
- b. disparage
- c. ignore
- d. honor

5. Scanned (line 25) is best defined as
- a. raced
- b. ran from
- c. glanced at
- d. avoided

6. Mortal (line 27) is best defined as
- a. fatal
- b. minor
- c. divine
- d. major

Definitions

Note carefully the spelling, pronunciation, part(s) of speech, and definition(s) of each of the following words. Then write the word in the blank space(s) in the illustrative sentence(s) following. Finally, study the lists of synonyms and antonyms given at the end of each entry.

1. acute
(ə kyüt')

(*adj.*) with a sharp point; keen and alert; sharp and severe; rising quickly to a high point and lasting for a short time

One who is an _____ **acute** _____ observer of human nature may notice subtle changes in people's behavior.

SYNONYMS: clever, penetrating
ANTONYMS: dull, blunted, mild, stupid, obtuse

2. bluster
(bləs' tər)

(*v.*) to talk or act in a noisy and threatening way; to blow in stormy gusts; (*n.*) speech that is loud and threatening

When we saw harsh winds _____ **bluster** _____ around our tent, we decided to change our plans for the weekend.

Dad's manner is all _____ **bluster** _____, but beneath it all, he's really a kind-hearted man.

SYNONYMS: (*v.*) spout, rant, brag, swagger; (*n.*) bravado

3. bungle
(bəŋ' gəl)

(*v.*) to act or work clumsily and awkwardly; to ruin something through clumsiness

If we _____ **bungle** _____ this project, we may never get another chance to prove ourselves as a worthy team.

SYNONYMS: blunder, botch, mess up

4. commentary
(käm' ən ter ē)

(*n.*) a series of notes clarifying or explaining something; an expression of opinion

Our spiritual leader gave us a helpful _____ **commentary** on the true meaning of the Ten Commandments.

SYNONYMS: explanation, remarks, narration, description, account, review, analysis

5. duration
(dù rā' shən)

(*n.*) the length of time that something continues or lasts

Even though the story was hard to follow, my friends decided to stay for the _____ **duration** _____ of the opera.

6. eerie
(ē' rē)

(*adj.*) causing fear because of strangeness; weird, mysterious

It is a lot of fun to tell _____ **eerie** _____ ghost stories around a campfire.

SYNONYMS: frightening, spooky, creepy

7. facet
(fas' ət)

(*n.*) one aspect or side of a subject or problem; one of the cut surfaces of a gem

One important _____ facet _____ of problem solving is to recognize when a solution makes no sense.

SYNONYMS: angle, characteristic, factor, element, cut

8. fidelity
(fi del' ə tē)

(*n.*) the state of being faithful; accuracy in details, exactness

The _____ fidelity _____ of scratchy old records can't match the clarity of CDs or DVDs.

SYNONYMS: loyalty, faithfulness
ANTONYMS: disloyalty, treachery, inexactness

9. fray
(frā)

(*n.*) a brawl, a noisy quarrel; (*v.*) to wear away by rubbing; make ragged or worn; to strain, irritate

After the two loudest students began arguing, the whole class jumped into the _____ fray _____.

A faucet that drips continuously can _____ fray _____ anyone's nerves.

SYNONYMS: (*n.*) scuffle; (*v.*) unravel

10. headstrong
(hed' strôŋ)

(*adj.*) willful, stubborn

Even the most patient caregiver may feel challenged when faced with a _____ headstrong _____ child.

SYNONYMS: obstinate, mulish, unruly
ANTONYMS: obedient, docile, submissive

11. inhabitant
(in hab' ə tənt)

(*n.*) one living permanently in a given place

Although she enjoys traveling to exotic places, she's a lifelong _____ inhabitant _____ of this small town.

SYNONYMS: resident, native, occupant, tenant
ANTONYMS: stranger, outsider, visitor, foreigner

12. numb
(nəm)

(*adj.*) having lost the power of feeling or movement; (*v.*) to dull the feelings of; to cause to lose feeling

Bitter cold may leave your toes _____ numb _____, so try to wear woolen socks.

This injection will _____ numb _____ the area so that the doctor can stitch the cut painlessly.

SYNONYMS: (*adj.*) unfeeling, insensible, dazed; (*v.*) deaden
ANTONYMS: (*adj.*) sensitive, alert

13. pacify
(pas' ə fī)

(*v.*) to make peaceful or calm; to soothe

The factory owners hope to _____ pacify _____ the angry protesters with promises of higher wages and shorter working hours.

SYNONYMS: mollify, placate
ANTONYMS: anger, arouse, stir up, foment, ignite

14. ravenous
(rav′ ə nəs)

(*adj.*) greedy; very hungry; eager for satisfaction

Exercising vigorously for several hours gives me a
_____ravenous_____ appetite.

SYNONYMS: starved, famished, voracious, wolfish
ANTONYMS: not hungry, well-fed, satisfied, satiated

15. refute
(ri fyüt′)

(*v.*) to prove incorrect

After analyzing the situation, I now know a foolproof way to
_____refute_____ the original claim.

SYNONYMS: disprove, rebut
ANTONYMS: prove, support, confirm, corroborate

16. remorse
(ri mors′)

(*n.*) deep and painful regret for one's past misdeeds; pangs of
conscience

When the driver realized what a terrible accident he had
caused, he was overcome with _____remorse_____.

SYNONYM: guilt
ANTONYMS: clear conscience, guiltlessness

17. setback
(set′ bak)

(*n.*) something that interferes with progress; a disappointment,
unexpected loss or defeat; a steplike recession in a wall

A broken toe can be a major _____setback_____
for a skater who hopes to qualify for the Olympics.

SYNONYMS: failure, reversal
ANTONYMS: advance, gain, progress, triumph

18. smug
(sməg)

(*adj.*) overly self-satisfied, self-righteous

Just because he got the lead in the school play doesn't
justify his irritating air of _____smug_____
superiority.

SYNONYMS: conceited, complacent
ANTONYMS: discontented, disgruntled

19. synopsis
(si năp′ sis)

(*n.*) a brief statement giving a general view of some subject,
book, etc.; a summary

The teacher's guide gives a _____synopsis_____
of the plot of each story in the collection.

SYNONYMS: outline, digest, abstract

20. tarry
(tar′ ē)

(*v.*) to delay leaving; to linger, wait; to remain or stay for a while

He will be tempted to _____tarry_____
longer if he thinks that this might be their last visit together.

SYNONYMS: dawdle, dally
ANTONYMS: rush, hasten, leave, depart

Completing the Sentence

From the words for this unit, choose the one that best completes each of the following sentences. Write the word in the space provided.

1. By _____**blustering**_____ in a loud, confident voice, he tried to convince us that he had nothing to do with the accident.

2. The program contained a(n) _____**synopsis**_____ of the opera, so that we were able to follow the action even though the singing was in Italian.

3. No one can question her complete _____**fidelity**_____ to basic American ideas and ideals.

4. His _____**smug**_____ expression showed how highly he valued his own opinions and scorned the views of others.

5. Some children are as docile as sheep; others are as _____**headstrong**_____ as mules.

6. Our team suffered a tough _____**setback**_____ when our best player was hurt in the first few minutes of play.

7. Because of our inexperience and haste, we _____**bungled**_____ the little repair job so badly that it became necessary to replace the entire motor.

8. Is it true that the _____**inhabitants**_____ of Maine are sometimes called "Maniacs"?

9. After eating a light breakfast and hiking for hours in the crisp mountain air, you can imagine how _____**ravenous**_____ we were by lunchtime.

10. Since the convicted felon had shown no _____**remorse**_____ for his crimes, the judge sentenced him to the maximum prison term allowed.

11. Anyone who has never had a sprained ankle will find it hard to imagine how _____**acute**_____ the pain is.

12. After the dentist gave me an injection of novocaine, the whole side of my jaw turned _____**numb**_____.

13. I had a(n) _____**eerie**_____ feeling that we were being followed and that something bad might happen.

14. The accused person must be given every chance to _____**refute**_____ the charges against him or her.

15. Because I _____**tarried**_____ at the book fair, I was ten minutes late for my piano lesson.

16. When my two sisters began their bitter quarrel, only Mother had enough nerve to enter the _____**fray**_____ and tell them to stop.

17. Although the rain was heavy, it was of such short _____**duration**_____ that it didn't interfere with our plans.

18. Do you think it is a good idea to try to _____ pacify _____ the weeping child by giving her a lollipop?

19. Warmth and understanding are two outstanding _____ facets _____ of her personality.

20. The newscaster on my favorite TV program not only tells the facts of the news but offers a(n) _____ commentary _____ that helps us to understand it.

Synonyms

*Choose the word from this unit that is **the same** or **most nearly the same** in meaning as the **boldface** word or expression in the given phrase. Write the word on the line provided.*

1. reflected off the **cuts** of the diamond — facets

2. shock that left them **dazed** and speechless — numb

3. lip-smacking sounds of the **voracious** eaters — ravenous

4. to endure yet another **reversal** — setback

5. always **dawdle** over juice and doughnuts — tarry

6. after they **botched** the paint job — bungled

7. offer a brief **outline** of the plan — synopsis

8. flashing that **conceited** grin of hers — smug

9. gave some **remarks** after the speech — commentary

10. no sense of **guilt** for what happened — remorse

11. began to **unravel** at the cuffs — fray

12. the cause of such **bravado** — bluster

13. what it's like to be **occupants** of a houseboat — inhabitants

14. decided to stay for the **length** of the party — duration

15. at the **frightening** howl of a lone wolf — eerie

Antonyms

*Choose the word from this unit that is **most nearly opposite** in meaning to the **boldface** word or expression in the given phrase. Write the word on the line provided.*

16. discussions with the **submissive** guide — headstrong

17. could never **support** their opinion — refute

18. the perfect medication for my **mild** headache — acute

19. tried to **arouse** the crowd — pacify

20. the reasons for their **disloyalty** — fidelity

Choosing the Right Word

*Circle the **boldface** word that more satisfactorily completes each of the following sentences.*

1. With a winter storm (**blustering,** bungling) outside, what could be more welcome than a warm room, a good meal, and my favorite TV program?

2. The idea that most people usually behave in a calm and reasonable way is (**refuted,** numbed) by all the facts of history.

3. We cannot assume that all the people that one sees on the streets of a large city are actually (facets, **inhabitants**) of the place.

4. There is so much wear and tear on the ropes in this pulley system that they become (**frayed,** refuted) in only a few days.

5. On the camping trip out West some of the children were frightened when they first heard the (smug, **eerie**) howls of coyotes at night.

6. "It's your job to help (**pacify,** fray) the conquered area," the general said, "not to add fuel to an already explosive situation."

7. The victims of the disaster were so (**numbed,** tarried) by the scope of the tragedy that they scarcely showed any emotion at all.

8. When I realized how deeply I had hurt my friend with my careless insult, I suffered a pang of (**remorse,** duration).

9. I keep telling you things for your own good, but you're just too (eerie, **headstrong**) to listen.

10. We know that we are going through a period of economic instability, but there is no way of telling what its (**duration,** remorse) will be.

11. If you read no more than a(n) (inhabitant, **synopsis**) of the plot of any one of Shakespeare's plays, you will get very little idea of what it is all about.

12. Each time she answered a question correctly, she rewarded herself with a (**smug,** ravenous) little smile of self-congratulation.

13. After the way you (**bungled,** blustered) the job of arranging the class trip, I can never again trust you with anything important.

14. The strength of this book lies in the author's ability to describe and explain different (setbacks, **facets**) of human experience.

15. Since it had seemed that winter would (**tarry,** pacify) forever, we were all heartily glad when it finally quit dragging its heels and departed.

16. Florence's illness, after she had been chosen for the leading role in the class show, was a serious (**setback,** commentary) to our plans.

17. The character Scrooge in Charles Dickens's *A Christmas Carol* starts out as a(n) (acute, **ravenous**) miser, but he undergoes a great change.

18. Although I don't agree with all her ideas, I must admire her unshakable (**fidelity,** synopsis) to them.

19. His (headstrong, **acute**) analysis of the housing problem in our town gave us a clear idea of what we would have to overcome.

20. The fact that so many people are still living in poverty is indeed a sad (fidelity, **commentary**) on our civilization.

*Read the following passage, in which some of the words you have studied in this unit appear in **boldface** type. Then complete each statement given below the passage by circling the letter of the item that is **the same** or **almost the same** in meaning as the highlighted word.*

An Olympic Star

(Line)

James Cleveland Owens had always been called J. C. In 1922, his family left their farm in Alabama to become **inhabitants** of Ohio. His **acute** Southern accent must have confused his new teacher, who thought that his name was "Jesse." The new name stuck. And by 1936, everyone knew Jesse Owens, who had become a real-life legend. (5)

Owens was a sickly child, but poor health during his early years proved not to be a **setback**. As he grew, so did his speed and strength. Owens developed a

talent for running and jumping. Record-breaking successes in high school and college track and field prepared him for the (10) 1936 Olympic Games, which were held in Berlin, Germany, where Adolf Hitler's Nazi Party was in control. Owens won four gold medals for the U.S.—the most won by any single Olympic athlete at that time. (15)

To this day, many consider Owens' performance at the 1936 Olympics to be the greatest moment in all Olympic history. He was never **smug** about his successes and continued to inspire others for the **duration** (20) of his life. There were many **facets** to Owens' accomplishments. After the Olympics he traveled the world to promote the importance of sports for young people. He started the Jesse Owens Games, a playground sports (25) event for children through age 15. The Jesse

Jesse Owens, on his way to winning four Olympic gold medals in Berlin, 1936

Owens Foundation continues to grant scholarships to young people who can't afford college. Since Jesse Owens' impact endures even today, it is fitting that in 1990, he posthumously received a fifth gold medal—the Congressional Gold Medal—to honor his humanitarian contributions. (30)

---

1. Inhabitants (line 2) is best defined as
a. farmers
c. residents
b. teachers
d. workers

2. The meaning of **acute** (line 2) is
a. cute
c. sharp
b. mild
d. annoying

3. Setback (line 7) most nearly means
a. illness
c. impediment
b. medicine
d. sport

4. The meaning of **smug** (line 19) is
a. happy
c. discontented
b. satisfied
d. conceited

5. Duration (line 20) most nearly means
a. beginning
c. length
b. end
d. story

6. Facets (line 21) is best defined as
a. aspects
c. locations
b. demands
d. obstacles

Definitions

Note carefully the spelling, pronunciation, part(s) of speech, and definition(s) of each of the following words. Then write the word in the blank space(s) in the illustrative sentence(s) following. Finally, study the lists of synonyms and antonyms given at the end of each entry.

1. agenda
(ə jen' də)

(*n.*) the program for a meeting; a list, outline, or plan of things to be considered or done

The _____**agenda**_____ for today's assembly includes a plan for recycling in the classroom.
SYNONYMS: schedule, docket

2. amiable
(ā' mē ə bəl)

(*adj.*) friendly, good-natured

Marty, whose sense of humor and good spirits never fail, is an _____**amiable**_____ companion.
SYNONYMS: pleasant, agreeable
ANTONYMS: unfriendly, ill-humored, gruff, hostile

3. befuddle
(bi fəd' əl)

(*v.*) to confuse, make stupid

A difficult scientific experiment with many steps is likely to _____**befuddle**_____ most beginners.
SYNONYMS: bewilder, boggle, stupefy
ANTONYMS: enlighten, set straight

4. blight
(blīt)

(*n.*) a disease that causes plants to wither and die; a condition of disease or ruin; (*v.*) to destroy, ruin

Dutch elm disease was a _____**blight**_____ that forever changed the look of my neighborhood.

Though she received several letters of rejection, she determined not to let them _____**blight**_____ her hopes of going to college.
SYNONYMS: (*n.*) eyesore; (*v.*) spoil, nip
ANTONYMS: (*v.*) foster, promote, nourish, encourage

5. boisterous
(boi' strəs)

(*adj.*) rough and noisy in a cheerful way; high-spirited

The _____**boisterous**_____ schoolchildren made it clear to their teacher how much they enjoyed the class trip.
SYNONYMS: loud, unruly, disorderly
ANTONYMS: quiet, calm, peaceful, well-behaved, sedate

6. clarity
(klar' ə tē)

(*n.*) clearness, accuracy

The vet explained with great _____**clarity**_____ how best to housebreak our new puppy.
SYNONYMS: lucidity, precision
ANTONYMS: confusion, murkiness, ambiguity

7. compliant
(kəm plī′ ənt)

(*adj.*) willing to do what someone else wants; obedient

A _____ **compliant** _____ child is easy to discipline, even when in an unfamiliar environment.

SYNONYMS: meek, docile, submissive
ANTONYMS: disobedient, obstinate, rebellious, perverse

8. conserve
(kən sərv′)

(*v.*) to preserve; to keep from being damaged, lost, or wasted; to save

Responsible citizens try to _____ **conserve** _____ our precious natural resources.

SYNONYMS: guard, care for
ANTONYMS: waste, squander, dissipate

9. debut
(dā′ byü)

(*n.*) a first public appearance; a formal entrance into society; (*v.*) to make a first appearance

The talented flute player in the marching band finally made her _____ **debut** _____ as a soloist today.

Many theaters will _____ **debut** _____ the film tonight.

SYNONYM: (*n.*) coming-out
ANTONYMS: (*n.*) retirement, departure

10. gory
(gôr′ ē)

(*adj.*) marked by bloodshed, slaughter, or violence

The Civil War battle of Antietam is, to this day, the most _____ **gory** _____ one-day fight in our history.

SYNONYMS: bloody, gruesome
ANTONYM: bloodless

11. gross
(grōs)

(*adj.*) overweight; coarse, vulgar; very noticeable; total; (*n.*) an overall total (without deductions); twelve dozen; (*v.*) to earn

They responded to the _____ **gross** _____ injustice in an unsatisfactory manner.

A _____ **gross** _____ of pencils lasts all year.

She expects to _____ **gross** _____ $3000 in tips.

SYNONYMS: (*adj.*) fat, sheer, utter, flagrant
ANTONYMS: (*adj.*) slender, thin, delicate, fine, partial; (*n., v.*) net

12. induce
(in düs′)

(*v.*) to cause, bring about; to persuade

Can drinking warm milk _____ **induce** _____ sleep?

SYNONYMS: prevail upon, influence
ANTONYMS: prevent, deter, hinder

13. leeway
(lē′ wā)

(*n.*) extra space for moving along a certain route; allowance for mistakes or inaccuracies; margin of error

Experienced planners allow _____ **leeway** _____ of a week or so in case a project runs into snags or delays.

SYNONYMS: latitude, elbowroom

14. limber
(lim′ bər)

(*adj.*) flexible; (*v.*) to cause to become flexible

Dancers work hard to develop _____limber_____ bodies.

Runners _____limber_____ up before a race.

SYNONYMS: (*adj.*) supple, pliable; (*v.*) stretch
ANTONYMS: (*adj.*) stiff, rigid, wooden; (*v.*) stiffen

15. maze
(māz)

(*n.*) a network of paths through which it is hard to find one's way; something very mixed-up and confusing

Ancient Rome was a _____maze_____ of narrow streets and winding alleys.

SYNONYMS: labyrinth, puzzle, tangle

16. oracle
(ôr′ ə kəl)

(*n.*) someone or something that can predict the future

According to Greek legend, people sought prophecy at the great _____Oracle_____ at Delphi.

SYNONYMS: prophet, seer, sibyl

17. partisan
(pärt′ ə zən)

(*n.*) a strong supporter of a person, party, or cause; one whose support is unreasoning; a resistance fighter, guerrilla; (*adj.*) strongly supporting one side only

That mayoral candidate is a strong _____partisan_____ of term limits.

_____Partisan_____ hometown fans can be hostile to those from out of town.

SYNONYMS: (*n.*) fan, booster; (*adj.*) partial, biased
ANTONYMS: (*n.*) critic, foe; (*adj.*) impartial, neutral

18. reimburse
(rē im bərs′)

(*v.*) to pay back; to give payment for

When Mom goes on business trips, she records the cost of hotels and meals so her company will _____reimburse_____ her.

SYNONYMS: repay, refund, compensate

19. vacate
(vā′ kāt)

(*v.*) to go away from, leave empty; to make empty; to void, annul

We have a lot of cleaning up to do before we _____vacate_____ the apartment at the end of the month.

SYNONYMS: depart, give up, abandon
ANTONYMS: occupy, keep, hold, hang on to

20. vagabond
(vag′ ə bänd)

(*n.*) an idle wanderer; a tramp; (*adj.*) wandering; irresponsible

The _____vagabond_____ carried his few belongings in a shabby cardboard suitcase.

The _____vagabond_____ life interests some people, but it doesn't appeal to me.

SYNONYMS: (*n.*) vagrant, hobo; (*adj.*) unsettled, footloose
ANTONYMS: (*n.*) homebody, resident; (*adj.*) settled

Completing the Sentence

From the words for this unit, choose the one that best completes each of the following sentences. Write the word in the space provided.

1. Why do you always ask me what's going to happen? I'm no _____ oracle _____!

2. For years, his restless spirit led him to wander the highways and byways of this great land like any other footloose _____ vagabond _____.

3. If you would be kind enough to buy a loose-leaf notebook for me while you are in the stationery store, I'll _____ reimburse _____ you immediately.

4. The crowd is so _____ partisan _____ that the umpire is booed every time he makes a decision against the home team.

5. Trying to untangle a badly snarled fishing line is like trying to find one's way through a(n) _____ maze _____.

6. Because our energy resources are limited, the American people must try to do everything possible to _____ conserve _____ fuel.

7. Each of the items on the _____ agenda _____ for our meeting today will probably require a good deal of discussion.

8. Ms. Fillmer explained with such _____ clarity _____ how to go about changing a tire that I felt that even someone as clumsy as I could do it.

9. I was not prepared for the _____ gory _____ sight that met my eyes at the scene of that horrible massacre.

10. The high standard of excellence that the woman had set for herself left her no _____ leeway _____ for mistakes.

11. None of us could possibly overlook the _____ gross _____ error that the waiter had made in adding up our check.

12. No matter what you may say, you cannot _____ induce _____ me to do something that I know is wrong.

13. The high point of the social season was the formal _____ debut _____ of young ladies at the annual Society Ball.

14. Before the game starts, the players _____ limber _____ up by doing a few deep knee bends, sit-ups, and other exercises.

15. If the Superintendent of Schools should _____ vacate _____ his position by resigning, the Mayor has the right to name someone else to the job.

16. Because of her outgoing and _____ amiable _____ personality, she is liked by everyone.

17. How can a mind _____ befuddled _____ by alcohol make the type of snap decisions needed to drive safely in heavy traffic?

68 ■ Unit 6

18. You certainly have a right to cheer for your team, but try not to become too _____boisterous_____ and unruly.

19. We cannot allow the lives of millions of people to be _____blighted_____ by poverty.

20. Because you are working with older and more experienced people, you should be _____compliant_____ with their requests and advice.

Synonyms

*Choose the word from this unit that is **the same** or **most nearly the same** in meaning as the **boldface** word or expression in the given phrase. Write the word on the line provided.*

1. offended by that **flagrant** insult _____gross_____

2. **persuade** them to speak softly _____induce_____

3. a hidden **eyesore** behind thick shrubs _____blight_____

4. when he saw the **gruesome** ~~surgery~~ *spectacle* _____gory_____

5. can't rely on their **biased** viewpoint _____partisan_____

6. had never consulted the **prophet** before _____oracle_____

7. following a **tangle** of clues _____maze_____

8. enough **latitude** for a beginner to succeed _____leeway_____

9. no choice but to **depart** the cabin _____vacate_____

10. known for being a **docile** pet _____compliant_____

11. **compensate** you for your time _____reimburse_____

12. directions written with **precision** _____clarity_____

13. a **hobo** who hopped freight trains _____vagabond_____

14. publishes the **schedule** a week in advance _____agenda_____

15. for her **coming-out** party at the country club _____debut_____

Antonyms

*Choose the word from this unit that is **most nearly opposite** in meaning to the **boldface** word or expression in the given phrase. Write the word on the line provided.*

16. a **sedate** group of bikers _____boisterous_____

17. to **squander** our limited food supplies _____conserve_____

18. the guitar player's **rigid** fingers _____limber_____

19. **enlighten** us with new passwords and commands _____befuddle_____

20. socializing with our **gruff** neighbors _____amiable_____

Choosing the Right Word

*Circle the **boldface** word that more satisfactorily completes each of the following sentences.*

1. Poland received top priority on Adolf Hitler's (**agenda,** **maze**) of military conquests in the fall of 1939.

2. Students must take many required courses, but they also have a little (**oracle,** **leeway**) to choose courses that they find especially interesting.

3. At the end of the long series of discussions and arguments, we felt that we were trapped in a (**blight,** **maze**) of conflicting ideas and plans.

4. This matter is so important to all the people of the community that we must forget (**partisan,** **boisterous**) politics and work together.

5. What I thought was going to be a(n) (**amiable,** **vagabond**) little chat with my boss soon turned into a real argument.

6. One of the biggest problems facing the United States today is how to stop the (**blight,** **agenda**) that is creeping over large parts of our great cities.

7. Since he is an expert gymnast and works out every day, his body has remained as (**limber,** **gory**) as that of a boy.

8. Because she is usually so (**compliant,** **partisan**), we were all surprised when she said that she didn't like our plans and wouldn't accept them.

9. Over the years, so many of the columnist's predictions have come true that he is now looked on as something of a(n) (**debut,** **oracle**).

10. As we moved higher up the mountain, I was overcome by dizziness and fatigue (**induced,** **grossed**) by the thin air.

11. In her graphic description of the most gruesome scenes in the horror film, Maria left out none of the (**amiable,** **gory**) details.

12. After all the deductions had been made from my (**gross,** **limber**) salary, the sum that remained seemed pitifully small.

13. Many a student dreams about spending a (**vagabond,** **partisan**) year idly hitchhiking through Europe.

14. The disc jockey promised to (**vacate,** **debut**) the band's long-awaited new CD as soon as it was released by the recording company.

15. An experienced backpacker can give you many useful suggestions for (**befuddling,** **conserving**) energy on a long, tough hike.

16. The landlord ordered all tenants to (**vacate,** **reimburse**) the premises by noon.

17. Don't let the (**clarity,** **leeway**) of the water fool you into supposing that it's safe for drinking.

18. Mr. Roth, the librarian, cracks down hard on (**compliant,** **boisterous**) students.

19. If you want to get a clear picture of just what went wrong, you must not (**induce,** **befuddle**) your mind with all kinds of wild rumors.

20. I will feel fully (**reimbursed,** **conserved**) for all that I have done for her if I can see her in good health again.

Vocabulary in Context

*Read the following passage, in which some of the words you have studied in this unit appear in **boldface** type. Then complete each statement given below the passage by circling the letter of the item that is **the same** or **almost the same** in meaning as the highlighted word.*

Send in the Clowns

(Line)

Do you have a good sense of humor and enjoy working with people? Do you have an **amiable** disposition? Can your behavior be characterized as **boisterous**? Are you ready to learn to juggle, paint your face, and sculpt balloons? If so, you might
(5)   have what it takes to become a clown.

The art of clowning has been around for centuries. A clown performed as a jester in Pharaoh's court during Egypt's Fifth Dynasty, about 2500 B.C. Court jesters have performed
(10)   in China since 1818 B.C. Clowns who performed as court jesters were often the only ones allowed to speak against the ruler's policies. The fools in Shakespeare's plays were often the ones with the smartest things to say!
(15)   There are three basic types of clowns. *Whiteface* clowns cover their face with white makeup and then use different colors to highlight their facial features. They try to look like dolls who have come to life. *Auguste*
(20)   clowns are more human looking; their base makeup is a fleshy tone, but they exaggerate their facial features with additional makeup. Their hair is often wild, and they wear brightly

A full wig and sociable nature contribute to the appeal of this *Auguste* clown.

colored, mismatched, and oversized clothes. The *character* clown is a third type.
(25)   This type is often a tramp or a hobo, a **vagabond** down on his or her luck. Makeup is flesh-based with gray tones to simulate dirt and tears.

Clowns may seem clumsy and **befuddled**, but good clowning requires a **limber** body and quick mind. Clown antics are like well-tuned gymnastics or dance routines, which often don't allow **leeway** for mistakes. They demand strong muscles and great
(30)   timing. Without advanced preparation, clowns could get injured. Worse, they might not be the least bit funny!

---

1. The meaning of **amiable** (line 2) is
a. strict
c. agreeable
b. peaceful
d. hostile

2. Boisterous (line 2) most nearly means
a. ridiculous
c. peaceful
b. nervous
d. high-spirited

3. Vagabond (line 25) is best defined as
a. person
c. employee
b. student
d. vagrant

4. The meaning of **befuddled** (line 27) is
a. confused
c. innocent
b. enlightened
d. silly

5. Limber (line 27) most nearly means
a. wooden
c. trained
b. flexible
d. quick

6. Leeway (line 29) is best defined as
a. excuse
c. rules
b. latitude
d. witness

Analogies

In each of the following, circle the item that best completes the comparison.

See pages T38–T48 for explanations of answers.

1. **hero** is to **idolize** as
a. partisan is to ignore
b. inhabitant is to reimburse
c. buddy is to discredit
d. villain is to despise

2. **repent** is to **remorse** as
a. desire is to hatred
b. enjoy is to anxiety
c. fear is to pleasure
d. boast is to pride

3. **inhabitant** is to **live** as
a. resident is to leave
b. employee is to own
c. guest is to dwell
d. tourist is to visit

4. **devastate** is to **ruined** as
a. conserve is to musty
b. blight is to soggy
c. bungle is to noisy
d. vacate is to empty

5. **mortal** is to **death** as
a. acute is to decay
b. fluid is to change
c. permanent is to duration
d. elusive is to time

6. **numb** is to **feel** as
a. paralyzed is to move
b. injured is to hear
c. blind is to taste
d. lame is to see

7. **dancer** is to **limber** as
a. pickpocket is to smug
b. loudmouth is to boisterous
c. showoff is to acute
d. spoilsport is to amiable

8. **gross** is to **refinement** as
a. boisterous is to noise
b. smug is to contentment
c. amiable is to friendliness
d. petty is to significance

9. **bulldozer** is to **topple** as
a. derrick is to blight
b. plow is to devastate
c. crane is to raise
d. truck is to conserve

10. **vagabond** is to **wander** as
a. beggar is to explore
b. nomad is to tarry
c. drifter is to roam
d. homebody is to travel

11. **loyal** is to **fidelity** as
a. intelligent is to stupidity
b. brave is to cowardice
c. thankful is to gratitude
d. ignorant is to wisdom

12. **scan** is to **eye** as
a. observe is to ear
b. touch is to finger
c. smell is to mouth
d. taste is to nose

13. **gory** is to **blood** as
a. dull is to interest
b. eerie is to mystery
c. pale is to color
d. numb is to sensation

14. **hungry** is to **ravenous** as
a. tired is to exhausted
b. sleepy is to awake
c. thirsty is to drunk
d. dirty is to spotless

15. **liquor** is to **befuddle** as
a. coffee is to stimulate
b. tea is to deem
c. water is to generate
d. milk is to induce

16. **clarity** is to **clear** as
a. simplicity is to complicated
b. charm is to boring
c. brevity is to short
d. force is to weak

17. **mule** is to **headstrong** as
a. lamb is to compliant
b. wolf is to amiable
c. horse is to numb
d. mouse is to boisterous

18. **acquit** is to **innocence** as
a. arrest is to blamelessness
b. convict is to guilt
c. clear is to complicity
d. release is to suspicion

Word Associations

In each of the following groups, circle the word that is best defined or suggested by the given phrase.

1. state of being faithful
a. revocation   b. synopsis   c. maze   d. fidelity

2. to look over quickly
a. scan   b. generate   c. bungle   d. discredit

3. to throw doubt or uncertainty on
a. idolize   b. fray   c. conserve   d. discredit

4. to make a first appearance in public
a. strife   b. setback   c. debut   d. agenda

5. to find not guilty of a charge
a. induce   b. devastate   c. idolize   d. acquit

6. deep regret for some past misdeed
a. strand   b. ingratitude   c. bluster   d. remorse

7. one who speaks with wisdom and authority
a. inhabitant   b. partisan   c. oracle   d. mortal

8. to think or believe
a. deem   b. topple   c. vacate   d. pacify

9. friendly and pleasant
a. elusive   b. amiable   c. limber   d. gross

10. reminder of a special event
a. keepsake   b. ovation   c. reverie   d. synopsis

11. showing great insight or sharpness
a. acute   b. gory   c. numb   d. smug

12. to pay back
a. repent   b. reimburse   c. debut   d. refute

13. series of notes explaining a book
a. commentary   b. facet   c. plight   d. agenda

14. bringing about death
a. headstrong   b. acute   c. mortal   d. ravenous

15. to confuse or bewilder
a. tarry   b. befuddle   c. scan   d. fray

16. length of time that something lasts
a. leeway   b. duration   c. clarity   d. ovation

17. loud and noisy
a. boisterous   b. compliant   c. eerie   d. petty

18. one who lives in a particular place
a. vagabond   b. commentary   c. inhabitant   d. keepsake

19. condition of being lost in thought
a. remorse   b. reverie   c. strand   d. maze

20. to show sorrow for bad conduct
a. repent   b. tarry   c. generate   d. bluster

*Read the following passage, in which some of the words you have studied in Units 4–6 appear in **boldface** type. Then complete each statement given below the passage by circling the item that is **the same** or **almost the same** in meaning as the highlighted word.*

Oseola McCarty: How Frugality Led to Heroism

(Line)

Oseola McCarty left school after sixth grade to help care for ailing relatives. She was sorry not to be able to continue her education, but
(5) her family needed her. Pursuing an education was an **elusive** dream to this lifelong **inhabitant** of Mississippi. She eked out a living washing and ironing other people's clothing. She
(10) lived most of her life in a small house her uncle once owned.

For seventy-five years, Oseola McCarty served her customers. She walked wherever she had to go. She
(15) earned little money yet managed to put aside a small amount almost every week. She knew it was wise to plan for the future.

Oseola McCarty never felt right
(20) about taking money out of her bank account. The money she put into the bank quietly earned interest. What must have seemed like **petty** deposits of nickels and dimes
(25) eventually grew into a fortune. By the time McCarty was 87, she had nearly

$300,000! McCarty's dreams of education had never faded. She knew she was too old to attend
(30) college but felt no **remorse** about her life. Instead she thought of an **agenda** to help others attend college. She gave $150,000 of her life's savings to the University of Southern Mississippi.
(35) Suddenly, an elderly laundry woman was a local hero!

Oseola McCarty's generosity touched people. Many were moved to make their own contributions to
(40) increase the Oseola McCarty Scholarship Fund. Although she was finally rich, McCarty remained a straightforward, honest, and humble person. Her **commentaries** on life
(45) were right to the point. "If you want to feel proud of yourself," she once said, "you've got to do things you can be proud of." When McCarty died at the age of 91, people throughout the
(50) United States remembered her with pride and admiration.

---

1. The meaning of **elusive** (line 6) is
a. passionate   c. magical
b. steady   d. fleeting

2. Inhabitant (line 7) most nearly means
a. visitor   c. resident
b. student   d. fan

3. Petty (line 23) is best defined as
a. minor   c. attractive
b. major   d. normal

4. The meaning of **remorse** (line 30) is
a. failure   c. responsibility
b. loyalty   d. regret

5. Agenda (line 31) most nearly means
a. plan   c. opinion
b. dream   d. puzzle

6. Commentaries (line 44) is best defined as
a. setbacks   c. oracles
b. remarks   d. keepsakes

Choosing the Right Meaning

Read each sentence carefully. Then circle the item that best completes the statement below the sentence.

See pages T38–T48 for explanations of answers.

The fellow is so off-putting and mean that I am sure he must count his enemies by the gross. (2)

1. The word **gross** in line 2 is used to mean

a. total   (b. twelve dozen)   c. weight   d. score

On June 30, 1971, the Supreme Court vacated a lower court's restraining order, thus freeing newspapers to resume publication of the Pentagon Papers. (2)

2. The best definition for the word **vacated** in line 1 is

(a. annulled/voided)   b. deserted   c. emptied   d. gave up

At Dunkirk in the Spring of 1940, an armada of warships and civilian craft evacuated hundreds of thousands of Allied soldiers from the Northern French strand, where they had been pinned by the German army. (2)

3. In line 2 the word **strand** most nearly means

a. fiber   (b. shore)   c. abandonment   d. battle

The commentator's petty evaluation of the election results betrays a woeful ignorance of American political history. (2)

4. In line 1 the word **petty** most nearly means

a. unimportant   b. minor   (c. narrow-minded)   d. insignificant

Skyscrapers of the 1930s, such as the Empire State Building in New York, typically are crowned with setbacks that lead like steps to a spire at the summit. (2)

5. The word **setbacks** in line 2 is best defined as

a. defeats   b. reversals   c. disappointments   (d. recesses)

Antonyms

*In each of the following groups, circle the word or expression that is most nearly the **opposite** of the word in **boldface** type.*

1. limber
(a. stiff)
b. large
c. tiny
d. loose

2. headstrong
a. neat
b. intelligent
c. wealthy
(d. docile)

3. vacate
a. own
b. paint
c. clean
(d. occupy)

4. idolize
(a. despise)
b. bore
c. train
d. deceive

5. tarry
a. stay
(b. leave)
c. eat
d. loiter

6. setback
(a. advance)
b. defeat
c. problem
d. effort

7. strife
(a. harmony)
b. unemployment
c. plenty
d. trouble

8. partisan
a. separate
b. rare
c. biased
(d. neutral)

9. acute
a. strange
b. dull ⟵
c. new
d. sharp

11. blight
a. squander
b. bewilder
c. foster ⟵
d. starve

13. refute
a. disprove
b. lessen
c. confirm ⟵
d. change

15. ingratitude
a. wisdom
b. trust
c. thankfulness ⟵
d. money

10. conserve
a. store
b. waste ⟵
c. purchase
d. save

12. devastate
a. inhabit
b. liberate
c. develop ⟵
d. conquer

14. ovation
a. smiles
b. cheers
c. boos ⟵
d. cries

16. debut
a. employment
b. coming-out
c. retirement ⟵
d. investment

Word Families

A. *On the line provided, write the word you have learned in Units 4–6 that is related to each of the following nouns.*
EXAMPLE: pettiness—**petty**

1. bungler — bungle
2. reimbursement — reimburse
3. eerieness — eerie
4. inducement, inducer, inducibility — induce
5. conservation, conservationist, conservatory, conservative — conserve
6. befuddlement — befuddle
7. devastation, devastator — devastate
8. repentance, repenter — repent
9. gore, goriness — gory
10. acquittal, acquittance, acquitter — acquit
11. smugness — smug
12. pacifist, pacifier, pacification, pacifism — pacify
13. idolization, idolizer — idolize
14. blusterer — bluster
15. amiability, amiableness — amiable

B. *On the line provided, write the word you have learned in Units 4–6 that is related to each of the following verbs.*
EXAMPLE: inhabit—**inhabitant**

16. revoke — revocation
17. comply — compliant
18. comment — commentary
19. synopsize — synopsis
20. elude — elusive

Two-Word Completions

Circle the pair of words that best complete the meaning of each of the following passages.

See pages T38–T48 for explanations of answers.

1. In the third century, bands of savage barbarians repeatedly broke through the frontier defenses of the Roman province of Gaul, _____ the countryside with fire and sword, and either slew or carried off the _____.
a. scanned . . . partisans
b. pacified . . . vagabonds
c. devastated . . . inhabitants
d. blighted . . . oracles

2. The defense was able to _____ the prosecution's case so convincingly that the jury _____ the defendant after only five minutes of deliberation.
a. devastate . . . befuddled
b. refute . . . acquitted
c. topple . . . discredited
d. bungle . . . reimbursed

3. The TV special not only brought in huge sums of money to help relieve the _____ of millions of Africans suffering from the effects of a severe famine, but also _____ a great deal of sympathy for them.
a. setback . . . induced
b. plight . . . generated
c. duration . . . deemed
d. strife . . . conserved

4. "The Scholar Gypsy" tells the tale of a poor student who left school to join a band of _____. He and his companions roamed the countryside endlessly, never _____ in one place for long.
a. inhabitants . . . deeming
b. debutantes . . . vacating
c. partisans . . . generating
d. vagabonds . . . tarrying

5. When the new government came to power, its first order of business was to _____ a country that had been torn by _____ and revolution for over ten years.
a. pacify . . . strife
b. topple . . . ingratitude
c. strand . . . fidelity
d. conserve . . . remorse

6. "I want to maintain _____ to the book in bringing this story to the screen," the director instructed the scriptwriter. "However, I recognize that one has to have a little _____ when translating print into film."
a. clarity . . . synopsis
b. fidelity . . . leeway
c. strife . . . facet
d. partisan . . . commentary

Building with Classical Roots

re—back; again

This prefix appears in **repent** (page 53), **revocation** (page 53), **refute** (page 60), **remorse** (page 60), and **reimburse** (page 67). Some other words in which this prefix appears are listed below.

rebuke	refrain	renege	retract
redeem	relic	restraint	revive

From the list of words above, choose the one that corresponds to each of the brief definitions below. Write the word in the blank space in the illustrative sentence below the definition.

1. something that has survived the passage of time

We marveled at the delicate artistry in the Indian _____relics_____ we saw at the museum.

2. to give new life to; to restore

Lively cheers from a hopeful crowd may _____revive_____ the team's dampened spirits.

3. to take back something that has been said, offered, or published

The angry candidate demanded that the newspaper _____retract_____ the scandalous story.

4. to hold oneself back; a repeated verse, chorus

Thanksgiving is one of the hardest days for me to _____refrain_____ from overeating.

5. to go back on a promise

They were surprised when the buyer suddenly decided to _____renege_____ on the deal.

6. a device that restricts or confines; control over the expression of one's feelings or behavior

The police officers placed _____restraints_____ on the violent prisoner.

7. to scold, express sharp disapproval; a scolding

The babysitter had to _____rebuke_____ the children for misbehaving after dinner.

8. to buy back; to make up for; to fulfill a pledge

Consumers who _____redeem_____ discount coupons they clip from magazines and newspapers can cut their weekly grocery bills.

From the list of words on page 78, choose the one that best completes each of the following sentences. Write the word in the blank space provided.

1. The recruit's failure to salute earned him a stern _____rebuke_____ from the sergeant.

2. When she _____reneged_____ on her promise, we felt that we could no longer trust her to keep her word.

3. "If you do not immediately _____retract_____ those outrageous allegations," declared the lawyer, "my client will sue for libel."

4. The fans were asked to _____refrain_____ from rushing onto the court until the basketball game was officially over.

5. The rookie's brilliant play in the final game of the series more than _____redeemed_____ the crucial error he had made in the opener.

6. The rescue squad worked resolutely to _____revive_____ the child who had been overcome by smoke.

7. Dressed in their old uniforms, the aging veterans looked like _____relics_____ of a bygone age.

8. It took incredible _____restraint_____ on the part of the speaker not to respond to the taunts of the hecklers.

---

*Circle the **boldface** word that more satisfactorily completes each of the following sentences.*

1. The conductor's withering (**rebuke,** **refrain**) prompted the flutist to relinquish her solo to another player who was better rehearsed.

2. In less than a year, we will (**revive,** **redeem**) the mortgage, owning our house free and clear.

3. Archaeologists nearly missed the (**relic,** **restraint**) amid the stones and dust of the dig site.

4. As soon as they heard the familiar (**refrain,** **relic**) of the school song, the homecoming crowd stood to sing the anthem once again.

5. "If you (**retract,** **renege**) on your commitment to the team," the coach reasoned, "how can you expect me to rely on you in the future?"

6. The eager opening-night audience showed great (**restraint,** **rebuke**) as a technician repaired the broken projector.

7. The popularity of the show's theme song has served to (**renege,** **revive**) widespread interest in swing dancing.

8. Following the actor's dreadful performance on the screen test, the director had no choice but to (**retract,** **redeem**) the offer of the lead role.

Writer's Challenge

Read the following sentences, paying special attention to the words and phrases underlined. From the words in the box below, find better choices for these underlined words and phrases. Then use these choices to rewrite the sentences.

WORD BANK				
acquit	conserve	eerie	gory	ovation
acute	debut	elusive	limber	partisan
bungle	deem	facet	maze	petty
commentary	discredit	generate	numb	vagabond

Vietnamese Water Puppets

1. One appeal of the <u>hard to explain</u> art form of water puppetry is that it can engross children and adults on many levels.
elusive
_____

2. Vietnamese water puppetry provides <u>expressions of opinion</u> on the lives and traditions of early Vietnamese culture.
commentary
_____

3. Historians believe that water puppetry probably made its <u>first appearance</u> in ancient Vietnamese rice farming communities as a way to celebrate plentiful harvests.
debut
_____

4. <u>Unsettled</u> troupes of puppeteers, usually from the same family or clan, often passed their skills from generation to generation as they traveled the countryside to perform.
vagabond
_____

5. A compelling <u>side of the subject</u> of this art form is the key role water plays in hiding the apparatus that activates the puppets.
facet
_____

6. Puppeteers present their works from boats or platforms set on water, creating <u>weird</u> floating stages that rock and shimmer, lending a dreamlike quality to the theater.
eerie
_____

7. Most puppeteers work from the floating stages or rafts. But some learn to ignore the <u>lost feeling or movement</u> sensations in their own feet as they stand for hours in the water to manipulate their puppets.
numb
_____

Analogies

In each of the following, circle the item that best completes the comparison.

See pages T38–T48 for explanations of answers.

1. eerie is to **ghosts** as
a. frightening is to monsters
b. elusive is to cowboys
c. incomprehensible is to clowns
d. sage is to spies

2. elusive is to **grasp** as
a. hazy is to see
b. spicy is to taste
c. sharp is to smell
d. loud is to hear

3. irk is to **annoyance** as
a. befuddle is to understanding
b. ruffle is to joy
c. infuriate is to rage
d. pacify is to discontent

4. messenger is to **dispatch** as
a. partisan is to synopsis
b. oracle is to prophecy
c. bigot is to keepsake
d. oaf is to ovation

5. illusion is to **deceive** as
a. enigma is to mystify
b. vow is to devastate
c. repast is to disturb
d. leeway is to restrict

6. gloat is to **satisfaction** as
a. repent is to regret
b. forsake is to delight
c. confront is to fear
d. idolize is to amusement

7. famished is to **ravenous** as
a. contemporary is to prehistoric
b. global is to aquatic
c. dazed is to numb
d. stiff is to limber

8. hairline is to **recede** as
a. city is to besiege
b. tide is to ebb
c. building is to topple
d. task is to bungle

9. fray is to **boisterous** as
a. skyscraper is to petty
b. ocean is to arid
c. tempest is to sheepish
d. massacre is to gory

10. compress is to **swelling** as
a. splint is to snakebite
b. bandage is to broken leg
c. steak is to black eye
d. crutch is to bloody nose

Choosing the Right Meaning

Read each sentence carefully. Then circle the item that best completes the statement below the sentence.

See pages T38–T48 for explanations of answers.

Of Silvia, in *Two Gentlemen of Verona,* Shakespeare has the players sing, "She excels each mortal thing upon the dull earth dwelling." (2)

1. The word **mortal** in line 2 most nearly means
a. often deadly   b. potentially fatal   c. usually lethal   d. certain to die

A truly gifted mimic can adopt not only another's voice but that person's expressions and mannerisms as well. (2)

2. The word **mimic** in line 1 is best defined as
a. comedian   b. imitator   c. magician   d. ventriloquist

The naturalist and author John Burroughs (1837–1921) was one of the first to advocate the conservation of our country's natural resources. (2)

3. In line 2 the word **conservation** is best defined as

a. waste   b. study   c. supervision   d. preservation

Their disinterested expressions suggested that many of the soldiers returning from
the front were suffering the effects of battle fatigue.   (2)

4. In line 1 the word **disinterested** most nearly means

a. apathetic   b. impartial   c. unselfish   d. frightened

The new management introduced a number of cost-cutting measures designed to
wring a maximum of profit from the struggling business.   (2)

5. The word **maximum** in line 2 is best defined as

a. greatest possible amount   c. least possible amount
b. modest amount   d. record level

Two-Word Completions

*Circle the pair of words that best complete the meaning
of each of the following sentences.*

See pages T38–T48 for explanations of answers.

1. On that cold and _____ November morning, the sails on our boat
_____ and flapped in the wind like so many sheets on a giant
clothesline.

a. serene . . . constrained   c. eerie . . . generated
b. blustery . . . billowed   d. adverse . . . tarried

2. During the ten years that he spent conquering Gaul, Julius Caesar wrote a series of
_____ on his campaigns. In these accounts, he not only tells the
story of the war but also _____ the daily life and customs of the
peoples he subdued.

a. reveries . . . conserves   c. commentaries . . . depicts
b. barrages . . . discredits   d. mazes . . . designates

3. "Though I didn't expect to be _____ in any monetary way for the
help I'd given them," I replied, "I was totally taken aback by their complete lack of
_____ for what I'd done."

a. irked . . . remorse   c. confronted . . . clarity
b. reimbursed . . . gratitude   d. befuddled . . . diversity

4. When a series of natural disasters turned their once fertile valley into a "dust bowl,"
the _____ of the area _____ their homes and
sought a more hospitable environment in which to live.

a. partisans . . . denounced   c. hypocrites . . . vacated
b. oafs . . . devastated   d. inhabitants . . . forsook

5. The linesman's adverse calls so _____ one of the players in the
championship match that he began to shower the unfortunate official with an angry
_____ of verbal abuse.

a. infuriated . . . barrage   c. motivated . . . queue
b. pacified . . . dispatch   d. befuddled . . . strand

Enriching Your Vocabulary

Read the passage below. Then complete the exercise at the bottom of the page.

Compound Interest

Did you ever imagine that a dictionary and a laboratory had something in common? They have—both are full of compounds. The compounds in a laboratory are made by combining two or more chemical elements. The compounds in a dictionary are compound words. These come into the language when people put together two or more words to communicate a new idea.

Creating compounds in chemistry class

In chemistry, the compound may be completely different from either of the elements from which it is made. Water, for example, is made of the gases hydrogen and oxygen. In the English language, compound words sometimes mean exactly what you'd think they'd mean when you put two words together. For instance, a *footbridge* is a bridge you'd walk over. A *rubber band* is a band made of rubber. The meaning of the compound word is often different from the words that make it up. Is a *butterfly* some kind of floating food? Do scalp exercises make you *headstrong* (Unit 5)? Is a *high school* a school on a mountaintop?

The English language grows and changes over time. New words come into use, and old-fashioned words hide inside old books. Compound words prove that the English language is flexible and alive.

In each row, it is possible to make two compound words. Match the parts correctly and write the words on the lines. Use a dictionary if you are not sure.

1. fire   wood   boat   saw   firewood
                                             fireboat

2. thunder   lightning   clap   storm   thunderclap
                                             thunderstorm

3. every   one   big   where   everyone
                                             everywhere

4. head   wall   light   ache   headlight
                                             headache

5. house   add   boat   warming   houseboat
                                             housewarming

6. home   city   town   work   hometown
                                             homework

7. down   watch   play   load   downplay
                                             download

Definitions

Note carefully the spelling, pronunciation, part(s) of speech, and definition(s) of each of the following words. Then write the word in the blank space(s) in the illustrative sentence(s) following. Finally, study the lists of synonyms and antonyms given at the end of each entry.

1. authorize
(ô′ thə rīz)

(*v.*) to approve or permit; to give power or authority to

I wonder if Congress will someday _____**authorize**_____ U. S. citizens to cast official votes over the Internet.

SYNONYMS: order, entitle, empower
ANTONYMS: forbid, ban, prohibit

2. culprit
(kəl′ prit)

(*n.*) a person who has committed a crime or is guilty of some misconduct; an offender

Thanks to their efficient tracking methods, the police were able to catch the _____**culprit**_____ red-handed.

SYNONYMS: lawbreaker, wrongdoer

3. dawdle
(dôd′ əl)

(*v.*) to waste time; to be idle; to spend more time in doing something than is necessary

It's relaxing to _____**dawdle**_____ in the shower, but it wastes water.

SYNONYMS: delay, loiter, dillydally
ANTONYMS: hurry, hasten, speed up, bustle

4. dissect
(di sekt′)

(*v.*) to cut apart in preparation for scientific study; to analyze with great care

I can't wait to _____**dissect**_____ a frog in biology class next week.

SYNONYM: examine
ANTONYMS: sew together, fuse, weld

5. expend
(ek spend′)

(*v.*) to pay out, spend; to use up

The most experienced long-distance runners learn not to _____**expend**_____ their energy too soon.

SYNONYMS: utilize, consume, disburse
ANTONYMS: save, hoard

6. fatality
(fā tal′ ə tē)

(*n.*) an event resulting in death; an accidental death

The driver slammed on the brakes, but it was too late to prevent the traffic _____**fatality**_____.

SYNONYMS: casualty, mortality
ANTONYM: injury

7. gullible
(gəl′ ə bəl)

(*adj.*) easily fooled, tricked, or cheated

Are you _____gullible_____ enough to believe everything you hear on the radio?

SYNONYMS: trusting, innocent, naïve, credulous
ANTONYMS: suspicious, skeptical

8. illicit
(i lis′ it)

(*adj.*) not permitted, unlawful, improper

Students will be suspended for one week if they bring any _____illicit_____ materials to school.

SYNONYMS: illegal, unauthorized, forbidden
ANTONYMS: legal, lawful, permissible, aboveboard

9. immerse
(i mərs′)

(*v.*) to plunge or dip into a fluid; to involve deeply

I find it's easier to _____immerse_____ my entire body in a swimming pool than try to get used to the water slowly.

SYNONYMS: dunk, engross
ANTONYMS: dredge up, pull out

10. inflammatory
(in flam′ ə tôr ē)

(*adj.*) causing excitement or anger; leading to violence or disorder

The candidate made an _____inflammatory_____ speech that incensed all those who heard it.

SYNONYMS: provoking, incendiary, provocative
ANTONYMS: calming, soothing, lulling, quieting

11. memorandum
(mem ə ran′ dəm)

(*n.*) a note to aid one's memory; an informal note or report (*pl.,* memorandums *or* memoranda)

The principal posts a weekly _____memorandum_____ to remind teachers of programs, deadlines, and special events.

SYNONYM: reminder

12. pathetic
(pə thet′ ik)

(*adj.*) marked by strong emotion, especially pity and sorrow; able to move people emotionally; worthy of pity; woefully inadequate

It was a _____pathetic_____ sight to see so many starving people desperately begging for food.

SYNONYMS: moving, distressing, pitiable, heartrending
ANTONYMS: funny, hilarious, frightening

13. persevere
(pər sə vēr′)

(*v.*) to keep doing something in spite of difficulties; to refuse to quit even when the going is tough

The patient needs to _____persevere_____ with the painful exercises in order to be able to walk normally again.

SYNONYMS: plug away, pursue, stick to it
ANTONYMS: give up, despair, throw in the towel, quit

14. prevaricate
(pri var′ ə kāt)

(v.) to lie, tell an untruth; to mislead on purpose

His reputation has suffered because of his unfortunate tendency to _____ **prevaricate** _____ .

SYNONYMS: fib, stretch the truth, equivocate
ANTONYM: tell the truth

15. quash
(kwäsh)

(v.) to crush, put down completely

Swift military action was required to _____ **quash** _____ the revolt before anyone was injured.

SYNONYM: suppress
ANTONYMS: start, kindle, ignite, encourage

16. relish
(rel′ ish)

(n.) enjoyment or satisfaction; something that adds a pleasing flavor; (v.) to enjoy greatly

She opened the tiny box with _____ **relish** _____ , knowing that it contained a piece of jewelry.

Now that I've learned about Japan in class, I _____ **relish** _____ the chance to travel there.

SYNONYMS: (n.) pleasure, gusto; (v.) take delight in
ANTONYMS: (v.) dislike, loathe, hate, despise

17. reminisce
(rem ə nis′)

(v.) to recall one's past thoughts, feelings, or experiences

At the family reunion, we got to hear 94-year-old Tía Luzia _____ **reminisce** _____ about life in old Havana.

SYNONYMS: remember, recollect

18. scour
(skaủr)

(v.) to clean or polish by hard rubbing; to examine with great care; to move about quickly in search of

The pot roast was delicious, but it won't be any fun to _____ **scour** _____ the burned roasting pan.

SYNONYMS: scrub, search, comb
ANTONYMS: dirty, soil

19. tribute
(trib′ yüt)

(n.) something done or given to show thanks or respect; a payment

The best-selling author offered _____ **tribute** _____ to the teacher who inspired her.

SYNONYMS: praise, honor, homage, recognition, commendation, glorification, money, tax, levy
ANTONYMS: blame, criticism, reproach

20. writhe
(rīth)

(v.) to make twisting or turning movements in a way that suggests pain or struggle

It's so sad to see an injured bird _____ **writhe** _____ in pain.

SYNONYMS: twist, squirm, thrash

Completing the Sentence

From the words for this unit, choose the one that best completes each of the following sentences. Write the word in the space provided.

1. Our supervisor prepared a(n) _____memorandum_____ that reminded the salespeople of the procedures to be followed during the holiday season.

2. The children won't _____dawdle_____ over their homework if they know they'll be getting cheese and crackers as soon as they finish.

3. The dictator ordered his secret police to _____quash_____ any attempt to organize a protest rally.

4. Is it wise to _____expend_____ so much of your hard-earned money on things that you don't really want or need?

5. You may not _____relish_____ being told that your carelessness was responsible for the accident even though it happens to be true.

6. Because he was seen near the scene of the crime at the time the deed was committed, he was suspected of being the _____culprit_____.

7. Many people were injured in the explosion, but luckily there was not a single _____fatality_____.

8. How can you adequately pay _____tribute_____ to such an outstanding individual?

9. We tried to hold Tom steady, but he _____writhed_____ with pain as the doctor put splints on his broken leg.

10. This pass _____authorizes_____ you to visit certain rooms in this museum that are not open to the general public.

11. The story of the homeless child was so _____pathetic_____ that it moved us all to tears.

12. Cracking down on _____illicit_____ drug traffic is one of the biggest problems facing law-enforcement agencies in the United States.

13. After we had _____dissected_____ the animal, we had to point to each of its important organs and explain its main function.

14. I love to listen to my grandfather _____reminisce_____ about his boyhood adventures in Coney Island.

15. Before you _____immerse_____ yourself in the bath, be sure to test the temperature of the water.

16. Do you really think that I am _____gullible_____ enough to believe his foolish story about being a member of the Olympic team?

17. No matter how talented you may be, you will never be successful unless you learn to _____persevere_____ in what you undertake.

18. "Only a bigot would dare to make such a rude and _____inflammatory_____ remark, even in jest," I replied.

19. You may be tempted to _____prevaricate_____, but in the long run it will be to your advantage to own up to the truth about your unfortunate error.

20. We had to _____scour_____ the walls for hours to get rid of the dirt and grease with which they were encrusted.

Synonyms

*Choose the word from this unit that is **the same** or **most nearly the same** in meaning as the **boldface** word or expression in the given phrase. Write the word on the line provided.*

1. upsetting to learn the **heartrending** details _____pathetic_____
2. targeted the most **innocent** people _____gullible_____
3. their attempt to **suppress** all those wild rumors _____quash_____
4. will carefully **examine** their argument _____dissect_____
5. **plug away** despite many setbacks _____persevere_____
6. miracle that we suffered only one **casualty** _____fatality_____
7. is certainly no time to **fib** _____prevaricate_____
8. ideas for **disbursing** the remaining funds _____expending_____
9. desperate to **squirm** free from the ropes _____writhe_____
10. should **dunk** it in cold water for one hour _____immerse_____
11. a monthly **reminder** to all her patients _____memorandum_____
12. love to **recollect** about how we first met _____reminisce_____
13. responsible for the **forbidden** actions _____illicit_____
14. will **comb** the shelves to find that book _____scour_____
15. no proof that he is the **wrongdoer** _____culprit_____

Antonyms

*Choose the word from this unit that is **most nearly opposite** in meaning to the **boldface** word or expression in the given phrase. Write the word on the line provided.*

16. given **criticism** for his actions _____tribute_____
17. encourages the children not to **hurry** _____dawdle_____
18. made **calming** gestures to the group _____inflammatory_____
19. who would **loathe** a weekend at the beach _____relish_____
20. to **forbid** taking this kind of risk _____authorize_____

Choosing the Right Word

Circle the **boldface** word that more satisfactorily completes each of the following sentences.

1. His scheme to make money by preparing term papers for other students is not only completely (**gullible, illicit**) but immoral as well.

2. I am afraid that our ambitious plan to modernize the gym has become a (**memorandum, fatality**) of the School Board's economy drive.

3. Is there any sight more (**pathetic, illicit**) than a lonely old person peering out of a tenement window hour after hour?

4. We were amazed at the (**tribute, culprit**) that Edna received from the speaker who introduced her.

5. Although our coach can spend hours (**reminiscing, writhing**) about his victories, he doesn't have an equally good memory for his defeats.

6. The more he tried to protect himself by (**scouring, prevaricating**), the more he became entrapped in his own web of lies.

7. She was so deeply (**immersed, expended**) in the book she was reading that she did not even hear us enter the room.

8. In spite of all your talk about how hard it is to get into medical school, I intend to (**persevere, relish**) in my plans to become a doctor.

9. What good does it do for the president of the Student Council to issue (**fatalities, memorandums**) if no one takes the trouble to read them?

10. It was plain from the way that he (**dawdled, persevered**) over breakfast that he was in no hurry to visit the dentist.

11. Since the charges against the suspected mugger will probably not hold up in court, the district attorney has decided to (**authorize, quash**) them.

12. When the class comedian imitated my way of speaking, it was all I could do not to (**writhe, reminisce**) with embarrassment.

13. She (**expends, dawdles**) so much time and energy on small matters that she can't prepare properly for the things that are really important.

14. With the skill of a trained debater, she (**prevaricated, dissected**) her opponent's arguments one by one to reveal their basic weaknesses.

15. Dictators like Hitler and Mussolini used (**pathetic, inflammatory**) language to stir up the emotions of the crowds they addressed.

16. We learned in our social studies class that the Constitution (**dissects, authorizes**) the president to arrange treaties with foreign countries.

17. No one (**relishes, immerses**) being reminded of his or her mistakes, but if you are wise you will try to learn from such criticism.

18. She is so worried about appearing (**inflammatory, gullible**) that she sometimes refuses to believe things that are well supported by facts.

19. When it became known that four explorers were lost in the jungle, special search parties were sent out to (**quash, scour**) the area for them.

20. His sticky fingers and the crumbs around his mouth convinced us that he was the (**culprit, tribute**) in the Case of the Empty Cookie Jar.

Vocabulary in Context

*Read the following passage, in which some of the words you have studied in this unit appear in **boldface** type. Then complete each statement given below the passage by circling the letter of the item that is **the same** or **almost the same** in meaning as the highlighted word.*

Challenges of a Biographer

(Line)

It's likely that you have done research on the life of a famous person. If so, you probably **immersed** yourself in books and articles and put together facts and details into a report. But did you ever wonder how the works that guided you came to be? In many cases, they were written by professional biographers.

A biographer is, by turns, an explorer, a reporter, a judge, a psychologist, and a (5) storyteller. The biographer of a living person often interviews the subject, as well as his or her friends, family, and acquaintances. **Authorized** biographers may also get legal permission to examine the subject's personal papers, or attend private meetings. They may even live with the subject for a time for truly close-up study. (10)

A biographer who studies someone from the past has a harder task. This kind of biographer must **expend** another sort of energy—as a detective. He or she must dig into old documents, published articles, (15) personal diaries, or anything else that was written while the subject was alive. This type of first-hand material can be rare. The biographer **scours** public records for details about marriages, births, land purchases, (20) travel, legal cases, and so on. It's the biographer's job to link the data together in a sensible and accurate way.

Carl Sandburg won a Pulitzer Prize in 1939 for *Lincoln—The War Years*.

When the subject has been written about already, how can a biographer shed new light or (25) offer new interpretations? Perhaps a long-lost **memorandum** may surface. Maybe an old diary will turn up in someone's attic. Perhaps a **tribute** to the subject may be unearthed. When the subject is little-known or rarely studied, the biographer may face a lack of information. In either case, the biographer's efforts enable us to learn about the lives of people we might not otherwise know. (30)

---

1. The meaning of **immersed** (line 2) is
a. involved
b. exhausted
c. confused
d. understood

2. Authorized (line 7) most nearly means
a. impartial
b. forbidden
c. approved
d. gifted

3. Expend (line 13) is best defined as
a. save
b. utilize
c. choose
d. gain

4. The meaning of **scours** (line 19) is
a. polishes
b. borrows
c. photocopies
d. examines

5. Memorandum (line 26) most nearly means
a. relative
b. friend
c. falsehood
d. report

6. Tribute (line 27) is best defined as
a. homage
b. criticism
c. document
d. report

Definitions

Note carefully the spelling, pronunciation, part(s) of speech, and definition(s) of each of the following words. Then write the word in the blank space(s) in the illustrative sentence(s) following. Finally, study the lists of synonyms and antonyms given at the end of each entry.

1. affluence
(af' lü əns)

(*n.*) wealth, riches, prosperity; great abundance, plenty

Education, hard work, and a very strong desire to succeed can raise a person from poverty to _____affluence_____ .

SYNONYM: opulence
ANTONYMS: poverty, want, destitution, scarcity

2. arrears
(ə rērz')

(*n., pl.*) unpaid or overdue debts; an unfinished duty

Bad spending habits and unexpected expenses left my aunt in _____arrears_____ .

SYNONYMS: in default, in the red, late, overdue

3. cascade
(kas kād')

(*n.*) a steep, narrow waterfall; something falling or rushing forth in quantity; (*v.*) to flow downward (like a waterfall)

We were thrilled when we hit the jackpot, which produced a _____cascade_____ of loudly jangling coins.

I watched the clear, sparkling water _____cascade_____ down the mountainside.

SYNONYMS: (*v.*) plunge, rush, tumble
ANTONYMS: (*n.*) drip, drop; (*v.*) trickle, ooze

4. cringe
(krinj)

(*v.*) to shrink back or hide in fear or submissiveness

My father told me to be brave and not to _____cringe_____ when the doctor vaccinated me.

SYNONYMS: flinch, duck, cower, fawn
ANTONYMS: strut, swagger

5. crotchety
(kräch' ə tē)

(*adj.*) cranky, ill-tempered; full of odd whims

It is unfortunate that the teacher asked me to work with the most _____crotchety_____ partner in the class.

SYNONYMS: grumpy, grouchy, crabby, disagreeable
ANTONYMS: sociable, friendly, agreeable, amiable

6. format
(fôr' mat)

(*n.*) the size, shape, or arrangement of something

The clear _____format_____ of the website makes it easy for users to find its key features.

SYNONYMS: layout, design

7. immobile
(i mō' bəl)

(adj.) not movable; not moving

Models must remain _____immobile_____ for a long time in order for an artist to draw or paint them accurately.

SYNONYMS: fixed, stationary, unmoving, rooted
ANTONYMS: movable, portable, nimble, agile

8. impassable
(im pas' ə bəl)

(adj.) blocked so that nothing can go through

Fallen trees formed an _____impassable_____ barrier across the highway after the storm.

SYNONYMS: closed, impenetrable
ANTONYMS: unblocked, clear, open, fit for travel

9. innovation
(i nō vā' shən)

(n.) something new, a change; the act of introducing a new method, idea, device, etc.

Our furnace has an energy-saving _____innovation_____ that turns the heat on and off at certain intervals.

SYNONYMS: novelty, modernization, new wrinkle

10. jovial
(jō' vē əl)

(adj.) good-humored, in high spirits; merry

My _____jovial_____ friend is very entertaining and is always the life of the party.

SYNONYMS: jolly, cheerful, festive
ANTONYMS: gloomy, morose, melancholy, cheerless

11. manacle
(man' ə kəl)

(n., usually pl.) a handcuff, anything that chains or confines; (v.) to chain or restrain (as with handcuffs)

The kidnappers clamped _____manacles_____ on their hostages.

The guards were told to _____manacle_____ the prisoner to the chair.

SYNONYMS: (v.) put in chains, fetter
ANTONYMS: (v.) unchain, set free, emancipate, release

12. martial
(mär' shəl)

(adj.) warlike, fond of fighting; relating to war, the army, or military life

The army band plays _____martial_____ music as the troops formally march past the visiting general.

SYNONYMS: military, hostile, bellicose
ANTONYMS: peace-loving, peaceable, pacific, unwarlike

13. minimum
(min' ə məm)

(n.) the smallest possible amount; (adj.) the lowest permissible or possible

I need to sleep a _____minimum_____ of seven hours every night.

Sixteen is the _____minimum_____ age to get a driver's license in this state.

SYNONYM: (adj.) least
ANTONYMS: (n.) maximum; (adj.) highest, most

14. nimble
(nim' bəl)

(*adj.*) quick and skillful in movement, agile; clever

As the _____ nimble _____ climber scaled Mount Everest, it looked as if she was barely exerting any energy at all.

SYNONYMS: lively, keen, flexible
ANTONYMS: awkward, clumsy, stiff, inflexible

15. onset
(än' set)

(*n.*) the beginning, start (especially of something violent and destructive); an attack, assault

At the _____ onset _____ of the heavy storm, frightened people ran to find shelter.

SYNONYMS: outset, commencement
ANTONYMS: conclusion, close, end

16. partition
(pär tish' ən)

(*n.*) something that divides (such as a wall); the act of dividing something into parts or sections; (*v.*) to divide or subdivide into parts or shares

A cloth _____ partition _____ in the study gave each of us some privacy.

We can _____ partition _____ the backyard into four separate play areas.

SYNONYMS: (*n.*) divider, separation
ANTONYMS: (*v.*) join, combine, consolidate, merge

17. perishable
(per' ə shə bəl)

(*adj.*) likely to spoil or decay

You must keep _____ perishable _____ foods chilled or they will spoil.

SYNONYMS: short-lived, fleeting
ANTONYMS: long-lasting, durable, undying, permanent

18. retrieve
(ri trēv')

(*v.*) to find and bring back, get back; to put right, make good

I enjoy playing tennis, but I don't relish having to _____ retrieve _____ tennis balls every time you hit them over the fence!

SYNONYMS: recover, regain, fetch, remedy, rectify

19. sinister
(sin' ə stər)

(*adj.*) appearing evil or dangerous; threatening evil or harm

A _____ sinister _____ message left on our answering machine made us wonder if we were safe at home.

SYNONYMS: frightening, menacing, ominous
ANTONYMS: cheering, encouraging, reassuring, benign

20. taut
(tôt)

(*adj.*) tightly drawn, tense; neat, in good order

A _____ taut _____ chain kept the curious dog away from the swimming pool.

SYNONYMS: tight, strained, orderly, shipshape
ANTONYMS: loose, slack, drooping, messy, sloppy

Completing the Sentence

From the words for this unit, choose the one that best completes each of the following sentences. Write the word in the space provided.

1. Sherlock Holmes detected in the wicked scheme the _____**sinister**_____ hand of the evil Professor Moriarty.

2. I know that my payments on the car are in _____**arrears**_____, but I will catch up as soon as I get my next paycheck.

3. Unless you pull the ropes _____**taut**_____, the tennis net will sag.

4. The sunlight caught the waters of the stream as they _____**cascaded**_____ over the steep cliff and formed a brilliant rainbow.

5. The patients will have a much better chance to recover quickly if they receive treatment at the _____**onset**_____ of the fever.

6. The _____**jovial**_____ mood of our cheerful little gathering changed abruptly to sorrow when news of the tragedy came over the radio.

7. Frank Lloyd Wright was a great American architect who was responsible for many _____**innovations**_____ in the design of buildings.

8. I was able to _____**retrieve**_____ my baggage promptly after leaving the plane.

9. It's a pleasure to watch the expert typist's _____**nimble**_____ fingers move swiftly over the keyboard.

10. The more we tried to humor the _____**crotchety**_____ crossing guard, the more irritable and demanding he seemed to become.

11. Today _____**perishable**_____ foods are shipped in refrigerated trucks to prevent spoilage.

12. I don't expect you to be a hero, but do you have to _____**cringe**_____ in that cowardly fashion whenever anyone so much as disagrees with you?

13. Although we are sure that the prisoners will make no attempt to escape, the law requires us to place _____**manacles**_____ on them.

14. The feeling of _____**affluence**_____ I had when I was paid lasted only until I had finished taking care of my bills.

15. As a result of the record-breaking snowstorm, all roads in the area became _____**impassable**_____.

16. Can you explain why there is not only a maximum speed limit but also a(n) _____**minimum**_____ speed limit on many modern highways?

17. His back injury was so severe that he has been placed in a cast and will have to remain _____**immobile**_____ for months.

18. We made use of a(n) _____ partition _____ to break up the floor space into a large number of small offices.

19. During the war years, the government tried by all kinds of propaganda to arouse the _____ martial _____ spirit of the people.

20. We plan to change the _____ format _____ of our school magazine to make it more attractive and readable.

Synonyms

*Choose the word from this unit that is **the same** or **most nearly the same** in meaning as the **boldface** word or expression in the given phrase. Write the word on the line provided.*

1. recover data from my computer _____ retrieve _____

2. in the **impenetrable** section of the cave _____ impassable _____

3. under strict **military** law _____ martial _____

4. a **menacing** look in his eyes _____ sinister _____

5. installed to make it remain **stationary** _____ immobile _____

6. begged not to be **fettered** _____ manacled _____

7. in **default** after losing her job _____ arrears _____

8. so **short-lived** in this climate _____ perishable _____

9. as if confetti **tumbled** onto the stage _____ cascaded _____

10. resisting the latest **modernization** _____ innovation _____

11. stack of books as a temporary **divider** _____ partition _____

12. disagreeable because he was so tired _____ crotchety _____

13. according to the most recent **design** _____ format _____

14. as **flexible** as a ballet dancer _____ nimble _____

15. to **cower** when the doctor approaches _____ cringe _____

Antonyms

*Choose the word from this unit that is **most nearly opposite** in meaning to the **boldface** word or expression in the given phrase. Write the word on the line provided.*

16. assigned the **maximum** penalty _____ minimum _____

17. reacting to our **melancholy** host _____ jovial _____

18. taken as a sure sign of **poverty** _____ affluence _____

19. at the **conclusion** of the program _____ onset _____

20. massaging my **loose** muscles _____ taut _____

Choosing the Right Word

*Circle the **boldface** word that more satisfactorily completes each of the following sentences.*

1. Of all the different types of writing, humor may be the most (**perishable,** jovial) because each generation has its own idea of what is funny.

2. I felt that there was something thoroughly (**sinister,** immobile) about the way he kept trying to duck questions on that subject.

3. In the moment of danger, my nerves were so (**taut,** sinister) that I would have screamed if someone had touched me.

4. The first thing the bankrupt firm must do with its funds is pay the (**arrears,** formats) due on the employees' wages.

5. Although we are proud of our high standard of living, we should not forget that there are those who do not share in this (**affluence,** cascade).

6. Robin Hood's faithful band of merry men were not only (crotchety, **jovial**) companions, but brave fighters as well.

7. Her mind is so (impassable, **nimble**) that she always seems to be one step ahead of us in any matter under discussion.

8. The self-styled "tough guy" (**cringed,** manacled) in terror and begged the police not to shoot.

9. A high school student looking for a vacation job usually can't expect to earn more than the (perishable, **minimum**) wage.

10. Normally, I'm very even tempered, but I can become a little (**crotchety,** martial) when I'm tired or hungry.

11. Her shimmering blond hair fell upon her pretty shoulders like a(n) (onset, **cascade**) of gold.

12. Although we all recognize that there must be changes, it is a mistake to think that every (arrears, **innovation**) is necessarily an improvement.

13. In the 18th century, Russia, Prussia, and Austria made a series of deals to (**partition,** cringe) and annex Poland right out of existence.

14. More than once, our skillful running backs managed to find a way through our opponents' supposedly (**impassable,** affluent) line.

15. Despite all his efforts, he was never able to (**retrieve,** partition) the fine reputation he had lost by that crooked deal.

16. The speed with which the boxer darted about the ring made his lumbering opponent seem utterly (nimble, **immobile**) by comparison.

17. If you spend much time watching TV, you will come to realize that all the news programs share the same basic (**format,** minimum).

18. We learned in our history class that the ancient Romans were very fine soldiers and excelled in all the (**martial,** perishable) arts.

19. Instead of acting as though you were permanently (**manacled,** retrieved) to your small circle of friends, you should try to meet new people.

20. With the (affluence, **onset**) of the heat wave, vast numbers of city dwellers began to stream toward the beaches and mountains.

Read the following passage, in which some of the words you have studied in this unit appear in **boldface** type. Then complete each statement given below the passage by circling the letter of the item that is **the same** or **almost the same** in meaning as the highlighted word.

Birth of a Puzzle

(Line)

Crossword puzzles are so common that almost everyone knows how they work. Yet crosswords as we know them first appeared less than a hundred years ago. Before then, the only known word puzzles were simple British children's games. In these, letters could be arranged into connecting words. A clever child could read

(5) words both across and down.

In 1913, newspaper editor Arthur Wynne wanted a unique activity for the "Fun" page of his Sunday paper. He **retrieved** the old idea of the children's word puzzle. Wynne's **innovation** was to expand it into a larger written **format**. He drew interlocking boxes in a diamond shape. He gave clues to help solvers fill the

(10) boxes with letters to form linking words. Wynne's puzzle started a trend that others would perfect.

In 1924, Margaret Farrar published the first book of crossword puzzles. It became an instant best-seller. People did crossword puzzles to relax, to improve

(15) their vocabulary, and to keep their minds **nimble**.

Crossword puzzles quickly became a fad, and nearly every American newspaper featured them. In the days before television, people gathering to solve puzzles became a **jovial** social event.

(20) The fad grew into a familiar feature of daily life. Soon, serious puzzle solvers demanded more challenges. Puzzle makers began to develop larger diagrams with a **minimum** of blank spaces. They

Working together makes solving crossword puzzles even more fun.

wrote hard clues based on obscure facts, current events, quotations, puns, and

(25) riddles. In 1942, the *New York Times* added a Sunday puzzle, edited by Mrs. Farrar. This happened at an opportune time—during World War II—when war-weary readers were glad for a break from bad news. Farrar's puzzles were wildly popular. Today, you will find crossword puzzles everywhere—in newspapers, magazines, books, at online interactive websites, and even on

(30) place mats.

---

1. The meaning of **retrieved** (line 7) is
   a. copied
   c. brought back
   b. researched
   d. invented

2. The meaning of **innovation** (line 8) is
   a. change
   c. outline
   b. repetition
   d. separation

3. Format (line 8) most nearly means
   a. contract
   c. design
   b. novel
   d. box

4. Nimble (line 15) most nearly means
   a. stiff
   c. jolly
   b. blocked
   d. quick

5. Jovial (line 19) is best defined as
   a. gloomy
   c. crabby
   b. cheerful
   d. intellectual

6. Minimum (line 23) is best defined as
   a. great number
   c. equal number
   b. small number
   d. surplus

Definitions

Note carefully the spelling, pronunciation, part(s) of speech, and definition(s) of each of the following words. Then write the word in the blank space(s) in the illustrative sentence(s) following. Finally, study the lists of synonyms and antonyms given at the end of each entry.

1. avenge
(ə venj')

(*v.*) to get revenge for, get even for, settle a score; to punish someone or get satisfaction for a wrong or injury

In Shakespeare's *Hamlet*, the title character vows to _____**avenge**_____ his father's death.

SYNONYM: retaliate

2. cede
(sēd)

(*v.*) to give up, surrender; to hand over to another

Spain _____**ceded**_____ territory to France.

SYNONYMS: yield, deliver up, transfer

3. deluge
(del' yüj)

(*n.*) a great flood; a heavy fall of rain; anything that comes in vast quantity (like a flood); (*v.*) to flood

Owners are hoping this summer will bring a _____**deluge**_____ of visitors to their new theme park in Minneapolis.

A torrential downpour _____**deluged**_____ the entire town.

SYNONYMS: (*v.*) swamp, inundate
ANTONYMS: (*n.*) trickle, dribble

4. discretion
(dis kresh' ən)

(*n.*) good judgment; care in speech and action; freedom to judge or choose

My teacher suggested I use _____**discretion**_____ in dealing with my difficult classmate.

SYNONYMS: prudence, tact, discrimination

5. giddy
(gid' ē)

(*adj.*) dizzy; light-headed; lacking seriousness

After the long race, the marathoner felt _____**giddy**_____.

SYNONYMS: faint, frivolous, flighty
ANTONYMS: levelheaded, serious, earnest, sober

6. impact
(*n.,* im' pakt;
v., im pakt')

(*n.*) the striking of one object against another; the shock caused by a collision; (*v.*) to affect, especially forcefully

The _____**impact**_____ of the car crash destroyed both vehicles, but miraculously no one was hurt.

Budget cuts will _____**impact**_____ the number of hours the public library can stay open.

SYNONYMS: (*n.*) collision, blow, effect

7. intimidate
(in tim' ə dāt)

(*v.*) to make timid or frighten by threats; to use fear to get someone to do (or not to do) something

Bullies may try to _____ **intimidate** _____ us, but if we stick together, we can stand up to their threats.

SYNONYMS: bully, browbeat, hector

8. liberate
(lib' ə rāt)

(*v.*) to free from bondage or domination; to release

The police _____ **liberated** _____ the anxious hostages after sixteen hours of confinement.

SYNONYMS: untie, unshackle
ANTONYMS: imprison, fetter, shackle, bind

9. logical
(läj' ə kəl)

(*adj.*) reasonable; making use of reason and good sense

Our parents are constantly encouraging us to look for _____ **logical** _____ solutions to our problems.

SYNONYMS: rational, sensible
ANTONYMS: absurd, ridiculous, unsound, preposterous

10. misrepresent
(mis rep ri zent')

(*v.*) to give a false or untrue idea

If witnesses _____ **misrepresent** _____ the facts, the defense attorney has proof to support our story.

SYNONYMS: distort, falsify, twist, exaggerate

11. optional
(äp' shə nəl)

(*adj.*) left to one's own choice; not required

The hotel will charge us for breakfast and dinner, but lunch is _____ **optional** _____ .

SYNONYMS: voluntary, elective, discretionary
ANTONYMS: required, mandatory, compulsory

12. outright
(aût' rīt)

(*adj.*) complete; instantaneous; without reservation, thoroughgoing; (*adv.*) completely, instantaneously

When the teacher asked her why she didn't do her homework, she told an _____ **outright** _____ lie.

Even though they had already heard it several times, the hilarious joke made them laugh _____ **outright** _____ .

SYNONYMS: (*adj.*) total, out-and-out; (*adv.*) utterly, instantly
ANTONYMS: (*adj.*) partial, incomplete; (*adv.*) by degrees

13. rendezvous
(rän' dā vü)

(*v.*) to meet in accordance with a plan; (*n.*) a meeting by agreement; a meeting place

Let's all agree to _____ **rendezvous** _____ by the fountain on Saturday afternoon.

They kept their _____ **rendezvous** _____ a secret.

SYNONYMS: (*n.*) date, appointment, assignation

14. rotund
(rō tənd')

(*adj.*) rounded and plump; full or rich in sound

My friends like to display the largest and most _____ **rotund** _____ pumpkin outside their front door.

SYNONYMS: round, plump, chubby, portly, sonorous
ANTONYMS: thin, angular, lean, lanky, skinny, gaunt

15. saunter
(sôn' tər)

(*v.*) to stroll; walk in an easy, leisurely way; (*n.*) a stroll

The star _____ **sauntered** _____ past his adoring fans, pretending not to notice their cries of joy.

It's such a beautiful day to take a _____ **saunter** _____ .

SYNONYMS: (*v.*) ramble, amble; (*n.*) promenade
ANTONYMS: (*v.*) speed, race, hurry, dash, scurry, rush

16. sluggish
(sləg' ish)

(*adj.*) lazy; slow-moving; not active, dull

After a big lunch, I feel _____ **sluggish** _____ .

SYNONYMS: unhurried, lethargic, leisurely
ANTONYMS: active, energetic, lively, rapid, brisk

17. subordinate
(*adj., n.,* sə bôr' də nət; *v.,* sə bôr' də nāt)

(*adj.*) lower in rank or position, secondary; (*n.*) one who is in a lower position or under the orders of someone else; (*v.*) to put in a lower or secondary position

A corporal is _____ **subordinate** _____ to a sergeant.

Let's ask a _____ **subordinate** _____ to help us file.

Parents often _____ **subordinate** _____ their own wishes for the sake of their children's needs.

SYNONYMS: (*n.*) assistant, helper
ANTONYMS: (*adj.*) superior, higher; (*n.*) chief, supervisor

18. tint
(tint)

(*n.*) a delicate color or hue; a slight trace of something; (*v.*) to give color to something; to dye

He wants to paint his room a darker _____ **tint** _____ of blue.

I hope my ophthalmologist can _____ **tint** _____ my sunglass lenses pink.

SYNONYMS: (*n.*) shade, tone; (*v.*) color, stain
ANTONYMS: (*v.*) bleach, whiten

19. variable
(vâr' ē ə bəl)

(*adj.*) likely to undergo change; changeable; (*n.*) a value or quantity that varies; a symbol for such

Spring weather can be extremely _____ **variable** _____ .

In mathematics, the letter x can stand for a _____ **variable** _____ .

SYNONYMS: (*adj.*) fluctuating, shifting, inconstant
ANTONYMS: (*adj.*) constant, unchanging, steady

20. verge
(vərj)

(*n.*) the point at which something begins or happens; a border; (*v.*) to incline, tend toward, approach; to be in the process of becoming something else

I was on the _____ **verge** _____ of tears today.

That chatter _____ **verges** _____ on baby talk.

SYNONYMS: (*n.*) brink, threshhold, edge

Completing the Sentence

From the words for this unit, choose the one that best completes each of the following sentences. Write the word in the space provided.

1. By late September the leaves on the trees in my neck of the woods have begun to take on their normal autumn _____tint_____ .

2. Our "truth in advertising" laws are designed to discourage manufacturers from ____misrepresenting____ the virtues of their products.

3. Next year, when we have a stronger, more experienced team, we hope to _____avenge_____ the crushing defeat we have just suffered.

4. The two groups of hikers, setting out from different points, have planned a(n) _____rendezvous_____ at four o'clock at Eagle Rock.

5. After being defeated in a war that lasted from 1846 to 1848, Mexico was forced to _____cede_____ vast territories to the United States.

6. You may like to live where the sun shines all the time, but I prefer a more ____variable____ climate.

7. According to the Bible, Noah and his family were the only human beings to survive the great _____deluge_____ that once engulfed the world.

8. Even fans sitting high in the stands could hear the _____impact_____ when the big fullback crashed into the line.

9. We believe that the world is now on the _____verge_____ of new and exciting developments that may dramatically change the way we live.

10. Her argument was so _____logical_____ that she convinced us that her solution to the math problem was the correct one.

11. Uncle Eddie, with his _____rotund_____ figure, is often called on to play Santa Claus.

12. Every eye was on us as we _____sauntered_____ down Main Street in our new outfits.

13. As a young and inexperienced employee, you cannot expect to hold more than a(n) _____subordinate_____ job in that big company.

14. After the heavy meal, we felt so _____sluggish_____ that we just sat in the living room and watched whatever was on television.

15. The impact of the head-on collision was so severe that the drivers of both vehicles were killed _____outright_____ .

16. We can hold down the cost of the new car we want to buy by not ordering _____optional_____ features.

17. When they realized that sweet talk and flattery were getting them nowhere, they tried to _____intimidate_____ me into doing what they wanted.

18. Many older residents of Paris can still recall the day in 1944 when Allied troops _____ liberated _____ the city from German occupation.

19. Because of the lawyer's long experience in legal matters, we left it to his _____ discretion _____ how to proceed with the case.

20. Many people say that they become quite _____ giddy _____ when they look down from the top of a tall building.

Synonyms

*Choose the word from this unit that is **the same** or **most nearly the same** in meaning as the **boldface** word or expression in the given phrase. Write the word on the line provided.*

1. as **inconstant** as the latest fad — variable

2. an **assistant** to the vice principal — subordinate

3. on the **brink** of a new beginning — verge

4. made **total** fools of themselves — outright

5. could **bully** us into giving in — intimidate

6. kissed the baby's **chubby** cheek — rotund

7. the jarring sound of the **collision** — impact

8. as if they made an **appointment** with danger — rendezvous

9. had to **yield** that point in the debate — cede

10. decided to **stain** my T-shirt a pastel shade — tint

11. taught two **elective** classes after school — optional

12. spent a **lethargic** morning in bed — sluggish

13. thought of ways to **retaliate** the insult — avenge

14. her **tact** with difficult customers — discretion

15. not to **distort** the facts of the case — misrepresent

Antonyms

*Choose the word from this unit that is **most nearly opposite** in meaning to the **boldface** word or expression in the given phrase. Write the word on the line provided.*

16. gave a **preposterous** explanation — logical

17. a **trickle** of information — deluge

18. to **shackle** the young falcons — liberate

19. couldn't comprehend the **sober** mood — giddy

20. as they **scurry** through the mall — saunter

Choosing the Right Word

*Circle the **boldface** word that more satisfactorily completes each of the following sentences.*

1. We held a meeting to discuss why the sale of tickets to the class dance has been so (**sluggish,** rotund) and what we can do about it.

2. At the State Fair, we separated to visit different exhibits, but we agreed to (**saunter,** **rendezvous**) at the refreshment stand at five o'clock.

3. Only the (optional, **outright**) repeal of this unfair nuisance tax will satisfy the voters.

4. Many people, unhappy with what nature has given them, seek to improve their appearance by (**tinting,** ceding) their hair.

5. It is sad to see how, in just a few years, the lean young athlete has allowed himself to become flabby and (giddy, **rotund**).

6. In times of crisis, we may be called on to (deluge, **subordinate**) our personal interests to the needs of the nation as a whole.

7. Many Western films include a character who is out to (intimidate, **avenge**) a wrong done to a close friend or relative.

8. Letters of protest (**deluged,** tinted) the Mayor's office when he proposed an increase in the sales tax.

9. It is good for you to "stand up for your rights," but you should not do so in a way that (**verges,** subordinates) on discourtesy.

10. There are times in life when you should be guided more by your feelings, without trying to be strictly (outright, **logical**) about everything.

11. I plan to write a term paper that will discuss the different ways in which television has had a major (**impact,** verge) on American life.

12. We had regarded her as a rather (logical, **giddy**) young girl, but in this tough situation she showed that she had courage and good sense.

13. If you know that you are late for school, why do you (**saunter,** rendezvous) along as though you had all the time in the world?

14. This biased editorial has deliberately (**misrepresented,** avenged) the stand of our candidate on the important issues of the election.

15. The invitation to the party said that formal wear was (**optional,** variable).

16. I look forward to the time when my parents will agree that I have reached the "age of (**discretion,** misrepresentation)."

17. He soon learned that the moods of a youngster—happy one moment, miserable the next—can be as (**variable,** sluggish) as the winds.

18. Modern household appliances have done much to (**liberate,** deluge) homemakers from tedious and time-consuming chores.

19. The aged millionaire, wishing to spend his last years in peace and quiet, (**ceded,** impacted) all his business interests to his sons.

20. A fastball pitcher will often try to (**intimidate,** liberate) an opposing batter by "shaving" him with an inside pitch.

Vocabulary in Context

*Read the following passage, in which some of the words you have studied in this unit appear in **boldface** type. Then complete each statement given below the passage by circling the letter of the item that is **the same** or **almost the same** in meaning as the highlighted word.*

Exaggerated Kings

Why is this lion winking? Perhaps it is because he knows the truth!

(Line)

For centuries, people have regarded the lion as a noble creature. But have lions been **misrepresented** as the king of beasts? The truth about lions may surprise you.

Without a doubt, lions are handsome, powerful cats. The male lion's rich, thick mane makes it both beautiful and fierce looking. It would be a **logical** conclusion, then, to view the male as a great hunter and protector. But this is (5) not the case. Female lions do most of the hunting, often at night and in teams. Male lions rest or sleep up to twenty hours a day. The so-called "king" is actually a **sluggish** monarch much of the time. (10)

Lions generally live in groups known as *prides*, which are like family units. Females of several generations may stay in the same pride for life. Male lions wander away or are forced out by new, stronger males. A pride may have a **variable** number of (15) members, from as few as three to as many as thirty or more, depending on the amount of food in their territory. More food means larger prides.

These meat-eaters often feed on fresh kill that they bring down. However, some lions are **outright** (20) thieves. They steal meat from other predators to save themselves the effort of hunting. That doesn't seem like noble behavior! Nor does the fact that after female lions have made a kill, males chase them away so they can take the finest morsels for themselves.

Lions were once common to many parts of Europe, Asia, India, and Africa. (25) But human hunters and farmers, as well as widespread development in regions where lions once roamed, have all had a serious **impact** on the wild lion population. Today, wild lions are found only in parts of Africa, and in a protected wildlife preserve in India. Neither an endangered nor threatened species, the lion continues to occupy its throne. (30)

---

1. The meaning of **misrepresented** (line 2) is
  a. judged
  b. liberated
  c. construed
  d. falsified

2. Logical (line 4) most nearly means
  a. compulsory
  b. sensible
  c. senseless
  d. ridiculous

3. Sluggish (line 9) is best defined as
  a. royal
  b. energetic
  c. lazy
  d. plump

4. The meaning of **variable** (line 15) is
  a. changeable
  b. superior
  c. constant
  d. large

5. Outright (line 20) most nearly means
  a. devious
  b. accidental
  c. total
  d. partial

6. Impact (line 27) is best defined as
  a. hazard
  b. effect
  c. damage
  d. support

104 ■ Unit 9

Analogies

In each of the following, circle the item that best completes the comparison.

See pages T38–T48 for explanations of answers.

1. pathetic is to **pity** as
a. subordinate is to concern
b. outright is to joy
c. illicit is to laughter
d. sinister is to fear ⭕

2. rotund is to **shape** as
a. tiny is to size ⭕
b. wide is to length
c. wet is to volume
d. orange is to capacity

3. sluggish is to **speed** as
a. nimble is to skill
b. logical is to reason
c. giddy is to seriousness ⭕
d. optional is to meaning

4. diplomat is to **discretion** as
a. showoff is to modesty
b. daredevil is to cowardice
c. hothead is to rashness ⭕
d. spoilsport is to enthusiasm

5. variable is to **change** as
a. perishable is to decay ⭕
b. minimum is to time
c. outright is to disease
d. illicit is to aging

6. fatality is to **dead** as
a. onset is to tired
b. format is to dirty
c. injury is to hurt ⭕
d. memorandum is to hungry

7. bully is to **intimidate** as
a. coward is to avenge
b. swindler is to cheat ⭕
c. judge is to retrieve
d. patient is to dissect

8. dribble is to **deluge** as
a. invention is to innovation
b. dye is to tint
c. spray is to cascade ⭕
d. format is to design

9. perishable is to **spoil** as
a. fragile is to break ⭕
b. optional is to use
c. immobile is to shift
d. inflammatory is to extinguish

10. prisoner is to **manacle** as
a. dancer is to tie
b. nurse is to helmet
c. king is to crown ⭕
d. farmer is to tuxedo

11. slavery is to **liberate** as
a. trap is to release ⭕
b. problem is to create
c. accident is to observe
d. injury is to suffer

12. liar is to **prevaricate** as
a. showoff is to hide
b. pickpocket is to steal ⭕
c. spoilsport is to amuse
d. culprit is to rescue

13. immobile is to **move** as
a. impossible is to touch
b. impassable is to cross ⭕
c. important is to see
d. improper is to do

14. snake is to **writhe** as
a. lion is to cringe
b. leopard is to saunter
c. butterfly is to intimidate
d. snail is to dawdle ⭕

15. immerse is to **liquid** as
a. hide is to air
b. bury is to ground ⭕
c. freeze is to fire
d. illuminate is to cold

16. gullible is to **deceive** as
a. taut is to stretch
b. sluggish is to move
c. jovial is to surprise
d. crotchety is to annoy ⭕

17. affluence is to **wealthy** as
a. poverty is to penniless ⭕
b. knowledge is to ignorant
c. talent is to average
d. power is to political

18. martial is to **war** as
a. legal is to government
b. moral is to crime
c. financial is to money ⭕
d. judicial is to religion

Word Associations

In each of the following groups, circle the word that is best defined or suggested by the given phrase.

1. read the report
a. culprit   b. innovation   (c. memorandum)   d. affluence

2. will not allow ourselves to be bullied
a. avenged   b. impacted   c. immersed   (d. intimidated)

3. a highway death
a. deluge   b. memorandum   c. onset   (d. fatality)

4. enjoyed the military music
a. gullible   (b. martial)   c. illicit   d. jovial

5. pulled the rope tight
(a. taut)   b. nimble   c. crotchety   d. immobile

6. the effect of the new factory
a. innovation   b. manacle   c. subordinate   (d. impact)

7. on the brink of collapse
(a. verge)   b. manacle   c. variable   d. tribute

8. put down a revolt
(a. quash)   b. deluge   c. expend   d. partition

9. get even for a wrong
a. authorize   (b. avenge)   c. dawdle   d. cringe

10. the layout of the catalog
a. affluence   (b. format)   c. impact   d. memorandum

11. showed outstanding judgment
a. onset   (b. discretion)   c. relish   d. tint

12. divide the country
a. liberate   b. format   (c. partition)   d. reminisce

13. dye the canvas
a. cede   b. deluge   c. immerse   (d. tint)

14. a flood of letters
(a. deluge)   b. manacle   c. parcel   d. tribute

15. the blocked country road
a. inflammatory   b. illicit   c. jovial   (d. impassable)

16. in a merry mood
a. pathetic   (b. jovial)   c. sluggish   d. wholesome

17. the start of flu symptoms
(a. onset)   b. cascade   c. impact   d. encounter

18. a heartfelt commendation
a. memorandum   b. format   c. subordinate   (d. tribute)

19. a memorable date
a. fatality   (b. rendezvous)   c. impact   d. onset

20. strolling along
a. avenging   b. writhing   (c. sauntering)   d. immersing

Vocabulary in Context

*Read the following passage, in which some of the words you have studied in Units 7–9 appear in **boldface** type. Then complete each statement given below the passage by circling the item that is **the same** or **almost the same** in meaning as the highlighted word.*

Extinction of the Dodo

(Line)

Alas, the dodo bird is no more. None of these funny-looking relatives of the dove exist today. In fact, dodos have been extinct for over three
(5) centuries.

The **pathetic** dodo never got much respect in its time. People called it "disgusting." The clumsy-looking bird looked a bit like a deformed pigeon,
(10) but larger. Others thought it might be a kind of **rotund** turkey. Its hooked bill led still others to think it might be a flightless cockatoo. Had the dodo understood what people said about
(15) it, it probably wouldn't have **cringed** a bit. That's because of its strangely docile nature.

The dodo was slow moving and unusually trusting. Little would
(20) **intimidate** the easygoing bird. Its natural home was Mauritius, a small island in the Indian Ocean. Dutch and Portuguese sailors who visited Mauritius in their travels were
(25) fascinated by the dodo. Its odd looks made it seem almost imaginary, appealing to artists, naturalists, and writers.

But the dodo's trusting nature left it
(30) vulnerable. Several categories of **culprits** contributed to the extinction of the dodo. Enterprising sailors began to steal dodos from Mauritius. They sold them to eager collectors,
(35) who would pay handsomely for the homely birds. Also, the dodo was dinner for the colonists of and visitors to the island, and for the animals that they brought with them. By 1681, no
(40) more dodos lived on Mauritius, or anywhere else. The ones that had been held in captivity were never bred. They left no descendants.

Lack of scientific evidence led
(45) nineteenth-century naturalists to ask whether the dodo ever existed at all. With no bodies to **dissect**, and few bones to examine, skeptics came to denounce the dodo as a fraud. Later
(50) research proved that the dodo had indeed existed, but that its lack of natural enemies and overly trusting nature probably cost it a lasting place in the animal world.

---

1. The meaning of **pathetic** (line 6) is
   a. gullible   c. durable
   (b. pitiable)   d. terrible

2. Rotund (line 11) most nearly means
   a. skinny   (c. plump)
   b. tall   d. flighty

3. Cringed (line 15) is best defined as
   (a. flinched)   c. wept
   b. strutted   d. argued

4. The meaning of **intimidate** (line 20) is
   a. imprison   c. pursue
   b. avenge   (d. bully)

5. Culprits (line 31) most nearly means
   a. people   c. businessmen
   b. thieves   (d. wrongdoers)

6. Dissect (line 47) is best defined as
   a. bury   (c. analyze)
   b. train   d. compare

Choosing the Right Meaning

Read each sentence carefully. Then circle the item that best completes the statement below the sentence.

See pages T38–T48 for explanations of answers.

Not only was Abraham Lincoln a master of English prose, but by all accounts he possessed a keen sense of humor and relished a good story. (2)

1. The word **relished** in line 2 is used to mean
(a. enjoyed)   b. told   c. collected   d. concocted

Our teacher wrote "x + 9" on the board to give an example of a mathematical expression containing a variable. (2)

2. In line 2 the word **variable** is best defined as
a. difficult problem   b. mistake   (c. unknown value)   d. solution

With the death of Stonewall Jackson in May of 1863, Confederate commander Robert E. Lee lost his ablest subordinate. (2)

3. In line 2 the word **subordinate** is best defined as
a. adviser   b. strategist   c. ally   (d. lieutenant)

By the time of Lee's surrender at Appomattox in April 1865, the war-making capacity of the South had been destroyed outright. (2)

4. The word **outright** in line 2 most nearly means
a. quickly   (b. completely)   c. gradually   d. partially

Over the years countless students have recited the rotund lines of Edgar Allan Poe's famous poem "The Raven." (2)

5. The word **rotund** in line 1 most nearly means
a. plump   b. stout   c. round   (d. sonorous)

Antonyms

*In each of the following groups, circle the word or expression that is most nearly the **opposite** of the word in **boldface** type.*

1. manacle
(a. emancipate)
b. delete
c. befuddle
d. expand

2. illicit
(a. permissible)
b. explicit
c. illegal
d. coarse

3. optional
a. new
b. interesting
(c. required)
d. difficult

4. expend
a. spend
b. avoid
(c. save)
d. require

5. perishable
a. foreign
b. expensive
c. colorful
(d. durable)

6. liberate
(a. shackle)
b. study
c. rule
d. visit

7. relish
a. consider
(b. loathe)
c. examine
d. invent

8. gullible
a. rich
b. silly
c. tall
(d. suspicious)

9. persevere
a. pursue
b. quit ⟵
c. reply
d. spend

11. sluggish
a. thoughtful
b. friendly
c. active ⟵
d. sleepy

13. rotund
a. round
b. dark
c. frightening
d. lanky ⟵

15. crotchety
a. new
b. agreeable ⟵
c. former
d. overworked

10. pathetic
a. funny ⟵
b. unusual
c. inadequate
d. sad

12. affluence
a. wealth
b. poverty ⟵
c. heaviness
d. confusion

14. minimum
a. only
b. latest
c. usual
d. most ⟵

16. scour
a. dirty
b. cower ⟵
c. hide
d. believe

Word Families

A. On the line provided, write the word you have learned in Units 7–9 that is related to each of the following nouns.
EXAMPLE: intimidation—**intimidate**

1. retrieval, retriever, retrievability — retrieve
2. dissection, dissector — dissect
3. immersion — immerse
4. nimbleness — nimble
5. joviality — jovial
6. avenger — avenge
7. misrepresentation — misrepresent
8. liberation, liberator, liberationist — liberate
9. perseverance, perseveration — persevere
10. authorization — authorize
11. dawdler — dawdle
12. prevarication, prevaricator — prevaricate
13. logic — logical
14. reminiscence — reminisce
15. gullibility — gullible
16. option — optional

B. On the line provided, write the word you have learned in Units 7–9 that is related to each of the following verbs.
EXAMPLE: inflame—**inflammatory**

17. innovate — innovation
18. perish — perishable
19. minimize — minimum
20. vary — variable

Two-Word Completions

Circle the pair of words that best complete the meaning of each of the following passages.

See pages T38–T48 for explanations of answers.

1. The Emancipation Proclamation _____ Southern blacks once and for all from the _____ that bound them to a life of servitude and humiliation.
   a. immersed . . . arrears
   b. liberated . . . manacles
   c. subordinated . . . memoranda
   d. retrieved . . . tints

2. During "Operation Dragnet," the police _____ the entire city in search of the two _____ who had pulled off the daring bank robbery.
   a. immersed . . . fatalities
   b. quashed . . . innovators
   c. scoured . . . culprits
   d. deluged . . . subordinates

3. Joan of Arc spent most of her brief career as the "warrior maiden of France" attempting to _____ lands that the French had been forced to _____ to England as a result of English victories in the initial stages of the Hundred Years' War.
   a. partition . . . expend
   b. avenge . . . authorize
   c. liberate . . . misrepresent
   d. retrieve . . . cede

4. The _____ of their sudden collision left one of the players _____ on the ice in agony, while the other was hurled five feet into the air.
   a. format . . . cringing
   b. impact . . . writhing
   c. fatality . . . verging
   d. onset . . . scouring

5. The bully down the block is so big and so _____ that I find myself unconsciously _____ in fear every time he looks in my direction.
   a. intimidating . . . cringing
   b. rotund . . . prevaricating
   c. sinister . . . dawdling
   d. martial . . . sauntering

6. After Grandpa _____, then lost, half of his nest egg in an obviously crooked scheme, I stressed that he could no longer be so _____ when it came to taking the advice of financial "wizards."
   a. reminisced . . . jovial
   b. intimidated . . . taut
   c. deluged . . . giddy
   d. invested . . . gullible

Building with Classical Roots

log, logue—speech, word, discourse

This Greek root appears in **logical** (page 99). Some other words in which this root appears are listed below.

apology	dialogue	eulogy	neologism
decalogue	epilogue	monologue	prologue

From the list of words above, choose the one that corresponds to each of the brief definitions below. Write the word in the blank space in the illustrative sentence below the definition.

1. a long speech made by one person; a speech that monopolizes conversation; a series of jokes or comedic stories delivered by one comedian

The opening ____monologue____ given by talk-show hosts, consisting of light banter and political humor, has become a staple of late-night television.

2. a conversation between two or more people or characters; the lines in a script that are to be spoken; an airing of ideas or views

Abbott and Costello's wacky routine "Who's on first?" is one of the funniest baseball ____dialogues____ in American comedy.

3. a speech or written tribute composed to honor someone who has died

Lincoln's Gettysburg Address was delivered on November 19, 1863, to dedicate a national cemetery and as a ____eulogy____ to those who died at the Battle of Gettysburg.

4. words of regret to express remorse and ask pardon for an accident, fault, failure, or offense; an explanation, defense, or excuse

"If you'd like me to accept your ____apology____," he explained, "I need to believe that you know what you did wrong, and that you will strive to do better."

5. an introductory statement, act, or event; a preface; opening remarks

The novel's ____prologue____ offers background on the main character so that the action can begin immediately in Chapter 1.

6. a concluding section at the end of a play or literary work, intended to provide further comment, interpretation, or information; an afterword

After the curtain fell, a narrator gave a brief ____epilogue____ to tie up loose ends.

7. a newly invented word, expression, or usage; new meaning for an old word

Evolving technology has led to many ____neologisms____, such as CD-ROM, that have become part of our everyday language.

8. a set of ten authoritative rules or laws; (*usu. cap.*) The Ten Commandments (in the Bible)

The stained-glass window shows Moses holding the ____Decalogue____ above his head.

From the list of words on page 111, choose the one that best completes each of the following sentences. Write the word in the blank space provided.

1. The man scolded us with an angry ___monologue___ about the decline of manners.

2. The best way to achieve lasting peace is for both parties to engage in ongoing, meaningful ___dialogue___ to address their fundamental desires and demands.

3. The acting governor delivered a heartfelt ___eulogy___ at the funeral of her former boss.

4. An authentic ___apology___ should not be a bunch of meaningless words.

5. The author included a ___prologue___ to clarify her intentions in writing this book.

6. Stay tuned until the very end or you will miss the surprising ___epilogue___.

7. Many ___neologisms___ first achieve notice when they are introduced by popular culture's trendsetters.

8. The board of directors drafted a ___decalogue___ to specify the fundamental rules and procedures for the organization.

---

*Circle the **boldface** word that more satisfactorily completes each of the following sentences.*

1. The intensely dramatic (**monologue,** decalogue) lasted for nearly an hour-a stunning success for one actor alone on a bare stage.

2. What an unexpectedly productive (eulogy, **dialogue**) between the anti-war protesters and the police officers who were assigned to protect them!

3. The ushers have been instructed not to seat anyone who arrives at the theatre after the (epilogue, **prologue**) has begun.

4. No one who heard the inspiring (**eulogy,** neologism) given for the young hero will ever forget the deeply felt emotions of that sad moment.

5. The first British edition of *Moby Dick* accidentally omitted the (**epilogue,** apology), which tells how Ishmael alone survived, and justifies his first-person narrative.

6. The Biblical source of the (**Decalogue,** Dialogue) is Chapter 20 of the Book of Exodus.

7. Today's most original (monologue, **neologism**) can one day become woven into conventional standard usage.

8. When he realized that he had forgotten his mother's birthday, he drafted a thoughtful and loving (**apology,** prologue), which he tucked into a bouquet of roses for her.

Writer's Challenge

Read the following sentences, paying special attention to the words and phrases underlined. From the words in the box below, find better choices for these underlined words and phrases. Then use these choices to rewrite the sentences.

WORD BANK

affluence	discretion	impact	minimum	reminisce
arrears	format	inflammatory	nimble	rendezvous
authorize	giddy	innovations	perishable	taut
avenge	immerse	logical	relished	verge

Biltmore Estate

1. One of the oldest families in America, the Vanderbilts, <u>enjoyed</u> their enormous personal wealth—amassed largely from successes in the shipping and railroad businesses.

relished

2. The Vanderbilts used their <u>great abundance</u> to support and endow many worthy causes and to build some of the grandest homes in America.

affluence

3. Biltmore Estate, near Asheville, North Carolina, is America's largest private home. George Washington Vanderbilt <u>approved</u> its construction, hoping to create a lavish manor.

authorized

4. It took armies of artisans a <u>smallest possible amount</u> of six years to build the estate, which opened in December, 1895. Although the family began to move in, work continued for years to come.

minimum

5. The grand mansion has 250 rooms, including 43 bathrooms, 65 fireplaces, and such <u>new things</u> of the day as electric lighting, central heating, plumbing and refrigeration systems, and an indoor swimming pool.

innovations

6. The forestry principles that landscape architect Frederick Law Olmsted applied to the grounds had a major <u>effect</u> on the emerging field of forest conservation in America.

impact

 **Analogies**

In each of the following, circle the item that best completes the comparison.

See pages T38–T48 for explanations of answers.

1. nimble is to **agility** as
a. immobile is to liveliness
b. gross is to sensitivity
c. arid is to variety
d. limber is to flexibility ⟵

2. taut is to **leeway** as
a. variable is to change
b. cramped is to elbowroom ⟵
c. global is to area
d. optional is to choice

3. highwayman is to **waylay** as
a. assailant is to assault ⟵
b. inhabitant is to manipulate
c. culprit is to idolize
d. oaf is to forsake

4. crotchety is to **amiable** as
a. famished is to ravenous
b. mortal is to perishable
c. immediate is to instantaneous
d. sluggish is to energetic ⟵

5. jovial is to **merriment** as
a. sage is to joy
b. serene is to bliss ⟵
c. martial is to peace
d. sinister is to contentment

6. apparel is to **wear** as
a. equipment is to read
b. entertainment is to live
c. food is to eat ⟵
d. furniture is to break

7. synopsis is to **compress** as
a. memorandum is to discredit
b. ovation is to depict
c. commentary is to dissect ⟵
d. dispatch is to reimburse

8. manacle is to **constrain** as
a. spur is to motivate ⟵
b. leash is to liberate
c. chain is to generate
d. handcuff is to designate

9. setback is to **discourage** as
a. victory is to delight ⟵
b. loss is to please
c. triumph is to sadden
d. defeat is to thrill

10. maximum is to **minimum** as
a. immense is to petty ⟵
b. giddy is to eerie
c. pathetic is to pitiful
d. disinterested is to impartial

 **Choosing the Right Meaning**

Read each sentence carefully. Then circle the item that best completes the statement below the sentence.

See pages T38–T48 for explanations of answers.

Tacitus tells us in *The Annals* that Emperor Nero ordered the dispatch of scores of his enemies—both real and imagined. (2)

1. In line 1 the word **dispatch** is best defined as
a. promptness   b. communication   c. execution ⟵   d. conviction

Among those who perished at Nero's bidding was the philosopher and dramatist Lucius Annaeus Seneca, who had been the emperor's tutor. (2)

2. The word **perished** in line 1 most nearly means
a. profited   c. died ⟵
b. informed on others   d. were exiled

No visit to Paris is complete without a saunter down its most famous boulevard, the Champs-Elysees. (2)

3. In line 1 the word **saunter** is best defined as

a. scamper   (b. stroll)   c. race   d. hike

A brief scan of the rugged terrain that lay ahead was enough to tell us that a long, difficult hike was in store. (2)

4. In line 1 the word **scan** most nearly means

a. exploration   (b. examination)   c. discussion   d. mapping

Instructing an actor how to play a part, Prince Hamlet advises, "Let your own discretion be your tutor." (2)

5. The word **discretion** in line 2 is used to mean

(a. judgment)   b. freedom   c. choice   d. talent

Two-Word Completions

Circle the pair of words that best complete the meaning of each of the following sentences.

See pages T38–T48 for explanations of answers.

1. Though surrounded on all sides by superior forces, the inhabitants of the

_____ city were able to keep the enemy at bay for a long time by

maintaining a steady _____ of missiles from their walls and towers.

a. encompassed . . . rendezvous   c. restricted . . . oracle
b. partitioned . . . repast   (d. besieged . . . barrage)

2. "Despite all the problems and _____ we have experienced in

recent months, we must _____ in our endeavor to achieve the

goals we have set for the company this year," I said.

a. revocations . . . verge   c. keepsakes . . . cringe
(b. setbacks . . . persevere)   d. vocations . . . tarry

3. During the lengthy dry spell that the area experiences every summer, the vegetation

_____ completely away, and the landscape takes on a surprising

resemblance to the kind of _____ found on the moon.

a. frays . . . format   c. blusters . . . tribute
(b. withers . . . terrain)   d. cedes . . . duration

4. When the volcano erupted, huge quantities of molten lava and boiling mud

_____ like some fiery waterfall down the steep sides of the

mountain, _____ the region round about.

(a. cascaded . . . devastating)   c. billowed . . . vacating
b. deluged . . . befuddling   d. writhed . . . stranding

5. Though many of the hardships that the peoples of the world face today are purely

local, the _____ of those suffering from hunger and malnutrition is

of truly _____ proportions.

a. enigma . . . incomprehensible   (c. plight . . . global)
b. queue . . . adverse   d. maze . . . acute

Enriching Your Vocabulary

Read the passage below. Then complete the exercise at the bottom of the page.

The Right to a Fair Trial

There have always been rules about how people should treat one another. And there have always been folks who break the rules. So societies have come up with methods to keep order and to insure justice.

What can United States citizens do when they think someone has wronged them? The *plaintiff,* the person with the complaint, accuses the *defendant.* Sometimes the case is decided in court and is tried before a *judge* and a *jury.* The plaintiff and the *defendant* are both represented by an attorney. Both sides may present *evidence* to support their case and call witnesses to *testify* for them. A *jury* of twelve citizens and a *judge* would hear the evidence.

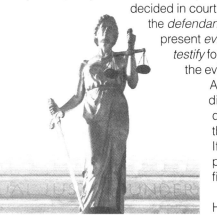

After all the arguments are heard, the jury would discuss the evidence and come to a *verdict,* a formal decision about the case. If the verdict is "not guilty," this means the defendant has been *acquitted* (Unit 4). If the verdict is "guilty," the judge would decide on a penalty for the *culprit* (Unit 7), who may have to pay a fine, do community service, or serve time in jail.

Our legal system is complicated and detailed. However, it is one of the most important benefits that American citizens have.

Lady of Justice in front of Supreme Court

In Column A below are 8 more legal terms. With or without a dictionary, match each word with its meaning in Column B.

Column A

__d__	**1.** oath
__b__	**2.** arraign
__f__	**3.** affidavit
__e__	**4.** statute
__g__	**5.** sequester
__h__	**6.** judicial
__a__	**7.** indict
__c__	**8.** mistrial

Column B

a. to accuse someone based on evidence

b. to call a defendant before a court of law to hear and answer charges

c. a trial that is ruled invalid because there was a problem with evidence or how it was presented

d. a solemn promise

e. a law that has been passed by a legislative body such as Congress

f. a written statement made under oath

g. to set apart, as members of a jury

h. having to do with judges, courts, and law

Definitions

Note carefully the spelling, pronunciation, part(s) of speech, and definition(s) of each of the following words. Then write the word in the blank space(s) in the illustrative sentence(s) following. Finally, study the lists of synonyms and antonyms given at the end of each entry.

1. abominable
(ə bäm′ ə nə bəl)

(*adj.*) arousing hatred; disgusting, detestable

Unfortunately there are many _____**abominable**_____ ideas circulating on the Internet.

SYNONYMS: hateful, despicable, loathsome
ANTONYMS: praiseworthy, delightful, charming

2. bumbling
(bəm′ bliŋ)

(*adj.*) blundering and awkward; (*n.*) clumsiness

The _____**bumbling**_____ burglars were so inept that they actually left some of their own money at the home they were planning to rob!

The old cartoon character Mr. Magoo was well known for his _____**bumbling**_____.

SYNONYMS: (*adj.*) clumsy, stumbling
ANTONYMS: (*adj.*) forceful, effective, skillful, adroit

3. consequence
(kän′ sə kwens)

(*n.*) a result, effect; importance

Does he truly comprehend the _____**consequences**_____ of his actions?

SYNONYMS: outcome, significance
ANTONYMS: cause, source

4. delude
(di lüd′)

(*v.*) to fool, deceive; to mislead utterly

Don't _____**delude**_____ yourself into thinking that you will become a famous concert pianist just because you played one song at the school's talent show.

SYNONYMS: trick, hoodwink

5. dole
(dōl)

(*v.*) to give out in small amounts; (*n.*) money, food, or other necessities given as charity; a small portion

Let's _____**dole**_____ out pieces of food to the hungry dog.

The homeless people lined up to receive their weekly _____**dole**_____ at the shelter.

SYNONYMS: (*v.*) ration, allot, distribute; (*n.*) handout

6. engulf
(en gəlf′)

(*v.*) to swallow up, overwhelm, consume

The truck was _____**engulfed**_____ in flames after its fuel tank exploded.

SYNONYMS: envelop, encompass, immerse

7. foil
(foil)

(*v.*) to defeat; to keep from gaining some end; (*n.*) a thin sheet of metal; a light fencing sword; a person or thing serving as a contrast to another

We hope that good police work will _____ **foil** _____ the criminals' plot.

Glum characters make a good _____ **foil** _____ for the upbeat star of that new comedy.

SYNONYMS: (*v.*) frustrate, thwart, counter; (*n.*) rapier
ANTONYMS: (*v.*) aid, abet, assist, advance, promote

8. formulate
(fôr′ myə lāt)

(*v.*) to express definitely or systematically; to devise, invent; to state as a formula

The town board is working to _____ **formulate** _____ a more economical energy policy for its citizens.

SYNONYMS: define, articulate, frame, specify

9. initiative
(i nish′ ə tiv)

(*n.*) the taking of the first step or move; the ability to act without being directed or urged from the outside

Dad was proud that I took the _____ **initiative** _____ to rake the leaves without being asked.

SYNONYMS: leadership, enterprise
ANTONYMS: laziness, sloth, shiftlessness

10. memento
(mə men′ tō)

(*n.*) something that serves as a reminder

This cap is a _____ **memento** _____ of our trip this past summer.

SYNONYMS: remembrance, keepsake, souvenir, token

11. nonconformist
(nän kən fôr′ mist)

(*n.*) a person who refuses to follow established ideas or ways of doing things; (*adj.*) of or relating to the unconventional

Jake is a _____ **nonconformist** _____ who is never swayed by other people's opinions or expectations.

Her _____ **nonconformist** _____ poetry appears in many small literary magazines.

SYNONYMS: (*n.*) maverick, individualist, bohemian
ANTONYMS: (*n., adj.*) traditionalist, conventionalist; (*adj.*)
traditional, conventional, conservative

12. null and void
(nəl and void)

(*adj.*) without legal force or effect; no longer binding

This contract becomes _____ **null and void** _____ at noon tomorrow.

SYNONYMS: canceled, invalid, repealed, abolished
ANTONYMS: in effect, binding, valid

13. panorama
(pan ə ram′ ə)

(*n.*) a wide, unobstructed view of an area; a complete survey of a subject; a continuously passing or changing scene; a range or spectrum

Displays of old picture postcards present an entertaining _____ **panorama** _____ of twentieth-century life.

SYNONYMS: vista, overview

14. posterity
(pä ster′ ət ē)

(*n.*) all of a person's offspring, descendants; all future generations

Let's keep the family photo album for _____ **posterity** _____.

ANTONYMS: ancestry, ancestors, forebears, the past

15. pry
(prī)

(*v.*) to pull loose by force; to look at closely or inquisitively; to be nosy about something

We can use this tool to _____ **pry** _____ the lid off a can of paint.

SYNONYMS: snoop, meddle

16. refurbish
(ri fər′ bish)

(*v.*) to brighten, freshen, or polish; to restore or improve

Every five years, the hotel _____ **refurbishes** _____ the décor of its elegant lobby.

SYNONYMS: remodel, renew, spruce up
ANTONYMS: dilapidate, run down

17. resourceful
(ri sôrs′ fəl)

(*adj.*) able to deal promptly and effectively with all sorts of problems; clever in finding ways and means of getting along

A _____ **resourceful** _____ guide will know how to handle any questions or surprises that come up on the tour.

SYNONYMS: inventive, ingenious, skillful
ANTONYMS: uninventive, incompetent, dull-witted

18. rigorous
(rig′ ər əs)

(*adj.*) severe, harsh, strict; thoroughly logical

"Boot camp" is the nickname for the place where new soldiers receive _____ **rigorous** _____ basic training.

SYNONYMS: tough, trying, challenging, stringent
ANTONYMS: easy, lax, indulgent, undemanding

19. subsequent
(səb′ sə kwent)

(*adj.*) coming after; following in time, place, or order

The county enjoyed peace and prosperity in the years _____ **subsequent** _____ to the war.

SYNONYMS: following, later, next, succeeding, ensuing
ANTONYMS: previous, prior, preceding

20. unerring
(ən er′ iŋ)

(*adj.*) making no mistakes, faultless, completely accurate

Even a pilot with _____ **unerring** _____ judgment can be surprised by sudden changes in the weather.

SYNONYMS: sure, certain, unfailing
ANTONYMS: faulty, fallible, unreliable

Completing the Sentence

From the words for this unit, choose the one that best completes each of the following sentences. Write the word in the space provided.

1. Professional baseball players get themselves into shape for the upcoming season by undergoing a _____**rigorous**_____ training period each spring.

2. Anyone who _____**pries**_____ into someone else's business runs the risk of opening a can of worms.

3. Huge clouds of smoke and ash from the angry volcano _____**engulfed**_____ the sleepy little villages that nestled on its flanks.

4. The alert employee _____**foiled**_____ an attempted robbery by setting off the alarm promptly.

5. Like so many other young people, he has been _____**deluded**_____ into the false belief that there is an easy way to success.

6. You may think that the crude way he has behaved is slightly amusing, but I think it is _____**abominable**_____ and inexcusable.

7. A truly _____**resourceful**_____ administrator always seems to be able to find an effective way of dealing with any problem that may come up.

8. At the time it occurred, that mistake didn't seem to be too important, but it had _____**consequences**_____ that still hurt me today.

9. From the observation deck of the skyscraper one may enjoy a sweeping _____**panorama**_____ of the city.

10. These old photographs may not look like much, but I treasure them as a(n) _____**memento**_____ of the last summer my entire family spent together.

11. We must _____**formulate**_____ a detailed response that leaves no doubt about our position on this important issue.

12. The first meeting will be in the school auditorium, but all _____**subsequent**_____ meetings will be held in the homes of our members.

13. Rather than sit back and wait for the enemy to attack him, the general took the _____**initiative**_____ and delivered the first blow.

14. What a disappointment to hear that dull and _____**bumbling**_____ speech when we were expecting a clear, forceful, and interesting statement!

15. Many an artist whose work has been overlooked in his or her own lifetime has had to trust to _____**posterity**_____ for appreciation.

16. The term "_____**nonconformist**_____" was first applied in the 1660s to English Protestants who dissented from the Church of England.

17. As a tennis player, Sue doesn't have much speed or power, but she hits the ball with _____**unerring**_____ accuracy.

18. During World War II, food became so scarce in Great Britain that the government _____ doled _____ it out to consumers in very small amounts.

19. All that you will need to _____ refurbish _____ that dilapidated old house is lots of time, lots of skill, lots of enthusiasm, and lots of money.

20. Since I was able to prove in court that the salesperson had lied to me, the contract I had signed was declared _____ null and void _____.

Synonyms

*Choose the word from this unit that is **the same** or **most nearly the same** in meaning as the **boldface** word or expression in the given phrase. Write the word on the line provided.*

1. the only **maverick** in the group — nonconformist

2. to discuss it at our **next** meeting — subsequent

3. **inventive** use of leftover materials — resourceful

4. must pass a **challenging** exam — rigorous

5. if they can **define** their goals — formulate

6. a dramatic **vista** of red rock formations — panorama

7. established for **future generations** — posterity

8. a precious **keepsake** of Sally's childhood — memento

9. if we decide to **spruce up** the kitchen — refurbish

10. huge waves that **envelop** the tiny beach — engulf

11. carefully **ration** out the medicine — dole

12. no longer **meddle** into my affairs — pry

13. judging the **significance** of this change — consequence

14. **hoodwink** them into believing his story — delude

15. a **clumsy** attempt at an apology — bumbling

Antonyms

*Choose the word from this unit that is **most nearly opposite** in meaning to the **boldface** word or expression in the given phrase. Write the word on the line provided.*

16. declared **valid** by the courts — null and void

17. to **promote** that wicked plot — foil

18. due to my **faulty** sense of direction — unerring

19. **charming** behavior for a twelve-year-old — abominable

20. anticipating your **laziness** — initiative

Choosing the Right Word

*Circle the **boldface** word that more satisfactorily completes each of the following sentences.*

1. With his serious face and his dignified way of speaking, he is an excellent (**foil,** **memento**) for the clownish comedian.

2. The war that began with Germany's invasion of Poland in 1939 spread until it had (**pried, engulfed**) almost the entire world.

3. It is too late to attempt to (**refurbish, formulate**) the old city charter; we must have a completely new plan for our city government.

4. Brad is the kind of (**rigorous, resourceful**) quarterback who can always come up with something new when it is a matter of victory or defeat.

5. If you think that you can get away with selling overpriced products to the people of this town, you are (**deluding, refurbishing**) yourself.

6. One of the signs of a truly democratic nation is that it gives protection and freedom to (**initiatives, nonconformists**) who espouse unpopular views.

7. She hopes to win the election by convincing voters that the city's troubles result from the (**bumbling, unerring**) policies of the present Mayor.

8. Do you think the United States should take the (**initiative, dole**) in trying to bring about a compromise peace in the Middle East?

9. In devising the Constitution, the Founding Fathers sought to "secure the blessings of liberty to ourselves and our (**posterity, foils**)."

10. Since you have failed to carry out your promises, I must tell you that the agreement between us is now (**resourceful, null and void**).

11. "We must (**engulf, formulate**) a plan to deal with this new situation and carry it out as quickly as possible," the president said.

12. He may look like an ordinary man, but he is in fact a figure of real (**panorama, consequence**) in the state government.

13. The lawyer made the point that her client had been at the scene of the crime before the murder but not (**subsequent, null and void**) to it.

14. By coaxing and questioning hour after hour, Tom finally managed to (**pry, delude**) the big secret from his sister.

15. What we lightly refer to as our "foreign policy" in fact embraces a vast (**panorama, consequence**) of aims and objectives, problems and concerns.

16. Why is it that such hardworking, self-reliant people now have to depend on a (**posterity, dole**) of food and other necessities from charitable agencies?

17. Perhaps he doesn't seem to be very bright, but he has an (**abominable, unerring**) instinct for anything that may make money for him.

18. All these things in the attic may seem like a lot of junk to you, but to me they are priceless (**mementos, nonconformists**) of childhood.

19. We all know that it is a long time since the speeding laws in our community have been (**subsequently, rigorously**) enforced.

20. Here I am on my first vacation in three years, and I have to put up with this (**abominable, bumbling**) weather day after day!

*Read the following passage, in which some of the words you have studied in this unit appear in **boldface** type. Then complete each statement given below the passage by circling the letter of the item that is **the same** or **almost the same** in meaning as the highlighted word.*

Annie Smith Peck: A Woman of Firsts

(Line)

Mountain climbing has always been a **rigorous** activity, even without today's high-tech gear. So imagine how rare it was when Annie Smith Peck climbed Mount Shasta in California in 1888. Peck became interested in mountain climbing when she first saw the Swiss Alps. Once she made that first climb in California

(5) and saw the marvelous **panorama** from the top, she was hooked for life.

Always a **nonconformist**, Peck refused to let the days' common prejudices against women keep her from her lofty goals. Born in 1850, she graduated from the University of Michigan with honors. Pursuing her interest in Greek and the

(10) Classics, she **subsequently** went on to study at the American School of Classical Studies in Athens, Greece, and was the school's first female student. She worked as a teacher, writer, and scholar, but it is as a mountain

(15) climber that **posterity** remembers her.

When she climbed Mount Orizaba in Mexico in 1897, Annie Smith Peck became the first woman in the Americas to climb a mountain over 18,000 feet high. By 1900,

(20) she had climbed twenty major mountains. Eight years later, she became the first person, man or woman, to climb the north peak of Mount Huarascan in Peru. Its summit, at 21,812 feet, marked the highest

The Swiss Alps, mountains that inspired Annie Smith Peck and countless others

(25) point ever reached in the Western Hemisphere. As a **consequence** of her accomplishments, the north peak of the mountain was renamed in her honor: *Cumbre Aña Smith*.

This spirited woman never let age hold her back. At sixty-one, Peck became the first person to climb Peru's Mount Coropuna. At the top she planted a flag that said,

(30) "Votes for Women." Peck climbed her last mountain in New Hampshire when she was eighty-two. Her death three years later marked the end of a long and remarkable life.

---

1. The meaning of **rigorous** (line 1) is
a. challenging
b. unpleasant
c. undemanding
d. enjoyable

2. Panorama (line 5) is best defined as
a. clouds
b. rocks
c. mountains
d. view

3. Nonconformist (line 6) most nearly means
a. follower
b. individualist
c. leader
d. feminist

4. Subsequently (line 10) is best defined as
a. suddenly
b. previously
c. surprisingly
d. later

5. Posterity (line 15) most nearly means
a. the past
b. the present
c. the future
d. the media

6. The meaning of **consequence** (line 25) is
a. cause
b. reminder
c. result
d. memory

Definitions

Note carefully the spelling, pronunciation, part(s) of speech, and definition(s) of each of the following words. Then write the word in the blank space(s) in the illustrative sentence(s) following. Finally, study the lists of synonyms and antonyms given at the end of each entry.

1. alias
(ā' lē əs)

(*n.*) an assumed name, especially as used to hide one's identity; (*adv.*) otherwise called

Mr. Plante was just one _____ **alias** _____ used by the elusive spy.

Superman, _____ **alias** _____ Clark Kent, began as a comic book character created in 1938.

SYNONYM: (*n.*) pseudonym
ANTONYMS: (*n.*) real name, given name, legal name

2. amble
(am' bəl)

(*v.*) to walk slowly, stroll; (*n.*) an easy pace; a leisurely walk

It's a lovely day to _____ **amble** _____ to work and enjoy the many sights and sounds along the way.

When we woke to see the sun shining, we planned a long _____ **amble** _____ in the park.

SYNONYMS: (*v.*) saunter; (*n.*) ramble
ANTONYMS: (*v., n.*) gallop, dash, sprint, run, race, rush

3. burly
(bər' lē)

(*adj.*) big and strong; muscular

That guy is as _____ **burly** _____ as a lumberjack, so he would be the perfect one to help me move my furniture.

SYNONYMS: strapping, hefty, beefy, brawny
ANTONYMS: weak, puny, delicate, frail

4. distort
(dis tôrt')

(*v.*) to give a false or misleading account of; to twist out of shape

A magazine known to _____ **distort** _____ the facts would be an unreliable source of information.

SYNONYMS: disfigure, misshape, falsify

5. dogged
(dôg' əd)

(*adj.*) persistent, stubbornly determined, refusing to give up

The troops fought with _____ **dogged** _____ determination and courage.

SYNONYM: untiring
ANTONYMS: wishy-washy, faltering, irresolute

6. dumbfounded
(dəm' faůnd əd)

(*adj.*) so amazed that one is unable to speak, bewildered

When the shocking news finally reached us, we were completely _____ **dumbfounded** _____ .

SYNONYMS: speechless, stunned, flabbergasted
ANTONYMS: unsurprised, expectant

7. extinct
(ek stiŋkt')

(*adj.*) no longer in existence; no longer active; gone out of use

The _____ extinct _____ volcano no longer threatens the area, but it changed the landscape forever.

SYNONYMS: died out, vanished
ANTONYMS: still alive, surviving, extant

8. fossil
(fäs' əl)

(*n.*) the petrified remains or traces of an animal or plant that lived in the past; an extremely old-fashioned person or thing; (*adj.*) having qualities that belong to a remote past

This fish _____ fossil _____ is a million years old yet is amazingly well preserved.

_____ Fossil _____ beliefs, such as that the world is flat, seem laughable today.

SYNONYM: (*n.*) relic   The workers discovered fossil
remains of an ancient beast.

9. grit
(grit)

(*n.*) very fine sand or gravel; courage in the face of hardship or danger; (*v.*) to grind; to make a grating sound

Cars stall if _____ grit _____ clogs a fuel line.

It upsets me to see Dad get angry and _____ grit _____ his teeth.

SYNONYMS: (*n.*) dirt, mettle
ANTONYMS: (*n.*) timidity, cowardice, faintheartedness

10. inevitable
(in ev' ə tə bəl)

(*adj.*) sure to happen, unavoidable

Is it _____ inevitable _____ that all comedies have happy endings?

SYNONYMS: inescapable, fated
ANTONYMS: avoidable, escapable, preventable

11. ingrained
(in grānd')

(*adj.*) fixed deeply and firmly; working into the grain or fiber; forming a part of the inmost being

My habit of biting my lower lip when I'm nervous is so _____ ingrained _____ that I don't notice doing it.

SYNONYMS: deep-seated, deep-rooted, indelible
ANTONYMS: superficial, shallow, skin-deep

12. meteoric
(mē tē ôr' ik)

(*adj.*) resembling a meteor in speed; having sudden and temporary brilliance similar to a meteor's

The doctor's _____ meteoric _____ rise to fame was legendary. The young actor's meteoric

SYNONYMS: brilliant, blazing
ANTONYMS: slow, sluggish, gradual

13. parody
(par' ə dē)

(*n.*) a humorous or ridiculous imitation; (*v.*) to make fun of something by imitating it

This clever and amusing book is a _____ parody _____ of ghost stories.

The audience roared with laughter at the hilarious parody.

The comedy film _____ parodies _____ political
life in England.
SYNONYMS: (*n.*) satire, travesty; (*v.*) lampoon, burlesque

14. prevail
(pri vāl')

(*v.*) to triumph over; to succeed; to exist widely, be in general
use; to get someone to do something by urging

We hope to _____ prevail _____ over all
obstacles we may encounter on this project.

SYNONYMS: win, rule, reign, overcome, conquer
ANTONYMS: be defeated, go under, succumb

15. rend
(rend)

(*v.*) to tear to pieces; split violently apart (*past tense*, rent)

The abominable tactics of this trial could ____ rend ____
public confidence in the legal system.

SYNONYMS: cleave, dismember, splinter, tear asunder

16. replenish
(ri plen' ish)

(v.) to fill again, make good, replace

Airport crews work quickly to _____ replenish _____
a plane's supply of food, water, and safety supplies.

SYNONYMS: refill, restock, refresh, restore
ANTONYMS: empty, drain, deplete, sap

17. rummage
(rəm' əj)

(*v.*) to search through, investigate the contents of; (*n.*) an active
search; a collection of odd items

It can be an adventure to _____ rummage _____
around our garage for remnants of our childhood.

She found an old saddle in the _____ rummage _____ .

SYNONYMS: (*v.*) delve into, sift through, poke around

18. skimp
(skimp)

(*v.*) to save, be thrifty; to be extremely sparing with; to give little
attention or effort to

If you _____ skimp _____ on regular meals,
you may be tempted to snack on too much junk food.

SYNONYMS: be stingy, scrimp, cut corners
ANTONYMS: be extravagant, splurge, lavish

19. sleuth
(slüth)

(*n.*) a detective

A skilled _____ sleuth _____ can find hidden
clues in unusual places.

SYNONYMS: investigator, gumshoe

20. vandalism
(van' dəl iz əm)

(*n.*) deliberate and pointless destruction of public or private
property

The city needs to create tougher laws to discourage
_____ vandalism _____ .

SYNONYMS: willful destruction, malicious defacement

Completing the Sentence

From the words for this unit, choose the one that best completes each of the following sentences. Write the word in the space provided.

1. There is an old saying that nothing is really _____ inevitable _____ except death and taxes.

2. We were nothing less than _____ dumbfounded _____ when we saw the immense damage that the hurricane had done in so brief a time.

3. As the buffalo began to decrease sharply in numbers, conservationists feared that it might become totally _____ extinct _____.

4. Whenever our team needs a few yards to make a first down, we call on our big, _____ burly _____ fullback to crash through the line.

5. The cruise ship stopped at the port both to give the passengers a chance to go ashore and to _____ replenish _____ the water supply.

6. If you truly want to improve your math grades, you should not continue to _____ skimp _____ so often on your homework.

7. We saw a bolt of lightning _____ rend _____ a huge limb from the mighty oak tree.

8. The old con artist had used so many _____ aliases _____ over the course of his criminal career that he sometimes forgot his real name!

9. After our furious gallop across the countryside, we allowed our tired horses to _____ amble _____ back to the stable.

10. We greatly admired the _____ dogged _____ determination and patience that the disabled veteran showed in learning to master a wheelchair.

11. The rock singer enjoyed a sudden _____ meteoric _____ rise in popularity, but his career faded just as quickly as it had blossomed.

12. Since coal was formed from the decayed bodies of plants that lived many millions of years ago, it is considered a kind of _____ fossil _____ fuel.

13. The grime on the mechanic's hands was so deeply _____ ingrained _____ that even a thorough scrubbing couldn't entirely remove it.

14. In the late 19th century, Sir Arthur Conan Doyle created one of the most famous _____ sleuths _____ in literature, Sherlock Holmes.

15. The old custom of celebrating the Fourth of July with a fireworks display still _____ prevails _____ in many American towns.

16. Even though so many people were criticizing and ridiculing him, he had the _____ grit _____ to continue doing what he felt was right.

17. Isn't it a shame that our School Board must spend thousands of dollars every year just to repair the damage caused by _____ vandalism _____?

18. Her face was so _____ distorted _____ with pain and suffering that at first I did not recognize her.

19. Her ability to _____ parody _____ the words and gestures of prominent Americans makes her an excellent comic impressionist.

20. Isn't it fun on a rainy day to _____ rummage _____ about in the attic and look for interesting odds and ends?

Synonyms

*Choose the word from this unit that is **the same** or **most nearly the same** in meaning as the **boldface** word or expression in the given phrase. Write the word on the line provided.*

1. deep-rooted sense of right and wrong	ingrained
2. ways to **falsify** the evidence	distort
3. tried to **lampoon** the governor	parody
4. memoirs of her **brilliant** career	meteoric
5. where science **reigns** over superstition	prevails
6. greedily **dismember** its prey	rend
7. protected by a **brawny** bodyguard	burly
8. untiring faith in technology	dogged
9. admiring the **mettle** of those hardy pioneers	grit
10. sift through the old catalogues	rummage
11. left the guide totally **flabbergasted**	dumbfounded
12. a valuable **relic** of life in the past	fossil
13. observing the sharp-witted **investigator**	sleuth
14. broken apart by **malicious defacement**	vandalism
15. to sign the document using a **pseudonym**	alias

Antonyms

*Choose the word from this unit that is **most nearly opposite** in meaning to the **boldface** word or expression in the given phrase. Write the word on the line provided.*

16. whether that outcome is **avoidable**	inevitable
17. after **depleting** the ice	replenishing
18. photographs of the **surviving** species	extinct
19. dash along the scenic river	amble
20. usually **splurge** on the desserts	skimp

Choosing the Right Word

Circle the **boldface** word that more satisfactorily completes each of the following sentences.

1. The defenders of the Alamo put up such a (**burly, dogged**) resistance that the enemy had a hard time capturing it.

2. To avoid a lot of unwanted attention, the famous rock star registered in the hotel under a(n) (**rummage, alias**).

3. An art historian who is trying to verify the authenticity of a painting acts more like a (**sleuth, fossil**) than a critic.

4. His (**dogged, meteoric**) success at such an early age left him unprepared to handle the disappointments and failures that came to him later in life.

5. It may be, as you say, that this volcano has been (**extinct, dumbfounded**) for many years, but isn't there some danger that it may come to life again?

6. Whether the window was broken accidentally or as an act of (**parody, vandalism**), the fact remains that it is broken and must be paid for.

7. I hope to pick up some real bargains at the (**rummage, grit**) sale being held in our civic center.

8. Although it is sometimes hard, we must have faith that in the long run justice and decency will (**skimp, prevail**).

9. Visiting the school I had attended so many years before made me feel like a creature from the far past—a living (**alias, fossil**).

10. "I'll have two franks with all the fixings," I said to the vendor, "and don't (**prevail, skimp**) on the mustard!"

11. I am exhausted now, but all I need is a satisfying meal, a hot shower, and a good night's sleep to (**replenish, rend**) my energies.

12. Is there anything more romantic than a nighttime (**amble, vandalism**) upon the moonlit decks of a mighty ocean liner?

13. No, I wasn't (**ingrained, dumbfounded**) to be chosen the most popular member of the class, but maybe I was just a little surprised!

14. The aging actor trying to play the part of a young man seemed no more than a (**sleuth, parody**) of the great performer he once was.

15. The prejudices of a bigot are sometimes so (**ingrained, alias**) that it is very difficult to get rid of them.

16. Isn't it foolish to think that just because of his (**meteoric, burly**) physique he has no interest in art or music?

17. We scorn all those who would deliberately bend the truth and (**distort, amble**) history in order to suit the political needs of their day.

18. Since it is possible for nations to settle their disagreements in a reasonable way, we refuse to believe that war is (**inevitable, dumbfounded**).

19. I know that you don't like the idea of working in a gas station, but you'll just have to (**replenish, grit**) your teeth and do it.

20. Suddenly, the stillness of the early morning hours was (**rent, rummaged**) by a single shot!

Vocabulary in Context

*Read the following passage, in which some of the words you have studied in this unit appear in **boldface** type. Then complete each statement given below the passage by circling the letter of the item that is **the same** or **almost the same** in meaning as the highlighted word.*

Delving into Dinosaur Truths

(Line)

Bone hunters first began to find, identify, and speculate about dinosaur **fossils** in the early 1800s. Since then, people the world over have offered a wide range of ideas and opinions about life in the age of dinosaurs. These great creatures have inspired painters, cartoonists, writers, filmmakers, musicians, and others. But not all ideas reflected scientific reality. (5)

Whether on purpose or out of ignorance, generations of misinformation have **distorted** our view of dinosaurs, which have been portrayed as stupid, vicious, and slow-moving creatures. Recent evidence now shows that some could run very fast and with grace. Many had well-developed brains. We now know that some were fierce predators, (10) while others were peaceful vegetarians.

In nature's great time line, dinosaurs were **extinct** long before human beings first appeared. Scenes of primitive people battling dinosaurs could never really have happened. Plots that may make for (15) absorbing entertainment, bold comedy, or gripping adventure should not be confused with reality.

It may be **inevitable** that creatures as big and as mystifying as dinosaurs would inspire art and invention. This is just what science fiction is—a (20) blend of fact and fantasy that entertains and stirs thought. Famous sci-fi adventures, such as *King Kong, Journey to the Center of the Earth, The Land That Time Forgot,* and the *Tarzan* tales, have become part of popular culture. They amuse both (25) scientists and escapists. Even a cartoon like "The Flintstones," in which sitcom cave families have cute dinosaurs as pets and as **burly** beasts of burden, amuses us. Must cartoons be accurate?

Maybe truth should **prevail** over entertainment value. To combat imaginative fiction being taken as truth, we need to do detailed research and ask probing questions. (30)

The fearsome tyrannosaurus rex: What was this huge creature *really* like?

---

1. The meaning of **fossils** (line 1) is
  (a.) remains   c. herds
  b. eggs   d. movies

2. The meaning of **distorted** (line 7) is
  a. encouraged   c. proved
  (b.) twisted   d. shaped

3. Extinct (line 12) most nearly means
  a. existent   c. born
  b. studied   (d.) gone

4. Inevitable (line 18) most nearly means
  a. understandable   (c.) unavoidable
  b. surprising   d. avoidable

5. Burly (line 27) is best defined as
  a. clever   c. amazing
  b. misshapen   (d.) muscular

6. Prevail (line 29) most nearly means
  (a.) win   c. draw
  b. lose   d. prepare

Definitions

Note carefully the spelling, pronunciation, part(s) of speech, and definition(s) of each of the following words. Then write the word in the blank space(s) in the illustrative sentence(s) following. Finally, study the lists of synonyms and antonyms given at the end of each entry.

1. abduct
(ab dəkt′)

(*v.*) to kidnap, carry off by force

Some people with vivid imaginations fear that hostile aliens will come to Earth to _____ abduct _____ humans.

SYNONYMS: seize, snatch

2. ambiguous
(am big′ yü əs)

(*adj.*) not clear; having two or more possible meanings

The purpose of a test is to determine whether students learned the material, not to confuse them with _____ ambiguous _____ questions.

SYNONYMS: vague, uncertain, unclear, equivocal
ANTONYMS: obvious, plain, clear, unequivocal

3. balk
(bôk)

(*v.*) to stop short and refuse to go on; to refuse abruptly; to prevent from happening; (*n.*) (in baseball) an illegal motion made by a pitcher

My horse _____ balked _____ when I urged it to go up the steep mountain slope.

The opposing team scored an additional run because of the pitcher's _____ balk _____.

SYNONYM: (*v.*) resist, hesitate, block

4. compact
(*v., adj.*, kəm pakt′;
n., käm′ pakt)

(*adj.*) closely and firmly packed together; small; (*v.*) to squeeze together; (*n.*) an agreement between parties; a small case containing a mirror and face powder; a small car

Computers are much more _____ compact _____ now than they were a generation ago.

Workers at the town dump were asked to _____ compact _____ the trash to save space.

SYNONYMS: (*adj.*) dense; (*v.*) compress
ANTONYMS: (*adj.*) oversize, enormous, humongous, bulky

5. confer
(kən fər′)

(*v.*) to consult, talk over, exchange opinions; to present as a gift, favor, or honor

The committee will _____ confer _____ before taking any action on the proposed new contract.

SYNONYMS: deliberate, award, bestow
ANTONYMS: withdraw, take away, withhold, deny

6. earmark
(ir′ mark)

(*v.*) to set aside for a special purpose; to mark an animal's ear for identification; (*n.*) an identifying mark or feature

Let's _____**earmark**_____ the money we received for the new building fund.

SYNONYMS: (v.) reserve; (n.) trait, attribute

7. frigid
(frij′ id)

(adj.) extremely cold; lacking in warmth or feeling

Antarctica has a very _____**frigid**_____ climate.

SYNONYMS: freezing, unresponsive
ANTONYMS: hot, balmy, torrid, warm, friendly

8. implement
(im′ plə mənt)

(n.) an instrument, tool; (v.) to put into effect

The harrow is a farm _____**implement**_____ that is used to pulverize and smooth soil.

The highway patrol will _____**implement**_____ the new speed limit as of July 1 of this year.

SYNONYMS: (n.) device, utensil; (v.) fulfill, accomplish, achieve, apply, carry out

9. incalculable
(in kal′ kyə lə bəl)

(adj.) too great to be counted; unpredictable, uncertain

Concerned scientists worry that global warming may cause _____**incalculable**_____ damage to our environment.

SYNONYMS: countless, measureless
ANTONYMS: measurable, countable, predictable

10. indisputable
(in dis pyüt′ ə bəl)

(adj.) beyond question or argument, definitely true

With such _____**indisputable**_____ evidence, Judge Lee must rule to drop all charges against my client.

SYNONYMS: irrefutable, undeniable, incontestable, inarguable
ANTONYMS: questionable, debatable, arguable

11. intensive
(in ten′ siv)

(adj.) thorough, deep; showing great effort; concentrated

It took _____**intensive**_____ physical therapy for the injured athlete to regain her strength and speed.

SYNONYMS: thoroughgoing, heightened, exhaustive
ANTONYMS: relaxed, easygoing, laid-back

12. maneuver
(mə nü′ vər)

(n.) a planned movement; a skillful plan; a scheme; (v.) to perform or carry out such a planned movement

The troops carried out a night _____**maneuver**_____ as part of the training mission.

It takes a steady hand to _____**maneuver**_____ the high-speed power drill.

SYNONYMS: (n.) move, tactic; (v.) guide, manipulate

13. sabotage
(sab′ ə täzh)

(n.) an action taken to destroy something or to prevent it from working properly; (v.) to take such destructive action

Foreign embassies worry about _____**sabotage**_____ .

Angry workers decided to _____ sabotage _____
the factory to protest its poor working conditions.
SYNONYMS: (*v.*) vandalize, cripple, subvert, destroy

14. scant
(skant)

(*adj.*) not enough; barely enough; marked by a small or insufficient amount

Somehow, we made the _____ scant _____
supply of food stretch for nearly a week.
SYNONYMS: inadequate, meager, skimpy, bare
ANTONYMS: abundant, plentiful, profuse, excessive

15. stealthy
(stel' thē)

(*adj.*) done in a way so as not to be seen or observed; sneaky, underhanded

The nervous robber took _____ stealthy _____
glances at the cash register.
SYNONYMS: sly, furtive
ANTONYMS: open, direct, aboveboard, forthright

16. strapping
(strap' iŋ)

(*adj.*) tall, strong, and healthy

That _____ strapping _____ young man will make
a very good wrestler.
SYNONYMS: sturdy, husky, brawny, athletic, hefty
ANTONYMS: weak, frail, fragile, delicate, puny

17. strident
(strīd' ənt)

(*adj.*) harsh, shrill; unpleasant sounding

The group's _____ strident _____ laughter
represented harsh ridicule, not cheery amusement.
SYNONYMS: piercing, grating
ANTONYMS: mellow, soothing, musical, honeyed

18. thrive
(thrīv)

(*v.*) to grow vigorously; to grow in wealth and possessions

Angela remains hopeful that her business will
_____ thrive _____ in today's Internet culture.
SYNONYMS: flourish, blossom, prosper
ANTONYMS: wither, die, fade, fail

19. titanic
(tī tan' ik)

(*adj.*) of enormous size, strength, power, or scope

The movie plot explores the _____ titanic _____
struggle between the forces of good and evil.
SYNONYMS: gigantic, huge, mighty, immense
ANTONYMS: tiny, miniature, diminutive, pint-size

20. valiant
(val' yənt)

(*adj.*) possessing or acting with bravery or boldness

Sir Galahad was a _____ valiant _____ knight
of King Arthur's Round Table.
SYNONYMS: brave, bold, courageous, gallant, heroic
ANTONYMS: timid, cowardly, fainthearted, "chicken"

Completing the Sentence

From the words for this unit, choose the one that best completes each of the following sentences. Write the word in the space provided.

1. No doubt our antipollution program will be expensive, but the cost of doing nothing would be simply _____**incalculable**_____ .

2. At first the zebras did not notice the _____**stealthy**_____ movements of the lions inching their way closer to the herd.

3. The millionaire has hired special guards to make sure that his children will not be _____**abducted**_____ .

4. When the winds begin to turn _____**frigid**_____ in November, our thoughts turn to our warm and sunny island off the coast of Florida.

5. Each year a portion of the school budget is _____**earmarked**_____ for the purchase of new books for the library.

6. When our team saw their _____**strapping**_____ 200-pound defensive linemen, we realized that we would have a hard time running against them.

7. In your training to become a dental assistant, you will become familiar with many of the _____**implements**_____ that dentists use.

8. I prefer the _____**compact**_____ edition of the dictionary because it is so much lighter and less bulky than the unabridged version.

9. Even mighty warships were endangered by the _____**titanic**_____ waves that loomed like mountains above them.

10. The new recruits were rudely awakened from their peaceful sleep by the _____**strident**_____ voice of the sergeant barking commands.

11. Why must you always be so _____**ambiguous**_____ when I want you to give me a straight yes-or-no answer?

12. In Shakespeare's words, "Cowards die many times before their deaths; the _____**valiant**_____ never taste of death but once."

13. I was amazed to see how skillfully Felicia _____**maneuvered**_____ that huge car through the heavy downtown traffic.

14. For a person who loves to argue as much as Gene does, there is nothing that is really _____**indisputable**_____ .

15. The president will _____**confer**_____ well-deserved honors on the retiring ambassador.

16. The cactus is an example of a plant having natural adaptations that enable it to _____**thrive**_____ even in a very dry climate.

17. Since I'm afraid of heights, I usually _____**balk**_____ at the idea of sitting in the first row of the topmost balcony in a theater.

18. The breakdown of all these machines at the same time cannot simply be a coincidence; we suspect deliberate _____ sabotage _____ .

19. Since the time we have to prepare for the final exams is exceedingly _____ scant _____ , we had better make the best of every hour.

20. As the day of the big game approached, our practice sessions became more and more _____ intensive _____ .

Synonyms

*Choose the word from this unit that is **the same** or **most nearly the same** in meaning as the **boldface** word or expression in the given phrase. Write the word on the line provided.*

1. forced to try dangerous **tactics** — maneuvers

2. **resist** because of fear — balk

3. lending us **measureless** support — incalculable

4. its **small** motor — compact

5. the **inarguable** star of the team — indisputable

6. a most **unresponsive** welcome — frigid

7. a plot to **kidnap** the king for ransom — abduct

8. to interpret that **vague** remark — ambiguous

9. as they put forth an **immense** effort — titanic

10. a **courageous** fight against the disease — valiant

11. may use that **device** to move the baggage — implement

12. made a **furtive** grab for the jewels — stealthy

13. all the **attributes** of a rascal — earmarks

14. tries to **cripple** the communications system — sabotage

15. the **heightened** search for the missing child — intensive

Antonyms

*Choose the word from this unit that is **most nearly opposite** in meaning to the **boldface** word or expression in the given phrase. Write the word on the line provided.*

16. to **deny** the award — confer

17. its **abundant** natural resources — scant

18. met a **delicate** peasant girl — strapping

19. spoken in **soothing** tones — strident

20. expected to **wither** in that environment — thrive

Choosing the Right Word

*Circle the **boldface** word that more satisfactorily completes each of the following sentences.*

1. Truthfulness and sincerity are the (**earmarks,** **compacts**) of an honest person.

2. As election day gets closer, the tone of the candidates' political oratory becomes more and more (**titanic,** **strident**).

3. What do you think the United States should do when its representatives are (**sabotaged,** **abducted**) and held for ransom?

4. I don't think democracy can (**balk,** **thrive**) in an atmosphere of racial and religious hatred.

5. Of all the evergreens that tower in America's forests, none can surpass the height and girth of the (**titanic,** **indisputable**) California redwoods.

6. Though the odds were greatly against them, the brave defenders of the fort waged a (**valiant,** **scant**) battle against the enemy's troops.

7. Because her condition was so poor after the operation, she was placed in the hospital's (**stealthy,** **intensive**) care unit.

8. The future is indeed (**incalculable,** **strapping**) but we must face it with faith and confidence.

9. After straining and sweating in the hot sun for an hour, we realized that we had pushed the stalled car only a(n) (**scant,** **intensive**) quarter mile.

10. Since *presently* means both "right now" and "in the future," any statement containing it must be considered (**strident,** **ambiguous**).

11. When we made our appeal for funds, their response was so (**incalculable,** **frigid**) that we realized we would have to find other ways of raising money.

12. Although our club is run more or less democratically, we don't have the time to (**confer,** **abduct**) about every minor detail.

13. Creeping (**stealthily,** **ambiguously**) through the underbrush, the enemy came within a few yards of the stockade before the guards saw them.

14. When their pitcher committed the (**balk,** **earmark**), the umpire advanced our runner from first to second base.

15. When a country has been overrun by a conquering army, the only way the people may have to strike back is by acts of (**ambiguity,** **sabotage**).

16. Before landing on the shore of New England, the first Pilgrim settlers signed an agreement called the "Mayflower (**Compact,** **Maneuver**)."

17. Why is that big, (**strapping,** **frigid**) fellow in the ad always kicking sand into the face of the 98-pound weakling?

18. In her floor exercise, the champion gymnast performed some of the most amazing (**earmarks,** **maneuvers**) I have ever seen.

19. We have worked out a good plan on paper; now we must decide how we are going to (**implement,** **balk**) it.

20. When he says that his analysis of the problem is (**indisputable,** **valiant**), all he means is that he's not willing to listen to anyone else's ideas.

Read the following passage, in which some of the words you have studied in this unit appear in **boldface** type. Then complete each statement given below the passage by circling the letter of the item that is **the same** or **almost the same** in meaning as the highlighted word.

Navajo Code Talkers

(Line)

In war, survival may depend on an army's ability to pass data in secret. Armies make **intensive** efforts to break each other's communication codes. Each wants to uncover what its enemy plans to do. During World War II, no intelligence group was more valuable to American troops in the South Pacific than the Navajo Code Talkers.

(5)   The Navajo Code Talkers were a remarkable group of Navajo soldiers who used their native language to create an unbreakable code. The Navajo language has many **earmarks** of a successful code: it is unwritten, complicated, and known only by a **scant** number of non-Navajos. The Japanese could never crack it. During

(10) the terrible battle of Iwo Jima, six Navajo Code Talkers sent and received 800 vital messages without a single error.

Philip Johnston got the idea of using the Navajo language for a code in 1941.

(15) He had grown up among the Navajo and spoke their language fluently. He believed that any code based on Navajo would be secure. After months of testing and training, the first group of twenty-nine

(20) Navajo Code Talkers **implemented** their distinctive system. They matched Navajo words to common military terms. For example, the Navajo word for

Navajo code talkers in the Pacific relay orders over a field radio during World War II.

"hummingbird" stood for fighter plane; "iron fish" meant submarine; "turtle" meant

(25) tank. They also created a secondary code in which Navajo words stood for English letters. Code Talkers could then spell specific words by stringing words together.

Some people found it odd that Native Americans made such **valiant** efforts to help a nation that had a history of harming them. Yet Navajo Code Talkers never **balked** at the chance to serve the United States. Their code remains one of the few in all of military

(30) history that was never broken. In 1982, President Ronald Reagan declared August 14 as Navajo Code Talkers Day to honor the contributions of these brave soldiers.

---

1. The meaning of **intensive** (line 2) is
   (a.) concentrated   c. truthful
   b. vague   d. half-hearted

2. The meaning of **earmarks** (line 7) is
   a. sounds   c. benefits
   b. actions   (d.) attributes

3. Scant (line 8) most nearly means
   (a.) meager   c. sturdy
   b. plentiful   d. clever

4. Implemented (line 20) most nearly means
   a. withheld   c. manipulated
   (b.) applied   d. destroyed

5. Valiant (line 27) is best defined as
   a. timid   (c.) heroic
   b. harsh   d. sly

6. Balked (line 28) is best defined as
   a. spoke   (c.) hesitated
   b. insisted   d. gave up

Analogies

In each of the following, circle the item that best completes the comparison.

See pages T38–T48 for explanations of answers.

1. compact is to **powder** as
a. wallet is to money
b. shoe is to keys
c. pocket is to pajamas
d. suitcase is to pet

2. scavenger is to **rummage** as
a. vagrant is to thrive
b. vandal is to confer
c. homebody is to amble
d. beggar is to panhandle

3. alias is to **criminal** as
a. nickname is to Mike
b. stage name is to sculptor
c. pen name is to author
d. surname is to animal

4. posterity is to **after** as
a. children are to before
b. classmates are to after
c. ancestors are to before
d. relatives are to after

5. snoop is to **pry** as
a. spoilsport is to amuse
b. busybody is to meddle
c. sleuth is to maneuver
d. showoff is to hide

6. pitchfork is to **implement** as
a. house is to furniture
b. engine is to automobile
c. door is to building
d. typewriter is to machine

7. consequence is to **after** as
a. cause is to before
b. initiative is to after
c. result is to before
d. origin is to after

8. thief is to **stealthy** as
a. maven is to strident
b. klutz is to bumbling
c. yenta is to ambiguous
d. kvetch is to extinct

9. scant is to **quantity** as
a. stealthy is to volume
b. frigid is to capacity
c. rigorous is to height
d. compact is to size

10. kidnapper is to **abduct** as
a. burglar is to rob
b. thug is to delude
c. pirate is to lie
d. thief is to murder

11. foil is to **fencing** as
a. hold is to wrestling
b. play is to baseball
c. signal is to football
d. bow is to archery

12. cold is to **frigid** as
a. tall is to long
b. hot is to fiery
c. small is to gigantic
d. narrow is to wide

13. incalculable is to **count** as
a. invisible is to hear
b. inevitable is to avoid
c. indisputable is to prove
d. invaluable is to own

14. dogged is to **persistence** as
a. abominable is to knowledge
b. ingrained is to enthusiasm
c. strident is to modesty
d. resourceful is to ingenuity

15. used up is to **replenish** as
a. run-down is to distort
b. done in is to formulate
c. worn-out is to refurbish
d. tied up is to maneuver

16. meteoric is to **speed** as
a. titanic is to size
b. strapping is to shape
c. burly is to duration
d. rigorous is to position

17. coward is to **valiant** as
a. fossil is to extinct
b. pickpocket is to stealthy
c. hero is to timid
d. wrestler is to burly

18. sheep is to **earmark** as
a. steer is to brand
b. horse is to saddle
c. mule is to plow
d. ox is to yoke

Word Associations

In each of the following groups, circle the word that is best defined or suggested by the given phrase.

1. said of someone who seems to be incapable of making a mistake
a. titanic   **b. unerring**   c. bumbling   d. ambiguous

2. what one of King Arthur's knights would probably be
a. abominable   b. null and void   **c. valiant**   d. inevitable

3. "This paperweight reminds me of the wonderful time I had last summer."
a. panorama   **b. memento**   c. parody   d. foil

4. rightly said of a dinosaur
a. extinct   b. rigorous   c. scant   d. ingrained

5. a trait that is fixed within a person
a. ingrained   b. ambiguous   c. intensive   d. null and void

6. "He seems to have a gift for doing the wrong thing, at the wrong time, in the wrong way."
a. strapping   **b. bumbling**   c. indisputable   d. rigorous

7. what might be done to a garment to express grief
a. confer   **b. rend**   c. grit   d. balk

8. so shocked and amazed that I couldn't speak
a. dumbfounded   b. resourceful   c. subsequent   d. meteoric

9. what a flood would probably do
a. dole   b. skimp   c. amble   **d. engulf**

10. an extinct fish found in a rock
a. rummage   **b. fossil**   c. alias   d. balk

11. food given in small amounts
a. balk   **b. dole**   c. earmark   d. grit

12. what we did when our water supply began to run out
a. formulate   b. thrive   **c. replenish**   d. prevail

13. what troops go out on to train for warfare
a. panoramas   b. parodies   **c. maneuvers**   d. initiatives

14. describing study that is thorough
a. dogged   **b. intensive**   c. strapping   d. subsequent

15. those who come after us, especially our descendants
a. abduction   b. implement   c. distortion   **d. posterity**

16. said of a person who is moving about very carefully in order to escape attention
a. stealthy   b. intensive   c. strident   d. dogged

17. a phony name that a con artist might use to avoid detection
a. initiative   b. consequence   **c. alias**   d. earmark

18. someone who is good at tracking down clues
a. sleuth   b. implement   c. grit   d. nonconformist

19. what a nosy person is likely to do
a. delude   b. balk   c. confer   **d. pry**

20. "They claim to be our friends, but are deliberately trying to make our program fail."
a. vandalism   **b. sabotage**   c. rummage   d. compact

Vocabulary in Context

*Read the following passage, in which some of the words you have studied in Units 10–12 appear in **boldface** type. Then complete each statement given below the passage by circling the item that is **the same** or **almost the same** in meaning as the highlighted word.*

(Line)
A Truly International Laboratory

"Science lab" usually means a clean, bright room in which researchers work with high-tech equipment. Antarctica, the fifth
(5) largest of the Earth's seven continents, is itself an enormous and **frigid** science lab. It has no native population. Few living things can survive in its brutal climate. But
(10) scientists are attracted to the rare features of this desolate continent.

Antarctica is more than 95% ice-covered all year long. It has had the lowest air temperature ever
(15) measured, as well as some of the highest winds. It has no industrial pollution, so its ice and snow are pure. All that ice makes it doubtful that any settlement or economic
(20) development will ever take place. But many tiny outposts have sprung up since the 1950s.

In that decade, twelve nations set up research stations all over Antarctica.
(25) Representatives of those nations got together to draft a **compact** devoting the continent to peaceful study. This pact went into effect in 1961. It forbids

military action and nuclear weapons. It
(30) promotes a free exchange of ideas.

Antarctic scientists **formulate** and carry out a wide range of tests. They study glaciers, weather patterns and conditions, icebergs, magnetism,
(35) volcanoes, the movement of rock plates, and animal and plant biology. They openly share their findings with the global scientific community.

Life in such a difficult place
(40) demands planning, special gear, and **grit**. Scientists must figure out how to do their research safely and effectively. They must guard their health and well being. Internet and
(45) satellite technologies surely help. Researchers so far from home can **confer** with the family, friends, and co-workers they left behind. They can stay up-to-date on world events. But
(50) they cannot easily come and go. Scientists often arrive before the Antarctic winter, when near-total darkness **engulfs** the area. They typically stay for six to ten long, cold,
(55) lonely months.

---

1. The meaning of **frigid** (line 7) is
a. unbending
b. thriving
c. experimental
d. freezing *(circled)*

2. Compact (line 26) most nearly means
a. reminder
b. agreement *(circled)*
c. travel
d. speech

3. Formulate (line 31) is best defined as
a. devise *(circled)*
b. memorize
c. frustrate
d. improve

4. The meaning of **grit** (line 41) is
a. humor
b. power
c. courage *(circled)*
d. intelligence

5. Confer (line 47) most nearly means
a. consult *(circled)*
b. study
c. live
d. play

6. Engulfs (line 53) is best defined as
a. empties
b. endangers
c. surrounds *(circled)*
d. avoids

Choosing the Right Meaning

Read each sentence carefully. Then circle the item that best completes the statement below the sentence.

See pages T38–T48 for explanations of answers.

Rather than retire from public life as he had hoped, George Washington was prevailed upon in 1789 to accept the presidency of the United States. (2)

1. The best definition for the phrase **prevailed upon** in line 2 is

a. commonly expected
b. successfully urged
c. reluctantly allowed
d. secretly ordered

It is no exaggeration to compare with canned sardines the thousands of commuters compacted in rush-hour subway cars. (2)

2. The word **compacted** in line 2 is best defined as

a. fleeing work
b. making deals
c. squeezed together
d. going home

Dr. Watson is often reminded by Sherlock Holmes that his astonishing solutions stem from observation and rigorous deduction, not hunches or gut feelings. (2)

3. In line 2 the word **rigorous** is used to mean

a. severe
b. logical
c. harsh
d. trying

One of the chief aims of American foreign policy in the period following World War II was to balk Soviet attempts to "export" communism to the Third World. (2)

4. In line 2 the word **balk** most nearly means

a. reverse
b. shy away from
c. monitor
d. block

New York City's Greenwich Village has long been a favorite destination for people whose nonconformist views set them apart from the mainstream. (2)

5. The word **nonconformist** in line 2 most nearly means

a. bohemian
b. revolutionary
c. foreign
d. quaint

Antonyms

*In each of the following groups, circle the word or expression that is most nearly the **opposite** of the word in **boldface** type.*

1. consequences
a. aims
b. criticisms
c. causes
d. results

2. frigid
a. balmy
b. icy
c. wasted
d. busy

3. strapping
a. sharp
b. strong
c. frail
d. husky

4. prevail
a. win
b. succumb
c. participate
d. campaign

5. subsequent
a. odd
b. prior
c. funny
d. disturbing

6. dumbfounded
a. astonished
b. saddened
c. amazed
d. expectant

7. indisputable
a. new
b. proven
c. debatable
d. strong

8. null and void
a. meaningless
b. illegal
c. vague
d. in effect

9. compact
a. efficient
b. enormous ⟨circled⟩
c. modern
d. costly

11. ambiguous
a. wordy
b. strange
c. clear ⟨circled⟩
d. brief

13. strident
a. loud
b. mellow ⟨circled⟩
c. strong
d. harsh

15. inevitable
a. costly
b. avoidable ⟨circled⟩
c. desired
d. foolish

10. replenish
a. empty ⟨circled⟩
b. count
c. budget
d. increase

12. burly
a. delicate ⟨circled⟩
b. fat
c. tough
d. muscular

14. skimp
a. splurge ⟨circled⟩
b. plan
c. annoy
d. decorate

16. nonconformist
a. clever
b. conventional ⟨circled⟩
c. radical
d. severe

Word Families

A. On the line provided, write the word you have learned in Units 10–12 that is related to each of the following nouns.

EXAMPLE: compactness—**compact**

1. stealthiness, stealth	stealthy
2. formula, formulation, formulator	formulate
3. extinction	extinct
4. refurbisher, refurbishment	refurbish
5. rigor, rigorousness	rigorous
6. stridency	strident
7. distortion, distorter	distort
8. resource, resourcefulness	resourceful
9. titan	titanic
10. burliness	burly
11. conference	confer
12. meteor, meteorite	meteoric
13. delusion, deluder	delude
14. inevitability, inevitableness	inevitable
15. scantness, scantiness	scant

B. On the line provided, write the word you have learned in Units 10–12 that is related to each of the following verbs.

EXAMPLE: dispute—**indisputable**

16. vandalize	vandalism
17. abominate	abominable
18. initiate	initiative
19. fossilize	fossil
20. bumble	bumbling

Two-Word Completions

Circle the pair of words that best complete the meaning of each of the following passages.

See pages T38–T48 for explanations of answers.

1. "Although we have devised a plan to deal with the situation," the official said, "we will not be able to _____ it until we get the funds that the government has _____ for the project."
   a. replenish . . . conferred
   b. implement . . . earmarked
   c. refurbish . . . maneuvered
   d. formulate . . . rummaged

2. Though such animals as the saber-toothed tiger and the woolly mammoth have been _____ since the close of the last Ice Age, many thousands of years ago, their _____ remains have been found in various parts of the world.
   a. extinct . . . fossilized
   b. scant . . . earmarked
   c. skimpy . . . distorted
   d. indisputable . . . unerring

3. When we saw the breathtaking _____ on that lovely autumn morning, we decided to _____ rather than rush and miss the impact of that stunning vista.
   a. parody . . . maneuver
   b. panorama . . . amble
   c. fossil . . . balk
   d. grit . . . compact

4. Kidnappers had made plans to _____ the official and hold him for ransom. Fortunately, however, the police were able to _____ the plot after an informant tipped them off about it.
   a. delude . . . balk
   b. abduct . . . foil
   c. sabotage . . . distort
   d. parody . . . pry

5. When I asked her where I could find the old book, her reply was so _____ that I had to spend over an hour _____ around the attic until I could find it.
   a. indisputable . . . earmarking
   b. bumbling . . . abducting
   c. intensive . . . prevailing
   d. ambiguous . . . rummaging

6. The way in which the nimble little star quarterback _____ around the _____ linebackers attempting to sack him reminded me of a bicycle weaving through heavy midtown traffic.
   a. engulfed . . . compact
   b. abducted . . . strapping
   c. maneuvered . . . burly
   d. foiled . . . frigid

7. I am always _____ by the amazing powers of observation and deduction exhibited by my favorite _____, the legendary Sherlock Holmes.
   a. deluded . . . fossil
   b. ingrained . . . foil
   c. dogged . . . vandal
   d. dumbfounded . . . sleuth

Building with Classical Roots

co, col, com, con, cor—with, together

This prefix appears in **consequence** (page 117), **compact** (page 131), and **confer** (page 131). Some other words in which this prefix appears are listed below.

coincidence	colleague	compute	confide
collaborate	composure	concurrent	correspond

From the list of words above, choose the one that corresponds to each of the brief definitions below. Write the word in the blank space in the illustrative sentence below the definition.

1. occurring at the same time; agreeing, coming

The convicted felon was sentenced to _____ **concurrent** _____ prison terms.

2. the chance occurrence of two things at the same time or place

"What a _____ **coincidence** _____ to bump into you here at the passport office!" she exclaimed.

3. to determine by arithmetic, calculate

The mechanic used a calculator to _____ **compute** _____ the total repair bill.

4. to exchange letters; to be in agreement

My cousin and I decided to _____ **correspond** _____ by e-mail since he moved to Montana.

5. calmness of mind, bearing, or appearance; self-control

Even the car alarms wailing outside did not ruffle the speaker's _____ **composure** _____.

6. to work with others; to aid or assist an enemy of one's country

They agreed to _____ **collaborate** _____ on the science project so they could pool their resources and ideas.

7. to tell something as a secret; to entrust a secret

I would never _____ **confide** _____ such details to anyone but a close friend.

8. a fellow worker, associate

The proud retiree was honored by her long-time _____ **colleagues** _____ at the library.

From the list of words above, choose the one that best completes each of the following sentences. Write the word in the space provided.

1. The composer George Gershwin often _____ **collaborated** _____ with his brother Ira to write some of America's best-loved songs.

2. The gossip columnist's success stemmed from her amazing ability to get even the most reclusive celebrities to _____ **confide** _____ in her.

3. Sherlock Holmes was often assisted in his investigations by his trusted friend and _____colleague_____ Dr. Watson.

4. The abacus is still widely used in China to _____compute_____ sums.

5. The culprits rehearsed their alibi until their stories _____corresponded_____ in every detail.

6. For a rookie making his first World Series appearance, the young pitcher showed remarkable _____composure_____ and maturity on the mound.

7. Powers exercised at one and the same time by states and the Federal government— for example, the power to tax—are said to be _____concurrent_____.

8. By the strangest _____coincidence_____, two of our nation's founders, Thomas Jefferson and John Adams, both died on exactly the same day—July 4, 1826.

Circle the **boldface** word that more satisfactorily completes each of the following sentences.

1. In terms of anatomical function, the wings of birds may be said to (**correspond,** **collaborate**) with the fins of fish.

2. To get recommendations for fine arts camp, she scheduled (**coincidental,** **concurrent**) appointments with her guidance counselor and her drama teacher.

3. One can sense how candidates may react under pressure by noticing their degree of (**composure,** **coincidence**) during unscripted town meetings and press conferences.

4. The architects, engineers, and designers found creative ways to (**collaborate,** **confide**) on a brilliant renovation of the old city hall.

5. What an amusing (**composure,** **coincidence**) that the newlyweds received as gifts three types of coffee makers—and neither of them even drinks the stuff!

6. "I'm not qualified to advise you on wallpapering," said the sales clerk at the home store, "but my (**colleague,** **concurrence**) over there is quite the expert."

7. The teacher showed us several strategies to help us mentally (**correspond,** **compute**) a tip at a restaurant.

8. The apprentice refused to (**confide,** **compute**) his anxieties to anyone but his older brother.

Read the following sentences, paying special attention to the words and phrases underlined. From the words in the box below, find better choices for these underlined words and phrases. Then use these choices to rewrite the sentences.

WORD BANK

abduct	distort	indisputable	replenish	skimp
amble	extinct	inevitable	resourceful	strident
confer	implement	initiative	rigorous	thrive
consequence	incalculable	panorama	scant	titanic

Mystic Seaport

1. Mystic Seaport is located where three of five shipyards once lined the Mystic River in Connecticut. About 600 vessels were launched from there from 1784 to 1919, an <u>undeniably true</u> record unmatched by other similar-sized American towns.
indisputable

2. It was the <u>first step</u> of three Mystic residents in 1929 to start a museum to preserve the remnants of the area's maritime history.
initiative

3. Over time, the efforts of this <u>inventive</u> trio grew into what is now Mystic Seaport, The Museum of America and The Sea.
resourceful

4. Mystic's coastal regions once <u>grew vigorously</u> in the business of shipbuilding.
thrived

5. So as not to <u>disfigure</u> or romanticize the past, Mystic Seaport features living history exhibits to help today's visitors get a true feel for life in a maritime town in the 1850s.
distort

6. Tourists may <u>walk slowly</u> along wooden docks, gravel roads, and stone lanes to experience a recreation of 19th-century Mystic.
amble

7. Soon, Mystic Seaport plans to <u>put into effect</u> more interactive exhibits and displays, to expand its research facilities, and to make some of its vast collection accessible over the Internet.
implement

Analogies — *In each of the following, circle the item that best completes the comparison.*

See pages T38–T48 for explanations of answers.

1. dumbfounded is to **shock** as
a. befuddled is to confusion
b. irked is to pleasure
c. pacified is to disgust
d. infuriated is to satisfaction

2. thrive is to **wither** as
a. skimp is to restrict
b. idolize is to detest
c. reminisce is to recall
d. refute is to disprove

3. gory is to **sight** as
a. sinister is to taste
b. meteoric is to feel
c. strident is to sound
d. martial is to smell

4. deluge is to **engulf** as
a. blizzard is to bake
b. earthquake is to devastate
c. drought is to swamp
d. avalanche is to fry

5. serene is to **ruffle** as
a. dogged is to persevere
b. gullible is to delude
c. resourceful is to motivate
d. valiant is to intimidate

6. culprit is to **commit** as
a. nonconformist is to obey
b. oaf is to foil
c. sage is to bungle
d. sleuth is to solve

7. global is to **world** as
a. cosmic is to universe
b. lunar is to sun
c. aquatic is to star
d. colonial is to planet

8. partisan is to **defend** as
a. hypocrite is to pry
b. pacifist is to attack
c. vagabond is to tarry
d. oracle is to predict

9. vandalism is to **destroy** as
a. initiative is to harm
b. fossil is to foil
c. sabotage is to wreck
d. memento is to injure

10. keepsake is to **memento** as
a. agenda is to decision
b. fidelity is to treachery
c. fatality is to death
d. debut is to journey

Choosing the Right Meaning — *Read each sentence carefully. Then circle the item that best completes the statement below the sentence.*

See pages T38–T48 for explanations of answers.

After the Emancipation Proclamation of 1863, Union victories in the South were often occasions for the mass liberation of slaves. (2)

1. The word **liberation** in line 2 is used to mean
a. freeing
b. arrest
c. transportation
d. migration

From a nearby hilltop scouts could see an enemy regiment drawn up in a long battle line at the forest's verge. (2)

2. The word **verge** in line 2 most nearly means
a. path
b. clearing
c. edge
d. center

Riflemen preparing for battle thoroughly cleaned their weapons to make sure they were free of grit. (2)

3. The best definition for the word **grit** in line 2 is
a. courage
b. determination
c. mettle
d. dirt

Packing winds in excess of 100 miles per hour, Hurricane Andrew tore through
Florida in 1992, leaving wholesale devastation in its wake. (2)

4. In line 2 the word **devastation** most nearly means

a. grief   (b. destruction)   c. flooding   d. misery

In fencing matches the two competitors bring the tips of their foils together to signal
that they are ready to commence. (2)

5. In line 1 the word **foils** is best defined as

a. weapons   b. pistols   c. daggers   (d. swords)

Two-Word Completions

*Circle the pair of words that best complete the meaning
of each of the following sentences.*

See pages T38–T48 for explanations of answers.

1. Though a number of people claim to have spotted his tracks or even sighted him, the
yeti, or "_____ snowman," has proved to be one of nature's most
_____ creatures, and may not even exist!

a. burly . . . pathetic   c. immobile . . . incomprehensible
(b. abominable . . . elusive)   d. ingenious . . . ambiguous

2. "In the frozen wastes of Antarctica," the world-famous explorer remarked,
"temperatures are so _____ that a person's hands and feet can
become _____ with cold after only a brief exposure to the elements."

(a. frigid . . . numb)   c. gross . . . sluggish
b. acute . . . extinct   d. rigorous . . . null and void

3. "I wouldn't go near that particular joint," I warned them, "because it is known to be a
favorite _____ of hoods, pushers, and other _____
or disreputable characters."

a. terrain . . . smug   c. earmark . . . affluent
(b. rendezvous . . . sinister)   d. queue . . . petty

4. Though the storm itself was of very brief _____, it dumped so
much snow on the city while it lasted that roads and highways all over town were
virtually _____ for a week.

a. format . . . indisputable   (c. duration . . . impassable)
b. onset . . . inflammatory   d. stamina . . . incalculable

5. That terrible _____ of war, like the atomic bomb, should in fact
prove to be our most reliable guardians of the peace is one of the most puzzling
_____ of modern life.

a. misgivings . . . consequences   c. illusions . . . facets
b. vows . . . innovations   (d. implements . . . enigmas)

Enriching Your Vocabulary

Read the passage below. Then complete the exercise at the bottom of the page.

You Name It!

Everybody and everything has a name. There are names that describe one's achievements, that explain where we are from, and that hide our true identities.

What words do we use to describe types of names? Your pet Chihuahua puppy is named Spike. He only has one name, but you, his owner, also have a *surname*, or last name. One type of surname is the *patronymic*, which is formed by adding a prefix or a suffix to the name of an ancestor. Peterson or "son of Peter" and O'Neal or "of Neal" are patronymics.

Someone who wants to hide his true identity could adopt an *alias* (Unit 11), a false name. A performer may choose a *stage name* that is more catchy or glamorous than her real name. That's what Caryn Johnson did. (You know her as Whoopi Goldberg.) Authors are famous for using *pen names*. Samuel Clemens—Mark Twain—is one of the best known.

Pennsylvania, Rome, and America all have something in common. These place names are based on the names of real or legendary people. Pennsylvania is named after William Penn. Rome is named after Romulus, one of its mythical founders. America is named after the explorer Amerigo Vespucci. Such place names are called *eponyms*.

Mark Twain (1835–1910), famous American humorist

Here is a questionnaire about names. Read each question and write the answer on the lines. Use a dictionary if you need to.

1. What is your *appellation*? <u>Students' answers should reflect their understanding</u> <u>that *appellation* means name.</u>

2. Do you have a *nickname?* If not, think of one you would like. Write it here. <u>Students'</u> <u>answers should include a *nickname* they are called or would like to be called.</u>

3. Do you have a *title*? Do you think you might have a title at some time in the future? If so, write it here. <u>Students' answers should include titles such as *Dr., Ms., Mr., Sen.,*</u> <u>and so on.</u>

4. Are you someone's *namesake*? If so, write that person's name here. If not, use your imagination and write the name of someone you could be named for. <u>Students'</u> <u>answers should reflect their understanding that a *namesake* is someone</u> <u>named after another person.</u>

5. What would it mean if someone called you by a *misnomer*? <u>Students' answers</u> <u>should reflect the fact that a *misnomer* is the wrong name.</u>

6. Do you ever use a *pseudonym* or a *nom de plume*? If so, what is it? If not, which one would you choose? <u>Students' answers should reflect that *pseudonym* and *nom*</u> <u>*de plume* are both assumed names.</u>

Definitions

Note carefully the spelling, pronunciation, part(s) of speech, and definition(s) of each of the following words. Then write the word in the blank space(s) in the illustrative sentence(s) following. Finally, study the lists of synonyms and antonyms given at the end of each entry.

1. adhere
(ad hēr′)

(*v.*) to stick to, remain attached; to be devoted or loyal as a follower or supporter

Things will work out better if we _____ **adhere** _____ to our original plan.

SYNONYMS: cling, hold fast
ANTONYMS: unfasten, unglue, abandon, betray

2. affirm
(ə fərm′)

(*v.*) to declare to be true, state positively; to confirm

Unexpected kindness from a stranger during a time of need can _____ **affirm** _____ one's faith in human nature.

SYNONYMS: assert, ratify
ANTONYMS: deny, disavow, reject, veto, disallow

3. atrocity
(ə träs′ ət ē)

(*n.*) an extremely wicked, brutal, or cruel act; something very bad or unpleasant

The Nazis took great pains to keep detailed records of each kind of _____ **atrocity** _____ they committed.

SYNONYMS: outrage, enormity, monstrosity
ANTONYMS: good deed, kindness, kind act

4. audition
(ô dish′ ən)

(*n.*) a trial hearing for a performer; (*v.*) to conduct or perform such a hearing

Kent will hold the final _____ **audition** _____ for Ibsen's *The Doll House* today.

Will you _____ **audition** _____ for the lead role in the school play?

SYNONYMS: (*n.*) tryout, screen test

5. cope
(kōp)

(*v.*) to struggle successfully against; to prove to be a match for, deal with satisfactorily; (*n.*) a long religious cloak; a canopy

Education and experience provide us with the skills we need to _____ **cope** _____ with difficult situations.

We exchanged wedding vows under a blue _____ **cope** _____ .

SYNONYMS: (*v.*) make do, manage, get along, handle

6. deter
(di tər′)

(*v.*) to discourage, scare off, or prevent through fear or doubt

Traffic jams won't _____ **deter** _____ us from coming to your birthday party.

ANTONYMS: encourage, urge on

7. disquieting
(dis kwī'ət iŋ)

(*adj.*) causing uneasiness or worry

A _____ disquieting _____ incident at school put all the teachers and students on edge.

SYNONYMS: troubling, disturbing, alarming
ANTONYMS: calming, reassuring, soothing, comforting

8. empower
(em paù' ər)

(*v.*) to give power or authority to; to enable; to permit

Signing this legal paper will _____ empower _____ me to set up my own bank account.

SYNONYMS: authorize, license
ANTONYMS: forbid, prohibit, ban, disqualify

9. fluent
(flü' ənt)

(*adj.*) speaking or writing easily and smoothly, flowing gracefully

Susannah can speak _____ fluent _____ Japanese, French, and Russian.

SYNONYMS: eloquent, articulate, glib
ANTONYMS: halting, tongue-tied, choppy

10. lag
(lag)

(*v.*) to move slowly or fall behind; to bring up the rear; (*n.*) a falling behind; the amount by which someone or something is behind; an interval

Please try not to _____ lag _____ behind the others.

There is a three-hour _____ lag _____ from the time I send you an e-mail until you receive it.

SYNONYMS: (*v.*) trail, straggle; (*v., n.*) delay
ANTONYMS: (*v.*) keep up, outstrip, outdo

11. mangle
(maŋ' gəl)

(*v.*) to injure very seriously by cutting, tearing, crushing, etc.; to bring to ruin

Workers could _____ mangle _____ their hands in this equipment if they don't pay attention to what they're doing.

SYNONYMS: damage, mutilate, butcher, disfigure, rend

12. misapprehension
(mis ap ri hen' shən)

(*n.*) a wrong idea, misunderstanding

A lingering _____ misapprehension _____ may cause ill will between friends.

SYNONYM: misconception

13. optimist
(äp' tə mist)

(*n.*) one who expects things to turn out for the best; someone who looks on the bright side of things

An _____ optimist _____ holds a rosy view of life.

ANTONYMS: pessimist, prophet of doom

14. prowl
(praül)

(v.) to roam about stealthily in search of something

A panther can _____ **prowl** _____ freely at night because its dark fur prevents it from being seen.

SYNONYMS: rove, skulk, slink, lurk

15. stupefy
(stü′ pə fī)

(v.) to make stupid, dull, or groggy; to surprise or astonish

The doctor prescribed strong painkillers to _____ **stupefy** _____ the patient after her major surgery.

SYNONYMS: stun, daze, shock, amaze, astound
ANTONYMS: awaken, arouse, stimulate, enliven

16. sulky
(səl′ kē)

(adj.) in a bad or nasty mood, resentful; gloomy

A _____ **sulky** _____ child does not make a very good playmate.

SYNONYMS: grouchy, sullen, peevish, petulant
ANTONYMS: cheerful, sociable, sunny, amiable

17. supplement
(səp′ lə ment)

(n.) something added to complete a thing or make up for a lack; a section added to a book or document; (v.) to provide such an addition or completion

The sports _____ **supplement** _____ is my favorite part of this magazine.

Many people _____ **supplement** _____ their regular diet by taking daily vitamins.

SYNONYMS: (n.) addition, extension; (v.) add to

18. surge
(sərj)

(v.) to have a heavy, violent, swelling motion (like waves); (n.) a powerful forward rush

Runners who train hard and who have good stamina often _____ **surge** _____ ahead of the pack.

A sudden _____ **surge** _____ of electrical current could make a computer crash.

SYNONYMS: (v.) flood, rush, burst, gush; (n.) wave
ANTONYMS: (v.) recede, ebb; (n.) recession, slowdown

19. trait
(trāt)

(n.) a quality or characteristic (especially of personality); a distinguishing feature

Your most appealing _____ **trait** _____ is your unfailing sense of humor.

20. unscrupulous
(ən skrü′ pyə ləs)

(adj.) dishonest; not guided or controlled by moral principles

Avoid dealing with _____ **unscrupulous** _____ merchants whenever possible.

SYNONYMS: crooked, corrupt, shady
ANTONYMS: fair, honest, trustworthy, aboveboard

Completing the Sentence

From the words for this unit, choose the one that best completes each of the following sentences. Write the word in the space provided.

1. He is so careless in handling his textbooks that by the end of the term he has practically _____ **mangled** _____ all of them.

2. The Constitution _____ **empowers** _____ the president to name the people who will fill many of the most important positions in the government.

3. As soon as the doors were opened, the shoppers, eager for the advertised bargains, _____ **surged** _____ into the store in great waves.

4. If you are having so much trouble with a program of four major courses, how do you expect to _____ **cope** _____ with a fifth course?

5. Do you think that it is possible to become _____ **fluent** _____ in a foreign language without actually living in a country where it is spoken?

6. Since she has a large family, she finds it necessary to _____ **supplement** _____ her income by working at a second job at night and on weekends.

7. We were so _____ **stupefied** _____ by the bad news that for a few moments we just sat there without moving or speaking.

8. In spite of our best efforts, collections for the Community Fund this year have _____ **lagged** _____ far behind last year's figures.

9. As the robber _____ **prowled** _____ the streets looking for victims, he was unaware that undercover police officers were watching his every move.

10. Throughout her long and noble career, her outstanding _____ **trait** _____ has been her deep love for her fellow human beings.

11. In spite of all his talents, he will never gain high public office because so many voters feel that he is _____ **unscrupulous** _____ and cannot be trusted.

12. Now that the job has been completed, I have finally become skillful in hanging the paper so that it _____ **adheres** _____ firmly to the wall.

13. It is hard to be a(n) _____ **optimist** _____ when nothing works out for you.

14. Naturally we were upset when we received the _____ **disquieting** _____ news that our uncle had been taken to the hospital.

15. On Broadway, _____ **auditions** _____ that are open to any performer who just walks in off the street are referred to as "cattle calls."

16. The witness solemnly _____ **affirmed** _____ that the evidence she was about to give was true.

17. If you think that I would go to a party without being invited, you are under a complete _____ **misapprehension** _____.

18. The unfavorable weather reports did not _____deter_____ us from holding the picnic that we had planned for so long.

19. When he gets in one of those _____sulky_____ moods, he is as unreasonable and unpleasant as a cranky child.

20. Drunken soldiers roamed the streets of the fallen city, committing one _____atrocity_____ after another on the terrified population.

Synonyms

Choose the word from this unit that is **the same** or **most nearly the same** in meaning as the **boldface** word or expression in the given phrase. Write the word on the line provided.

1. while they **damaged** the stolen bicycle —————— mangled

2. did not welcome her **peevish** attitude —————— sulky

3. **outrage** that stunned the world —————— atrocity

4. the most unique **feature** of the breed —————— trait

5. hikers who **straggle** behind the group —————— lag

6. clinging to that **misconception** —————— misapprehension

7. as the crowds **rush** forward —————— surge

8. which contained some **troubling** news —————— disquieting

9. scheduled **tryouts** for the chorus —————— auditions

10. unsure how to **manage** with the sick puppy —————— cope

11. hoping that the special effects will **amaze** you —————— stupefy

12. a special **addition** to the regular menu —————— supplement

13. to **skulk** along the corridor —————— prowl

14. **authorized** to make major decisions —————— empowered

15. able to **cling** to slippery surfaces —————— adhere

Antonyms

Choose the word from this unit that is **most nearly opposite** in meaning to the **boldface** word or expression in the given phrase. Write the word on the line provided.

16. as only the **pessimist** would believe —————— optimist

17. attempted to **encourage** their mission —————— deter

18. their reputation as **trustworthy** mechanics —————— unscrupulous

19. **halting** public-speaking skills —————— fluent

20. to **deny** that we were there —————— affirm

Choosing the Right Word

*Circle the **boldface** word that more satisfactorily completes each of the following sentences.*

1. Shortly after World War II, Japan began the great economic (**surge,** trait) that has put her among the world's top industrial nations.

2. All those smooth words and vague promises are not going to (**adhere, deter**) us from doing what we know is needed to improve conditions.

3. The City Council has approved funds for a new playground, but we expect a (**lag,** surge) of several months before construction begins.

4. There is no one (**optimist, trait**) that makes him so likable; it is the overall effect of his personality.

5. It is far better to know you are ignorant of something than to act on the basis of wrong information and (**misapprehensions,** auditions).

6. Come what may, I will (**adhere,** affirm) to the great ideas and ideals for which our ancestors suffered so much.

7. My definition of a(n) (**optimist,** misapprehension) is someone who looks at an almost empty bottle of juice and says, "This bottle is one-quarter full."

8. The worst way to deal with disappointments is to become (fluent, **sulky**); the best way is to smile and make up your mind to try again.

9. When everything went wrong for Stan, and he saw absolutely no way out of his troubles, he muttered to himself, "I just can't (mangle, **cope**)!"

10. After the conductor (**auditioned,** supplemented) all the candidates for the position of first violinist, he made his final choice.

11. Everything that I have learned about Abraham Lincoln from history books (stupefies, **affirms**) my reverence for this great president.

12. I agree fully with what the previous speaker has said, but I should like to (cope, **supplement**) his ideas with a few remarks of my own.

13. Who (prowled, **empowered**) you to speak for everyone in our class?

14. Although José has been living in this country for only a few years, I would love to be half as (**fluent,** sulky) in Spanish as he is in English.

15. The play went along smoothly until it came to Mark Antony's funeral oration, which Fred (empowered, **mangled**) beyond all recognition.

16. Jackals and other scavengers now (**prowl,** deter) through the ruins of what was once a great city.

17. A loud groan went through the class when we got the (unscrupulous, **disquieting**) news that there would be a full-period test later in the week.

18. My friend took one look at the statue I fashioned from stray pieces of junk and exclaimed, "That's not a sculpture; it's a(n) (lag, **atrocity**)!"

19. A true friend would not have been so (sulky, **unscrupulous**) as to take unfair advantage of your trust and confidence.

20. Have all these years of peace and good living (disquieted, **stupefied**) us to such an extent that we are not even prepared to defend ourselves?

*Read the following passage, in which some of the words you have studied in this unit appear in **boldface** type. Then complete each statement given below the passage by circling the letter of the item that is **the same** or **almost the same** in meaning as the highlighted word.*

Mary Cassatt

(Line)

Throughout her life, American painter Mary Cassatt demonstrated several important **traits** that contributed to her success. A passion for painting, hard work, and extensive study **empowered** her to achieve success in an age when few women had careers. She first studied art in Pennsylvania, where she was born in 1844. To **supplement** (5)

Mary Cassatt's *Maternal Kiss* (1897) hangs in the Philadelphia Museum of Art.

her training, she traveled to Europe and visited great art museums in Rome and Madrid. Above all, she spent time in Paris, then the center of the modern art world.

Her confidence **surged** when, in 1868, her painting *A Mandolin Player* was accepted for (10) exhibit in a famous Paris art show. She decided to settle in Paris and to devote herself to a life of art. Degas saw Cassatt's work, and in 1877 he asked her to join the Impressionists, a group of artists who used (15) shimmering color and bold brush strokes and experimented with light, shadow, and form. Cassatt's prestigious colleagues included Monet, Renoir, Cezanne, and Van Gogh.

In Mary Cassatt's day, most women (20) married and raised families; few women had careers. That did not **deter** her. Cassatt decided not to marry, making the conscious choice of art over family.

At first, Mary Cassatt painted typical scenes: social events, nightlife, people at (25) work, and scenes of the theatre. Eventually, she decided not to **adhere to** these themes alone. She chose instead to portray domestic life. Although she did not have a family of her own, her tender mother-and-child portraits became her most beloved pictures. Cassatt produced over 200 works during her career. When her vision began to fail in 1911, she was forced to give up art. She died near Paris in 1926. (30)

---

1. The meaning of **traits** (line 2) is
a. features
b. talents
c. ideas
d. trials

2. Empowered (line 3) most nearly means
a. forced
b. told
c. enabled
d. disabled

3. Supplement (line 4) is best defined as
a. hurry
b. cut back
c. repeat
d. add to

4. The meaning of **surged** (line 9) is
a. began
b. ended
c. rushed
d. receded

5. Deter (line 22) is best defined as
a. encourage
b. discourage
c. wake
d. shake

6. Adhere to (line 26) most nearly means
a. paint
b. stick to
c. abandon
d. avoid

Definitions

Note carefully the spelling, pronunciation, part(s) of speech, and definition(s) of each of the following words. Then write the word in the blank space(s) in the illustrative sentence(s) following. Finally, study the lists of synonyms and antonyms given at the end of each entry.

1. abstain
(ab stān')

(*v.*) to stay away from doing something by one's own choice

I find it hard to _____**abstain**_____ from these tempting and delicious desserts.

SYNONYMS: avoid, decline, resist, refrain from
ANTONYMS: yield to, give in to, indulge in

2. accommodate
(ə käm' ə dāt)

(*v.*) to do a favor or service for, help out; to provide for, supply with; to have space for; to make fit or suitable

That van is the ideal vehicle for carpooling because it can _____**accommodate**_____ nine passengers.

SYNONYMS: oblige, lodge, house, adapt
ANTONYMS: disoblige, inconvenience, trouble

3. allegiance
(ə lēj' əns)

(*n.*) the loyalty or obligation owed to a government, nation, or cause

At a festive yet solemn ceremony, fifty new citizens swore _____**allegiance**_____ to their adopted nation.

SYNONYMS: obedience, devotion, fidelity

4. amalgamate
(ə mal' gə māt)

(*v.*) to unite; to combine elements into a unified whole

Two small companies will _____**amalgamate**_____ into one large corporation on June 1.

SYNONYMS: merge, consolidate
ANTONYMS: divide, separate, carve up, break up

5. append
(ə pend')

(*v.*) to attach, add, or tack on as a supplement or extra item

We were dismayed when our teacher decided to _____**append**_____ an additional assignment to our already huge load of homework.

ANTONYMS: detach from, disconnect

6. commemorate
(kə mem' ə rāt)

(*v.*) to preserve, honor, or celebrate the memory of

Each May we _____**commemorate**_____ Grandpa's life by lighting a special candle for him that burns for 24 hours.

SYNONYM: memorialize
ANTONYMS: dishonor, forget, overlook

7. enumerate
(i nü' mə rāt)

(*v.*) to count; to name one by one, list

These booklets _____**enumerate**_____ and compare all the high-tech features that new televisions can offer.

SYNONYMS: check off, spell out, specify

8. exalt
(eg zôlt')

(*v.*) to make high in rank, power, character, or quality; to fill with pride, joy, or noble feeling; to praise, honor

Let us now _____ **exalt** _____ the heroes for their courage and character in the face of all this adversity.

SYNONYMS: elevate, raise, uplift
ANTONYMS: lower, cast down, humble, degrade, demote, depose

9. extort
(ek stôrt')

(*v.*) to obtain by violence, misuse of authority, or threats

The kidnappers tried to _____ **extort** _____ a huge sum of money in return for releasing their prisoners safely.

SYNONYMS: blackmail, coerce, bilk, "shake down"

10. far-fetched
(fär fecht')

(*adj.*) strained or improbable (in the sense of not being logical or believable), going far afield from a topic

No one will believe the _____ **far-fetched** _____ excuse you just gave!

SYNONYMS: unlikely, hard to swallow
ANTONYMS: likely, probable, plausible, credible

11. glum
(gləm)

(*adj.*) depressed, gloomy

The losing team wore _____ **glum** _____ expressions on their faces as the final buzzer sounded.

SYNONYMS: dejected, morose, melancholy
ANTONYMS: cheerful, merry, rosy, sunny

12. replica
(rep' lə kə)

(*n.*) a copy, close reproduction

We visited a life-size _____ **replica** _____ of the *Mayflower*, the Pilgrim ship docked near Plymouth, Massachusetts.

SYNONYMS: duplicate, imitation
ANTONYMS: original, prototype

13. responsive
(ri spän' siv)

(*adj.*) answering or replying; reacting readily to requests, suggestions, etc.; showing interest and understanding

The host of the charming inn was _____ **responsive** _____ to our every wish.

SYNONYMS: sympathetic, open, receptive
ANTONYMS: insensitive, unsympathetic

14. sanctuary
(saŋk' chə wer ē)

(*n.*) a sacred or holy place; refuge or protection from capture or punishment; a place of refuge or protection

The exhausted refugees found _____ **sanctuary** _____ in a local church.

SYNONYMS: shrine, haven

15. self-seeking
(self sēk' iŋ)

(*adj.*) selfishly ambitious

That _____ self-seeking _____ politician will promise just about anything to win a few more votes.

SYNONYMS: selfish, opportunistic, gold-digging
ANTONYMS: unselfish, selfless, altruistic

16. submissive
(səb mis' iv)

(*adj.*) humbly obedient; tending to give in to authority, obeying without protest

In some cultures, boys and men still expect girls and women to behave in a totally _____ submissive _____ manner.

SYNONYMS: meek, compliant, servile, subservient
ANTONYMS: rebellious, defiant, insubordinate

17. tally
(tal' ē)

(*v.*) to count up; to keep score; to make entries for reckoning; to correspond or agree; (*n.*) a total or score

They will _____ tally _____ the votes after 9 P.M.

Our teacher keeps an accurate _____ tally _____ of all of our absences.

SYNONYMS: (*v., n.*) total, record

18. taskmaster
(task' mas tər)

(*n.*) one whose job it is to assign work to others; one who uses his or her power to make people work very hard

The crusty old boss was a harsh _____ taskmaster _____ but also an efficient manager.

SYNONYMS: supervisor, overseer, slave driver

19. transform
(trans fôrm')

(*v.*) to change completely in appearance or form; to make into something else

A heavy rain could _____ transform _____ the parched yellow fields into a lush green landscape again.

SYNONYMS: alter, convert
ANTONYMS: maintain, preserve

20. upheaval
(əp hēv' əl)

(*n.*) a sudden, violent upward movement; great disorder or radical change

The sudden change in leadership caused dramatic social and economic _____ upheaval _____ in the government.

SYNONYMS: confusion, disruption, chaos
ANTONYMS: tranquility, peace and quiet

Completing the Sentence

From the words for this unit, choose the one that best completes each of the following sentences. Write the word in the space provided.

1. Every entertainer likes a(n) _____ **responsive** _____ audience that shows it appreciates and enjoys a performance.

2. Good employees don't need a(n) _____ **taskmaster** _____ to keep them working.

3. I would like to _____ **accommodate** _____ you, but I don't think it is right to allow you to copy my homework.

4. We learned in our science class how _____ **upheaval** _____ of the earth's crust has resulted in the formation of mountains.

5. When we visited New York City, we bought a small _____ **replica** _____ of the Statue of Liberty as a memento of our trip.

6. In just a few years, she was _____ **transformed** _____ from an awkward tomboy into a charming young woman.

7. A portion of the forest has been set aside as a bird _____ **sanctuary** _____ for the protection of endangered species in the area.

8. I love basketball games, but I have decided to _____ **abstain** _____ from attending them until I can get my grades up to where they should be.

9. On Memorial Day, Americans gather in ceremonies across the country to _____ **commemorate** _____ the nation's war dead.

10. Imagine how _____ **glum** _____ we felt when a sudden wave of warm weather melted all the snow and ruined our plans for a winter carnival!

11. Under the U.S. Constitution, officials are never _____ **exalted** _____ to a point where they are more important or more powerful than the law.

12. Anne usually seems to be quiet and _____ **submissive** _____, but she has a way of flaring up when she feels that anyone is being unfair to her.

13. Is there anything more despicable than trying to _____ **extort** _____ money from innocent people by threatening them with bodily harm?

14. When Ben Franklin said, "God helps those who help themselves," he did not mean that the most important thing in life is to be _____ **self-seeking** _____.

15. I enjoyed the first part of the detective story, but the surprise ending was so _____ **far-fetched** _____ that I couldn't accept it.

16. I know that Mother has given you all kinds of instructions before you leave for camp, but let me _____ **append** _____ some extra advice of my own.

17. Can you see why it was logical for various labor unions in the clothing and textile industries to _____ **amalgamate** _____ into a single organization?

18. Though an injured hand kept Larry from actually bowling, he took part in the tournament by keeping a careful _____tally_____ of the scores.

19. Remember that the Pledge of _____Allegiance_____ is not a formula to be repeated mechanically but a summary of our sacred duty to our country.

20. The driving instructor _____enumerated_____ carefully the bad habits and practices that are likely to lead to accidents.

Synonyms

*Choose the word from this unit that is **the same** or **most nearly the same** in meaning as the **boldface** word or expression in the given phrase. Write the word on the line provided.*

1. elevated as a standard of beauty — exalted

2. as **specified** on the packing slip — enumerated

3. that **imitation** of a Picasso sculpture — replica

4. an arrogant and **opportunistic** person — self-seeking

5. lit candles in the quiet **shrine** — sanctuary

6. fear of displeasing the **overseer** — taskmaster

7. has clearly proven his **devotion** — allegiance

8. chose to **refrain** from voting — abstain

9. to **house** an exchange student from Senegal — accommodate

10. forgotten amidst the **disruption** of moving — upheaval

11. how to **coerce** innocent victims — extort

12. made her feel so **dejected** — glum

13. may **convert** it into a family resort — transform

14. if we **total** up all the book orders — tally

15. always **receptive** to new ideas — responsive

Antonyms

*Choose the word from this unit that is **most nearly opposite** in meaning to the **boldface** word or expression in the given phrase. Write the word on the line provided.*

16. questioning such a **likely** conclusion — far-fetched

17. separate the two chemical elements — amalgamate

18. meant to be **detached** — appended

19. as they usually **overlook** the holiday — commemorate

20. reputation of being a **rebellious** student — submissive

Choosing the Right Word

Circle the **boldface** word that more satisfactorily completes each of the following sentences.

1. Each member of the basketball team was awarded a trophy to (**transform, commemorate**) the championship season.

2. Ms. Wilentz is the kind of manager who does not try to (**extort, exalt**) cooperation from the people under her, but earns it by being a real leader.

3. The detective's suspicion was aroused when the suspect's story failed to (**tally, commemorate**) with the known facts of the case.

4. If you look so (**far-fetched, glum**) just because you can't go to the party, how are you going to react when something really bad happens?

5. In Robert Louis Stevenson's classic story, a chemical potion (**tallies, transforms**) the good Dr. Jekyll into the evil Mr. Hyde.

6. Isn't it a little (**far-fetched, self-seeking**) to suggest that the pollution of our environment is mainly caused by creatures from outer space?

7. Unless the poor people of the country see some hope of improving their lives, there will probably soon be a great social (**sanctuary, upheaval**) there.

8. The Mayor had to choose between (**allegiance, tally**) to his political party and his judgment of what was best for the city.

9. The new hotel is spacious enough to (**accommodate, extort**) large groups of people attending conventions and banquets.

10. Experience has taught me that people who constantly boast about their unselfishness are often secretly quite (**submissive, self-seeking**).

11. Financiers are planning to (**accommodate, amalgamate**) various businesses in the United States and England into one huge multinational corporation.

12. The United States has a long history of providing (**upheaval, sanctuary**) to those fleeing persecution abroad.

13. He enjoys (**abstaining, enumerating**) all the factors that enabled him to rise from poverty to great wealth, but he always omits the very important element of good luck.

14. Since she sets extremely high standards for herself and is always pushing herself to do better, she is her own most severe (**taskmaster, replica**).

15. We cannot have a peaceful and just society so long as any one race is required to be (**responsive, submissive**) to another.

16. I didn't have time to write a letter to Lucy, but I (**appended, enumerated**) a few sentences to my sister's letter, expressing my congratulations.

17. Instead of working so hard to prepare (**replicas, allegiances**) of famous works of art, why don't you try to create something original?

18. Only seven members of the Security Council voted on the resolution; the others (**abstained, appended**).

19. When he felt low, he found that singing (**exalted, amalgamated**) his spirits.

20. It remains to be seen how (**responsive, glum**) the students will be to the new method of teaching mathematics.

Vocabulary in Context

*Read the following passage, in which some of the words you have studied in this unit appear in **boldface** type. Then complete each statement given below the passage by circling the letter of the item that is **the same** or **almost the same** in meaning as the highlighted word.*

"Let the Good Times Roll!"

(Line)

Most American pop music can trace its roots to folk music from many cultures. *Zydeco* music **amalgamates** aspects of French, Native American, German, African, and Caribbean musical styles into a unique new whole. It emerged in Southwest Louisiana as a separate style in the 1940s, but it owes much to the
(5) Creole and Cajun music that came hundreds of years earlier.

Creoles are French-speaking blacks from Louisiana. Creole music was played on fiddle and accordion. Cajuns descended from French settlers—the Acadians— who came to Canada in the 1600s. These pioneers sang old French folk music. When the
(10) British forced the Acadians out of Canada in 1755, many moved to Louisiana. Cajuns, as they became known, settled in the swampy delta. They eked out meager lives fishing and logging.

Clifton Chenier, the late King of Zydeco, coined
(15) the term *zydeco. Les haricots,* pronounced "lay-zariko," is the French word for green beans. An old French saying, "Les haricots sont pas salées" (the beans aren't salty), referred to times when people were so poor they even had to **abstain from** using
(20) salt pork to flavor their beans. Circumstances may have been difficult, but the mood certainly wasn't **glum**! Families would gather for a "La La" (house dance) to celebrate a harvest, a wedding, or any other event. One couldn't help but be **responsive** to the peppy music played on
(25) spoons, fiddles, accordions, washboards, animal bones, and triangles. Adults and children danced and celebrated long into the night.

Buckwheat Zydeco (r.) plays the accordion in Lafayette, Louisiana, while another musician plays a washboard, or *zydeco frottoir.*

Zydeco **accommodates** old Cajun and Creole dance tunes and homey instruments, but was **transformed** by the post-World War II elements of rhythm and blues. Chenier introduced the use of drums and guitars. Zydeco now borrows from country-western,
(30) disco, hip-hop, and reggae. Lyrics now include English along with, or instead of, French. As Zydeco musicians say, "Le bons temps roulez," or "Let the good times roll!"

---

1. The meaning of **amalgamates** (line 2) is
  a. rejects   c. combines
  b. copies   d. borrows

2. Abstain from (line 19) is best defined as
  a. avoid   c. indulge in
  b. escape   d. stop

3. Glum (line 22) most nearly means
  a. bored   c. depressed
  b. restless   d. cheery

4. The meaning of **responsive** (line 24) is
  a. indifferent   c. opposed
  b. receptive   d. insensitive

5. Accommodates (line 27) is best defined as
  a. combines   c. enjoys
  b. respects   d. adapts

6. Transformed (line 28) most nearly means
  a. changed   c. mocked
  b. produced   d. judged

 **Definitions**

Note carefully the spelling, pronunciation, part(s) of speech, and definition(s) of each of the following words. Then write the word in the blank space(s) in the illustrative sentence(s) following. Finally, study the lists of synonyms and antonyms given at the end of each entry.

1. beacon
(bē′ kən)

(*n.*) a light or other signal that warns and guides; a lighthouse; anything that guides or inspires

Sailors returning to port on a dark night search for the glow of a familiar _____**beacon**_____.

SYNONYMS: beam, flare

2. berserk
(bər sərk′)

(*adj., adv.*) violently and destructively enraged

A _____**berserk**_____ gunman terrified the crowd of subway riders.

The wounded lion went _____**berserk**_____ in his cage.

SYNONYMS: (*adj.*) mad, deranged
ANTONYMS: (*adj.*) sane, rational

3. celestial
(sə les′ chəl)

(*adj.*) having to do with the sky or heavens; heavenly; yielding great bliss or happiness

The sun is the brightest _____**celestial**_____ body in our solar system.

SYNONYMS: ethereal, stellar, blissful
ANTONYMS: earthly, terrestrial, infernal

4. chasten
(chā′ sən)

(*v.*) to punish (in order to bring about improvement in behavior, attitude, etc.); to restrain, moderate

Dad knows how to _____**chasten**_____ the stubborn child with a firm but soothing voice.

SYNONYMS: discipline, temper
ANTONYMS: praise, commend, reward

5. confiscate
(kän′ fə skāt)

(*v.*) to seize by authority; to take and keep

The police will _____**confiscate**_____ that car.

SYNONYMS: commandeer, expropriate
ANTONYMS: return, restore

6. data
(dā′ tə)

(*pl. n.*) information; facts, figures, statistics

For math class, we collected _____**data**_____ on the Internet sites students visited during the past week.

7. detract
(di trakt′)

(*v.*) to take away from; reduce in value or reputation

Nothing can _____**detract**_____ from your beauty!

SYNONYMS: subtract from, lower
ANTONYMS: increase, heighten, enhance

8. encounter
(en kaủn' tər)

(*n.*) a meeting (especially one that is unplanned); a meeting of enemies, battle; (*v.*) to meet or come upon

Remember our _____encounter_____ with that skunk?

We might _____encounter_____ other curious visitors to the Crystal Caverns in Virginia.

SYNONYMS: (*n.*) confrontation; (*v.*) happen upon
ANTONYMS: (*v.*) avoid, sidestep

9. epic
(ep' ik)

(*n.*) a long narrative poem (or other literary composition) about the deeds of heroes; an event or movement of great sweep; (*adj.*) on a grand scale, vast, titanic

Beowulf, the English _____epic_____, was written around the year 700.

It describes _____epic_____ struggles between the forces of good and evil.

SYNONYMS: (*n.*) saga, chronicle

10. pantomime
(pan' tə mīm)

(*n.*) a play or story performed without words by actors using only gestures; (*v.*) to express in this way

The very outspoken street performer amused us when she suddenly included _____pantomime_____ in her routine.

We _____pantomime_____ when we're unable to speak.

SYNONYMS: (*n.*) charade, mime show, dumb show

11. pessimist
(pes' ə mist)

(*n.*) one who believes or expects the worst; prophet of doom

A _____pessimist_____ sees a glass as half empty.

SYNONYM: killjoy
ANTONYMS: optimist, Pollyanna

12. precaution
(pri kô' shən)

(*n.*) care taken beforehand; a step or action taken to prevent something from happening

I advise you to take every _____precaution_____ necessary to prevent a household fire.

SYNONYMS: foresight, prudence, safeguard
ANTONYMS: recklessness, heedlessness

13. prosecute
(präs' ə kyüt)

(*v.*) to bring before a court of law for trial; to carry out

She was told she would not be _____prosecuted_____ if she restored the money.

SYNONYMS: put on trial, pursue
ANTONYMS: defend, abandon, give up

14. puncture
(pəŋk' chər)

(*n.*) a small hole made by a sharp object; (*v.*) to make such a hole, pierce

He used a needle to make a small ___puncture___ in the balloon.

I tried not to wince as the hypodermic needle ___punctured___ my skin.

SYNONYM: (*n.*) perforation

15. retaliate
(ri tal′ ē āt)

(*v.*) to get revenge; to strike back for an injury

I would ___retaliate___ for that cheap insult, but I fear it may only make matters worse.

SYNONYMS: avenge, pay back, get even with
ANTONYMS: pardon, forgive, turn the other cheek

16. sham
(sham)

(*adj.*) fake, not genuine; (*n.*) something false pretending to be genuine; a pretender; a decorated pillow covering; (*v.*) to pretend

The play includes a ___sham___ fight scene.

Her claim that she's a princess is a ___sham___ .

Don't ___sham___ an illness in order to miss a day of school.

SYNONYMS: (*adj.*) phony, counterfeit; (*n.*) fraud
ANTONYMS: (*adj.*) authentic, bona fide

17. uncouth
(ən küth′)

(*adj.*) unrefined, crude; awkward or clumsy

Although the quality of his work was good, his ___uncouth___ attitude cost him the job.

SYNONYMS: boorish, graceless
ANTONYMS: refined, polished, graceful, genteel

18. underscore
(ən′ dər skôr)

(*v.*) to draw a line under; to put special emphasis on; (*n.*) a line drawn under something

The dire situation in the hospital's emergency room ___underscores___ the importance of having enough doctors and nurses available.

The word with the ___underscore___ is in Spanish.

SYNONYMS: (*v.*) underline, stress, emphasize, accent
ANTONYMS: (*v.*) downplay, de-emphasize, soft-pedal

19. wholesome
(hōl′ səm)

(*adj.*) healthy; morally and socially sound and good; helping to bring about or preserve good health

He always eats ___wholesome___ foods.

SYNONYMS: nourishing, beneficial
ANTONYMS: harmful, unhealthy, baneful

20. wistful
(wist′ fəl)

(*adj.*) full of melancholy yearning or longing, sad, pensive

Her ___wistful___ look made me sad.

ANTONYMS: cheerful, happy, contented, satisfied

Completing the Sentence

From the words for this unit, choose the one that best completes each of the following sentences. Write the word in the space provided.

1. The police have done their job in arresting the suspect; now it is up to the district attorney to _____ **prosecute** _____ him and prove his guilt.

2. Though many people doubted that the new program would do any real good, I thought it was a very _____ **wholesome** _____ development.

3. Late that afternoon, one of the inmates went _____ **berserk** _____ and totally wrecked the infirmary.

4. Isn't it remarkable that a(n) _____ **epic** _____ poem such as the *Iliad*, written almost 3,000 years ago, still has interest for readers today?

5. Now that we have gathered a vast amount of _____ **data** _____, it is up to us to draw some useful conclusions from all this information.

6. After the war, all the property that had been _____ **confiscated** _____ by the government was turned back to its former owners.

7. Little did I realize when I _____ **encountered** _____ that old man on a lonely beach that this chance meeting would change my life.

8. With a(n) _____ **wistful** _____ expression on his face, the prisoner looked through his cell window at the patch of sky that meant freedom to him.

9. When she said she would "turn the other cheek," she simply meant that she would not _____ **retaliate** _____ for the injury done to her.

10. Freedom of speech is a(n) _____ **sham** _____ and a mockery if it does not apply to people whose opinions are very unpopular.

11. In the old days, whippings and other forms of physical punishment were used to _____ **chasten** _____ student misbehavior, even in college.

12. Nothing can _____ **detract** _____ from the fact that he stood by us in our hour of greatest need.

13. So there I was with a(n) _____ **puncture** _____ in one of my rear tires, on a lonely road, on a dark night, and during a violent rainstorm!

14. In polite society it is considered _____ **uncouth** _____ to balance peas on your knife at the dinner table.

15. My definition of a(n) _____ **pessimist** _____ is someone who worries about the hole in the doughnut and forgets about the cake surrounding it.

16. In ancient times, people gazed at the sky and studied the planets and other _____ **celestial** _____ bodies to predict the future.

17. Before we use the blowtorch in our industrial arts class, we are required to take the _____ **precaution** _____ of wearing goggles.

18. Although he could speak no English, he made us understand by the use of _____ pantomime _____ that he was extremely thirsty.

19. The workbook directions instruct the user to _____ underscore _____ the subject of each sentence in red and the predicate in blue.

20. Over the years, a great many ships have been saved from destruction by that tall _____ beacon _____ standing on the rocky coast.

Synonyms

*Choose the word from this unit that is **the same** or **most nearly the same** in meaning as the **boldface** word or expression in the given phrase. Write the word on the line provided.*

1. if it might **subtract** from its value — detract

2. a brief but awkward **confrontation** — encounter

3. should **emphasize** its safety features — underscore

4. crowds enjoying the **charade** — pantomime

5. sure to certify the **statistics** — data

6. a convincing, yet **phony** excuse — sham

7. due to a small **perforation** — puncture

8. with a strong desire to **avenge** — retaliate

9. took a **beneficial** family vacation — wholesome

10. kept an emergency **flare** in the trunk — beacon

11. had to **discipline** the rookie officer — chasten

12. a sprawling **saga** of pioneer life — epic

13. reasonable **safeguard** against theft — precaution

14. might **commandeer** our boat — confiscate

15. embarrassed by their **boorish** behavior — uncouth

Antonyms

*Choose the word from this unit that is **most nearly opposite** in meaning to the **boldface** word or expression in the given phrase. Write the word on the line provided.*

16. anticipated your **rational** behavior — berserk

17. forced to **abandon** the case — prosecute

18. watching the family's **cheerful** encounter — wistful

19. **optimists** who always share their views — pessimists

20. decorated with **earthly** figures — celestial

Choosing the Right Word

*Circle the **boldface** word that more satisfactorily completes each of the following sentences.*

1. The youth center that the charity organized was like a (**precaution, beacon**) to many young people desperately needing help and guidance.

2. The child gazed (**wistfully, wholesomely**) at the shiny toys in the store window.

3. Is it right to (**retaliate, confiscate**) against an evil act by performing evil acts of one's own?

4. Marie is not really pretty, but her sparkling personality and (**wholesome, berserk**) charm make her very attractive.

5. Many a perfectly healthy employee has been known to (**retaliate, sham**) illness to avoid going to work.

6. For some strange reason, the photocopier suddenly went (**berserk, wistful**) and started spewing vast quantities of paper all over the floor.

7. The report that he sent to the president of the company (**underscored, retaliated**) the need for better planning and more careful use of funds.

8. The settlement of the American West is one of the great (**pantomimes, epics**) of world history.

9. Our driving instructor has emphasized that the use of seat belts is not a "silly" (**encounter, precaution**) but a surefire way of saving lives.

10. The Bible tells us that the Lord is like a stern but loving parent, and that "whom He loveth, He (**chasteneth, detracteth**)."

11. During the long years of defeat, Lincoln searched for a general who would (**prosecute, underscore**) the war fearlessly until the Union was saved.

12. Her writing style is a little (**celestial, uncouth**), but what it lacks in polish and refinement is more than made up for by its wonderful humor.

13. The trouble with being a(n) (**underscore, pessimist**) is that you are so taken up with what is going wrong that you are unaware of what is going right.

14. It does not (**prosecute, detract**) in the least from his reputation as a great player to say that all the team members deserve equal credit.

15. Before we can plan properly for the upcoming school year, we must have accurate (**beacons, data**) on the results of last year's programs.

16. The news that I had been dropped from the football squad (**detracted, punctured**) my dream of becoming a great gridiron hero.

17. She had such a (**celestial, sham**) expression on her face that I thought she'd seen a vision of heaven.

18. As I watched through the soundproof hospital window, the skaters on the pond seemed to be carrying out a colorful (**pantomime, epic**).

19. If you try to smuggle goods into this country without paying the customs duties, the inspectors may (**puncture, confiscate**) the goods and fine you.

20. I knew that it would be difficult to raise funds for the recycling program, but I never expected to (**chasten, encounter**) so many tough problems.

Vocabulary in Context

*Read the following passage, in which some of the words you have studied in this unit appear in **boldface** type. Then complete each statement given below the passage by circling the letter of the item that is **the same** or **almost the same** in meaning as the highlighted word.*

Making a Difference

(Line)

Old-timers in Everett, Washington grew **wistful** when they recalled Pigeon Creek running "red with salmon." The fish once swam freely through its clear, fresh waters. But over the years, people threw dirt, garbage, and old motor oil into it, making Pigeon Creek into a muddy trash dump.

Students and teachers at Jackson Elementary School, near Pigeon Creek, (5) decided to do something. They were determined to **prosecute** an ambitious project they named Operation Pigeon Creek. They vowed to clean up the creek. They hauled garbage, posted "No Dumping" signs, wrote letters, handed out leaflets, and worked to make the community aware of their mission. They hoped that one day Pigeon Creek would become the (10) **wholesome** waterway it once was.

Silver salmon in Tongass National Forest, Alaska

The entire school took part. Younger kids studied the life cycle of salmon. They learned how water gets polluted and how it can be made cleaner. Older students did research on fresh water ecology (15) and learned to use water-testing equipment. They studied scientific **data** from Pigeon Creek.

Not everyone in the area supported Operation Pigeon Creek. Some believed that it was a waste of school time, energy, and funds. Even if Pigeon (20) Creek did get cleaner, it would never stay that way long enough for salmon to return, according to local **pessimists**. But the students would not give up. They tended a large fish tank in which they hatched and raised young salmon to release into Pigeon Creek. The project lasted the entire school year. (25)

One day, after more than twenty years as a nearly dead stream, Pigeon Creek welcomed back salmon. The first student to **encounter** a returning salmon nearly burst with excitement! News spread fast. The success story appeared on television, in magazines, and in newspapers. You can read about it in the Sierra Club book, *Come Back, Salmon,* by Molly Cone. (30)

---

1. The meaning of **wistful** (line 1) is
a. satisfied   c. angry
b. ashamed   d. sad

2. Prosecute (line 6) most nearly means
a. punish   c. pursue
b. emphasize   d. abandon

3. Wholesome (line 11) is best defined as
a. healthy   c. harmful
b. partial   d. complete

4. The meaning of **data** (line 17) is
a. meetings   c. papers
b. facts   d. lessons

5. Pessimists (line 23) most nearly means
a. believers   c. killjoys
b. dreamers   d. officials

6. Encounter (line 27) is best defined as
a. catch   c. raise
b. come upon   d. describe

Analogies

In each of the following, circle the item that best completes the comparison.

See pages T38–T48 for explanations of answers.

1. pin is to **puncture** as
a. saw is to chop
b. knife is to cut ⟵
c. rope is to release
d. ax is to drench

2. beacon is to **light** as
a. show is to foot
b. mailbox is to letter
c. hydrant is to water ⟵
d. step is to ladder

3. allegiance is to **adhere** as
a. time is to avoid
b. support is to dislike
c. blessing is to approve ⟵
d. consent is to refuse

4. data are to **inform** as
a. jokes are to amuse ⟵
b. headlines are to confuse
c. directions are to entertain
d. ideas are to puzzle

5. defeat is to **glum** as
a. setback is to joyful
b. victory is to jubilant ⟵
c. failure is to happy
d. success is to sulky

6. amazement is to **stupefy** as
a. praise is to chasten
b. confusion is to bewilder ⟵
c. boredom is to enthuse
d. puzzlement is to exalt

7. underscore is to **line** as
a. tally is to arrow
b. encircle is to ring ⟵
c. box is to triangle
d. check is to dot

8. wholesome is to **favorable** as
a. far-fetched is to unfavorable ⟵
b. self-seeking is to favorable
c. responsive is to unfavorable
d. glum is to favorable

9. boor is to **uncouth** as
a. celebrity is to unknown
b. genius is to unthinking
c. star is to unpopular
d. savage is to uncivilized ⟵

10. celestial is to **heaven** as
a. marine is to sky
b. colonial is to sea
c. terrestrial is to earth ⟵
d. urban is to country

11. monument is to **commemorate** as
a. trash basket is to guide
b. lamppost is to deter
c. crosswalk is to transform
d. milestone is to mark ⟵

12. cat is to **prowl** as
a. horse is to neigh
b. goat is to butt
c. ostrich is to fly
d. snake is to slither ⟵

13. audition is to **hear** as
a. preview is to see ⟵
b. misapprehension is to know
c. sanctuary is to feel
d. pantomime is to touch

14. supplement is to **more** as
a. append is to less
b. cope is to more
c. detract is to less ⟵
d. lag is to more

15. epic is to **deeds** as
a. lyric is to emotions ⟵
b. novel is to desires
c. play is to goals
d. opera is to ambitions

16. disquieting is to **disturb** as
a. boring is to delight
b. amazing is to depress
c. astounding is to stupefy ⟵
d. heartrending is to amuse

17. optimist is to **pessimist** as
a. trait is to characteristic
b. original is to replica ⟵
c. outrage is to atrocity
d. sham is to fake

18. crook is to **unscrupulous** as
a. swindler is to berserk
b. optimist is to glum
c. diplomat is to uncouth
d. manipulator is to self-seeking ⟵

Word Associations

In each of the following groups, circle the word that is best defined or suggested by the given phrase.

1. an exact reproduction of an aircraft carrier
(a. replica)   b. trait   c. sanctuary   d. epic

2. joined the competing companies to form one huge business organization
(a. amalgamate)   b. affirm   c. exalt   d. accommodate

3. a rush of energy
(a. surge)   b. audition   c. epic   d. pantomime

4. "Unless you pay me $500, I'm going to make trouble for you."
a. adhere   (b. extort)   c. enumerate   d. underscore

5. a measure taken in advance to prevent an accident
(a. precaution)   b. allegiance   c. puncture   d. encounter

6. great disorder and dislocation caused by a revolution
a. sham   (b. upheaval)   c. sanctuary   d. beacon

7. The knights swore lifelong loyalty to King Richard the Lion-hearted.
a. beacon   (b. allegiance)   c. tally   d. trait

8. My poor bicycle is damaged beyond recognition.
a. deterred   (b. mangled)   c. punctured   d. pantomimed

9. Before we make a decision, we must have all the facts.
a. tally   (b. data)   c. atrocity   d. misapprehension

10. She speaks French like a native.
a. celestial   b. responsive   (c. fluent)   d. uncouth

11. walked the streets of the city searching for helpless victims
a. surge   b. deter   (c. prowl)   d. retaliate

12. At 2:30, actors will have a chance to try out for different parts.
(a. audition)   b. pantomime   c. supplement   d. mangle

13. wishing for a place of refuge from the crazy world
a. taskmaster   b. replica   c. atrocity   (d. sanctuary)

14. That man does not seem to have any morals when it comes to business.
a. submissive   b. glum   (c. unscrupulous)   d. wistful

15. "That costly failure taught me that I'm not as smart as I thought I was."
(a. chasten)   b. accommodate   c. surge   d. fluent

16. He is only interested in people for what he can get out of them.
a. sulky   b. berserk   c. disquieting   (d. self-seeking)

17. How she longed to see her childhood home!
a. responsive   b. submissive   (c. wistful)   d. sulky

18. "Things are bad, and all the signs are that they're going to get worse."
(a. pessimist)   b. taskmaster   c. beacon   d. optimist

19. what a district attorney does with a legal case
a. commemorate   (b. prosecute)   c. confiscate   d. enumerate

20. acted out in silence
a. atrocity   b. encounter   (c. pantomime)   d. precaution

Vocabulary in Context

*Read the following passage, in which some of the words you have studied in Units 13–15 appear in **boldface** type. Then complete each statement given below the passage by circling the item that is **the same** or **almost the same** in meaning as the highlighted word.*

(Line)

What "Lead" to Goya's Illnesses

The masterful Spanish painter Francisco de Goya (1746–1828) **coped with** strange bouts of illness in his life. Might his illness have
(5) explained the dramatic changes in his work? His early paintings were gentle and bright. His graceful portraits were lovely. But over time, his work grew dark and moody. He
(10) began to paint angry scenes in thick dark colors. Art historians have long debated the reasons for this shift in Goya's style. Could it have been his health?
(15) Modern science has evidence to suggest that Goya may have had a severe case of lead poisoning. High levels of lead in the bloodstream can cause muscle and joint pains,
(20) headaches, hearing loss, dizziness, mental distress, nausea, **berserk** conduct, personality changes and, finally, death. This list **tallies** with the catalog of symptoms that Goya
(25) sadly suffered.

Goya's **disquieting** symptoms forced him to take breaks from painting. When he felt well enough to return to painting, he would rush
(30) back to his studio. There he would grind pigments again and paint enthusiastically to make up for the **lag** in his output.

Like most artists of the past, Goya
(35) made his paints himself. Grinding the pigments put him at risk to inhale lead dust, and to get it in his eyes, mouth, ears and on his skin. Goya was known to use an unusual amount
(40) of a pigment called lead white. It gave his works their characteristic pearly glow. But it also made him sick. Although other artists risked lead poisoning, few used as much
(45) lead white as Goya did.

It no longer seems **far-fetched** to think that Goya's physical condition changed his artistic vision. One can only wonder how modern medical
(50) knowledge might have prevented his illness and allowed him to express his later genius.

---

1. The meaning of **coped with** (line 3) is
a. laughed at   c. avoided
b. dealt with   d. discovered

2. Berserk (line 21) most nearly means
a. rational   c. deranged
b. boorish   d. merry

3. Tallies (line 23) is best defined as
a. degrades   c. merges
b. corresponds   d. astonishes

4. The meaning of **disquieting** (line 26) is
a. quiet   c. surprising
b. hidden   d. disturbing

5. Lag (line 33) most nearly means
a. delay   c. glut
b. belief   d. disappointment

6. Far-fetched (line 46) is best defined as
a. plausible   c. improbable
b. sympathetic   d. selfish

Choosing the Right Meaning

Read each sentence carefully. Then circle the item that best completes the statement below the sentence.

See pages T38–T48 for explanations of answers.

Flashing a sham police shield, the brazen intruder waltzed through the security checkpoint. (2)

1. The word **sham** in line 1 is used to mean

a. genuine   b. plastic   c. fake   d. expired

When civil war broke out in 1861, tens of thousands were responsive to calls for volunteers that issued from Washington and Richmond. (2)

2. The phrase **were responsive to** in line 1 most nearly means

a. received   b. understood   c. appreciated   d. answered

An encounter in 1959 between Vice President Nixon and Soviet Premier Nikita Khruschev over the merits of the market economy has come to be known as the "kitchen debate." (2)

3. In line 1 the word **encounter** most nearly means

a. confrontation   b. agreement   c. chance meeting   d. brawl

When men first walked on the moon on July 20, 1969, the newspapers across the country published supplements devoted to the historic event. (2)

4. In line 2 the word **supplements** is best defined as

a. extra sections   b. photographs   c. editorials   d. articles

Who would have guessed that the discovery of a minor break-in at the Watergate complex would lead to a scandal of such epic proportions? (2)

5. In line 2 the word **epic** is best defined as

a. poetic   b. vast   c. fantastic   d. tragic

Antonyms

*In each of the following groups, circle the word or expression that is most nearly the **opposite** of the word in **boldface** type.*

1. submissive
a. foreign
b. defiant
c. trustworthy
d. intelligent

2. detract from
a. change
b. enhance
c. study
d. hurt

3. prosecute
a. defend
b. arrest
c. try
d. jail

4. empower
a. authorize
b. forbid
c. strengthen
d. abandon

5. disquieting
a. disturbing
b. unexpected
c. comforting
d. latest

6. far-fetched
a. lame
b. plausible
c. wordy
d. foolish

7. exalted
a. pleasant
b. new
c. lowly
d. high

8. glum
a. cheerful
b. strange
c. sad
d. typical

9. affirm
a. examine
b. describe
c. defend
d. deny ⟵ (circled)

11. uncouth
a. criminal
b. strange
c. silly
d. genteel ⟵ (circled)

13. amalgamate
a. divide ⟵ (circled)
b. merge
c. devour
d. forbid

15. transformed
a. ruined
b. empty
c. preserved ⟵ (circled)
d. improved

10. atrocities
a. crimes
b. supplies
c. fatalities
d. kindnesses ⟵ (circled)

12. deter
a. finance
b. encourage ⟵ (circled)
c. study
d. stop

14. wholesome
a. harmful ⟵ (circled)
b. recent
c. surprising
d. desirable

16. celestial
a. heavenly
b. beautiful
c. infernal ⟵ (circled)
d. invisible

Word Families

A. *On the line provided, write the word you have learned in Units 13–15 that is related to each of the following nouns.*

EXAMPLE: glumness—**glum**

1. exaltation — exalt
2. appendage, appendix — append
3. affirmation, affirmative — affirm
4. deterrent, deterrence — deter
5. prowler — prowl
6. accommodation, accommodator, accommodativeness — accommodate
7. unscrupulousness — unscrupulous
8. adherent, adherence, adhesive — adhere
9. fluency — fluent
10. abstention, abstainer, abstinence — abstain
11. sulkiness — sulky
12. supplementation — supplement
13. affirmation — affirm
14. commemoration — commemorate
15. stupefaction — stupefy

B. *On the line provided, write the word you have learned in Units 13–15 that is related to each of the following verbs.*

EXAMPLE: audit—**audition**

16. replicate — replica
17. respond — responsive
18. submit — submissive
19. misapprehend — misapprehension
20. sulk — sulky

Two-Word Completions

Circle the pair of words that best complete the meaning of each of the following passages.

See pages T38–T48 for explanations of answers.

1. The _____ who had been lurking very suspiciously around the neighborhood was caught in the act of breaking into our house. The police _____ the set of burglar's tools that he had with him as evidence to back up the charges against him.
   - a. prowler . . . confiscated
   - b. optimist . . . underscored
   - c. sham . . . mangled
   - d. pessimist . . . enumerated

2. It's difficult to _____ all the reasons I like him because he has so many excellent _____.
   - a. pantomime . . . epics
   - b. enumerate . . . traits
   - c. puncture . . . data
   - d. amalgamate . . . lags

3. To say our new boss is a _____ is one thing. But you are wrong to say that you believe she is making us work very hard to _____ for past wrongs that were done to her.
   - a. sham . . . prosecute
   - b. atrocity . . . mangle
   - c. pessimist . . . exhort
   - d. taskmaster . . . retaliate

4. There's a wise old saying that a(n) _____ sees a partially filled glass of water as half full, while a _____ sees the same glass of water as half empty.
   - a. taskmaster . . . sham
   - b. optimist . . . pessimist
   - c. replica . . . tally
   - d. trait . . . beacon

5. The *Iliad*, Homer's famous _____ poem about the Trojan War, opens with the hero, Achilles, _____ moodily in his tent because he has not been accorded the proper reward for his brave deeds.
   - a. celestial . . . prowling
   - b. disquieting . . . shamming
   - c. epic . . . sulking
   - d. berserk . . . lagging

6. "The only way we are going to _____ people from driving a car while drunk," the speaker observed, "is to impose stiff penalties on such behavior and _____ offenders to the full extent of the law."
   - a. empower . . . accommodate
   - b. detract . . . chasten
   - c. exalt . . . puncture
   - d. deter . . . prosecute

Building with Classical Roots

pre—before

This prefix appears in **precaution** (page 111). Some other words in which this prefix appears are listed below.

prearrange	**prefer**	**preliminary**	**preoccupy**
precise	**prehistoric**	**premature**	**preside**

From the list of words above, choose the one that corresponds to each of the brief definitions below. Write the word in the blank space in the illustrative sentence below the definition.

1. to absorb one's attention completely or at the expense of other things

She was so ___preoccupied___ with the novel that she forgot to return my phone call.

2. belonging to the period before written history

The museum has a fascinating new exhibit that explains how scientists identify and classify the bones of ___prehistoric___ animals.

3. very definite or clear, exact; very careful; strict

The doctor left ___precise___ instructions on how to clean, dress, and care for the wound to avoid infection.

4. coming before the main business or action; introductory; something that comes before the main event, a "curtain-raiser"

Although the young boxer lost the ___preliminary___ bout, knowledgeable fans could readily see that he had promise.

5. to arrange ahead of time

One important task of a travel agent is to ___prearrange___ transportation and accommodations in order that the client can focus on enjoying the trip.

6. to like better, choose over something else; to put forward, press

Although many customers ___prefer___ to order healthy appetizers and main courses, restaurant owners report an increased interest in rich desserts.

7. to have authority over, oversee

Tomorrow is the first opportunity our principal will have to ___preside___ at the community school board meeting.

8. unexpectedly early in development; coming too soon

The expectant mother was alerted to the possibility of a ___premature___ birth, so she took extra good care of herself.

From the list of words on page 177, choose the one that best completes each of the following sentences. Write the word in the blank space provided.

1. The police decided to _____**prefer**_____ charges again the driver of one of the vehicles involved in the accident on Highway 11.

2. Cave paintings, deserted dwellings, and artifacts found in the Southwest are the only traces that remain of certain _____**prehistoric**_____ American Indian cultures.

3. Article I, Section 3, Clause 4 of the United States Constitution calls for the Vice President to _____**preside**_____ over the Senate, but not to vote except to break a tie.

4. They claimed that their meeting was accidental and unplanned, but the investigation later confirmed that they had in fact _____**prearranged**_____ it.

5. Although polls suggested an upset in the making, analysts cautioned that it would be _____**premature**_____ to declare the underdog the winner.

6. The thieves were so _____**preoccupied**_____ with dividing up the loot that they failed to notice that the police had surrounded their hideout.

7. The directions for assembling the bicycle were so _____**precise**_____ that we had no difficulty at all in putting it together.

8. A _____**preliminary**_____ hearing was held to determine whether there was sufficient evidence to try the accused.

---

*Circle the **boldface** word that more satisfactorily completes each of the following sentences.*

1. The (**premature, precise**) frost that damaged the citrus trees affected hundreds of groves in the region.

2. Most first-time airline passengers (**preoccupy, prefer**) a window seat to enjoy the view, but frequent flyers report that they find aisle seats to be more comfortable and convenient.

3. To honor the couple on their twentieth wedding anniversary, family members chipped in to (**prearrange, preside**) an elegant night on the town for the happy pair.

4. Musicians do not know for sure how (**prehistoric, premature**) music may have sounded, but archaeologists do have an assortment of ancient instruments that can offer clues.

5. The babysitter was totally (**prearranged, preoccupied**) with chatting on the phone, so we never hired him again.

6. It is the duty of the shop steward to (**preside, prefer**) over informal hearings that address issues of concern to his co-workers in the factory.

7. The (**prehistoric, preliminary**) findings suggest that new treatments may hold promise for the future, but doctors advise patients not to get their hopes up too soon.

8. "Smart" weapons are highly technical devices that allow trained users to plan extremely (**precise, preliminary**) strikes against desired targets.

Writer's Challenge

Read the following sentences, paying special attention to the words and phrases underlined. From the words in the box below, find better choices for these underlined words and phrases. Then use these choices to rewrite the sentences.

WORD BANK

abstain	audition	commemorate	enumerate	submissive
adhere	beacon	confiscate	fluent	supplement
affirm	berserk	empower	optimist	trait
allegiance	chasten	encounter	responsive	transform

The Meaning of a Special Pledge

1. Do young people truly grasp what they are saying when they promise <u>fidelity</u> "to the flag of the United States of America and to the republic for which it stands"?
allegiance

2. This pledge first appeared in the September 8, 1892 issue of *The Youth's Companion,* a once-popular family magazine. It was written to <u>state positively</u> the importance of raising of the flag at public school celebrations on Columbus Day.
affirm

3. It is estimated that more than ten million students recited the Pledge that day to <u>honor</u> the 400th anniversary of Columbus discovering America.
commemorate

4. Francis Bellamy of Rome, New York, who wrote the pledge, probably never imagined Americans to be so <u>sympathetic</u> to his words.
responsive

5. Bellamy envisioned a <u>guiding signal</u> to America's youth to support the essential American ideals of "liberty and justice for all."
beacon

6. Since then, Bellamy's Pledge has been <u>added to</u> with two revisions—in 1923 and in 1954—resulting in the words we recite today.
supplemented

7. Hopefully, Americans will always <u>be devoted</u> to the spirit of those words by supporting all that is great about our nation.
adhere

Analogies

In each of the following, circle the item that best completes the comparison.

See pages T38–T48 for explanations of answers.

1. surge is to **forward** as
a. billow is to back
b. deter is to forward
c. recede is to back
d. constrain is to forward

2. wistful is to **sadness** as
a. glum is to gloom
b. sheepish is to confidence
c. sluggish is to speed
d. frigid is to warmth

3. stupefy is to **dumbfounded** as
a. infuriate is to jubilant
b. motivate is to chastened
c. delude is to resourceful
d. irk is to irritated

4. berserk is to **control** as
a. logical is to clarity
b. numb is to sensation
c. nimble is to skill
d. dogged is to persistence

5. adapter is to **transform** as
a. hammer is to puncture
b. compactor is to compress
c. foil is to conserve
d. manacle is to topple

6. rigorous is to **stamina** as
a. adverse is to sincerity
b. inevitable is to discretion
c. gross is to initiative
d. intensive is to concentration

7. prowl is to **stealthy** as
a. amble is to hasty
b. saunter is to leisurely
c. maneuver is to inept
d. lag is to strident

8. adhere is to **forsake** as
a. amalgamate is to partition
b. avenge is to retaliate
c. prevaricate is to dissect
d. waylay is to liberate

9. allegiance is to **devoted** as
a. support is to disinterested
b. ingenuity is to arid
c. fidelity is to faithful
d. favor is to submissive

10. sulky is to **resentment** as
a. contrite is to remorse
b. responsive is to boredom
c. jovial is to anger
d. boisterous is to contentment

Choosing the Right Meaning

Read each sentence carefully. Then circle the item that best completes the statement below the sentence.

See pages T38–T48 for explanations of answers.

I didn't realize that the history text I had purchased was a used one until I opened it and found underscores on every other page. (2)

1. In line 2 the word **underscores** is defined as
a. overrulings   b. mistakes   c. notes   d. underlinings

Can you name the artist who prophesied that in the future everyone would experience a dole of fame—15 minutes' worth, to be exact? (2)

2. The word **dole** in line 2 is used to mean
a. small portion   b. handout   c. allowance   d. staggering amount

Scattered over the Gettysburg battlefield are monuments exalting the men—both Southerner and Yankee—who fought and died there. (2)

3. The word **exalting** in line 1 most nearly means
a. elevating   b. honoring   c. uplifting   d. naming

"The breeze with sea commenced to flirt
And ruffles trimmed the water's skirt." (A. E. Glug, "Flotsam and Jetsam")   (2)

4. The best definition for the word **ruffles** in line 2 is

a. driftwood   b. sand castles   (c. ripples)   d. seaweed

The opening scene of the pay is set in a run-down waterfront saloon frequented
by hoodlums and petty thieves.   (2)

5. In line 2, the word **petty** most nearly means

a. narrow-minded   b. piddling   c. big-time   (d. small-time)

Two-Word Completions

*Circle the pair of words that best complete the meaning
of each of the following sentences.*

See pages T38–T48 for explanations of answers.

1. The district attorney decided not to _____ the case when it
became clear that the evidence against the accused was too slight to win anything
but his _____ .

(a. prosecute . . . acquittal)   c. supplement . . . compliance
b. formulate . . . reimbursement   d. implement . . . ingratitude

2. There were so many _____ on both sides during the battle of
Antietam that it was the _____ conflict of the Civil War.

a. enigmas . . . smuggest   (c. fatalities . . . goriest)
b. setbacks . . . pettiest   d. assailants . . . eeriest

3. Some modern scientists believe that the _____ with which a gigantic
meteor crashed into the Earth millions of years ago set off the chain of events that led to
the _____ of the dinosaurs and the close of the Age of Reptiles.

a. misgivings . . . diversity   c. leeway . . . duration
(b. impact . . . extinction)   d. precaution . . . affluence

4. In classical times, the great temple of Apollo at Dephi housed the most famous
_____ in all Greece. Deep within the confines of this ancient
_____ , a priestess sitting on a golden tripod revealed the will of
the gods to all who sought her assistance.

a. sage . . . queue   c. beacon . . . fossil
b. panorama . . . terrain   (d. oracle . . . sanctuary)

5. According to Greek myth, Theseus was able to find his way back out of the
Labyrinth, a(n) _____ of passages and galleries built to house a
fearful monster, by following a(n) _____ of wool that he had slowly
unrolled from a large ball as he penetrated deeper and deeper into the bowels of the
confusing building.

a. rendezvous . . . barrage   (c. maze . . . strand)
b. format . . . earmark   d. agenda . . . facet

Enriching Your Vocabulary

Read the passage below. Then complete the exercise at the bottom of the page.

Myths Become Facts

The religions of ancient Greece and ancient Rome were crowded with gods and goddesses. The stories of these beings and their deeds are called *myths*, which inspired both awe and fear.

We often unknowingly refer to these mythical beings. For example, *Zeus*, the king of the gods in Greek mythology, was renamed *Jupiter*, or *Jove* by the ancient Roman religion. The

From left: Neptune, Uranus, Saturn, and Jupiter

word *jovial* (Unit 8) originally meant "to be like Jove" and over time has come to mean good-humored.

The ancient Greeks and ancient Romans were careful observers of the stars and planets. Jupiter, like the planets *Mercury, Venus, Mars, Saturn, Neptune*, and *Pluto* are named for Roman gods.

Centuries later, American scientists set out to reach the *titanic* (Unit 12) goal of landing a person on the moon and returning him safely to Earth. Mercury, the Roman god known for his speed, inspired the name of the first manned space project. The series of flights that actually took us to the moon was named after *Apollo*, the Greek god of prophecy, music, and healing. The

Apollo missions proved that space exploration is humanly possible, not just the stuff of myths and legends.

In Column A are 8 more words and names with roots in Greek and Roman mythology. Match each word with its meaning in Column B.

Column A

_g_	**1.** January
_a_	**2.** June
_d_	**3.** Athens
_h_	**4.** lunar
_e_	**5.** Europe
_c_	**6.** herculean
_b_	**7.** tantalize
_f_	**8.** museum

Column B

a. month named for Juno, the queen of Roman gods

b. to torment; the word comes from the plight of Tantalus, who was condemned to endure constant hunger and thirst

c. having great size, strength, or courage, such as that of the Greek god Hercules

d. city named for Athena, Greek goddess of wisdom

e. continent named for the princess Europa, whom the Greek god Zeus admired and pursued

f. where objects of art or wisdom are displayed, inspired by the Muses, Greek goddesses of art and science

g. month named for Janus, the Roman god of beginnings

h. having to do with the moon, after Luna, the Roman moon goddess

Selecting Word Meanings

*In each of the following groups, circle the word or expression that is **most nearly the same** in meaning as the word in **boldface** type in the given phrase.*

1. a **deluge** of congratulations
   a. shortage   b. trickle   (c. flood)   d. absence

2. provided the necessary **data**
   (a. information)   b. money   c. assistance   d. equipment

3. showed more **grit** than anyone else
   a. judgment   b. fear   (c. courage)   d. restlessness

4. an **instantaneous** decision
   (a. immediate)   b. poor   c. delayed   d. wise

5. a **gory** movie
   a. foreign   b. new   (c. bloody)   d. funny

6. found him **dawdling**
   (a. loafing)   b. working   c. fighting   d. napping

7. **restricted** his activities
   (a. limited)   b. widened   c. guided   d. ended

8. a **serene** mountain lake
   (a. peaceful)   b. polluted   c. cold   d. large

9. a skilled **mimic**
   a. athlete   b. politician   c. speaker   (d. imitator)

10. met with **scant** success
    a. much   (b. little)   c. popular   d. sudden

11. keep as a **memento**
    (a. reminder)   b. safeguard   c. pet   d. ornament

12. pay the **arrears**
    (a. overdue debts)   b. prices   c. fines   d. taxes

13. a **parody** of justice
    (a. mockery)   b. example   c. cause   d. fear

14. corrected the **misapprehension**
    a. plan   b. formula   c. examination   (d. misunderstanding)

15. **scour** the countryside
    a. visit   (b. search)   c. guard   d. invade

16. had many **misgivings**
    a. setbacks   (b. doubts)   c. victories   d. presents

17. **confronted** my accuser
    a. avoided   b. attacked   (c. faced)   d. ignored

18. an **arid** discussion
    a. informative   (b. barren)   c. heated   d. quiet

19. denounce as a traitor

a. seize   b. betray   c. sentence   (d. condemn)

20. the inevitable result

a. sudden   (b. unavoidable)   c. regrettable   d. unexpected

21. appended her signature

a. forged   (b. added)   c. erased   d. examined

22. read the synopsis

a. report   (b. summary)   c. editorial   d. advertisement

23. played a sluggish game

a. new   (b. slow)   c. winning   d. brilliant

24. the onset of the battle

a. conclusion   b. scene   (c. beginning)   d. noise

25. managed to retrieve the ball

a. inflate   (b. recover)   c. lose   d. buy

Antonyms

*In each of the following groups, circle the **two** words that are **most nearly opposite** in meaning.*

26. (a. affluence)   b. diversity   c. strife   (d. poverty)

27. (a. clarity)   b. trait   (c. murkiness)   d. sham

28. a. empower   (b. conserve)   (c. squander)   d. underscore

29. (a. abstain)   b. confiscate   (c. indulge)   d. enumerate

30. (a. strident)   b. responsive   c. incalculable   (d. mellow)

31. a. rotund   (b. compliant)   c. boisterous   (d. disobedient)

32. (a. skillful)   (b. bumbling)   c. optional   d. taut

33. a. inhabitant   b. oaf   (c. pacifist)   (d. warmonger)

34. a. expend   b. pacify   (c. occupy)   (d. vacate)

35. a. verge   b. deter   (c. idolize)   (d. detest)

36. a. clever   (b. frigid)   c. smug   (d. hot)

37. (a. maximum)   b. giddy   c. celestial   (d. minimum)

38. (a. partisan)   b. petty   c. sinister   (d. impartial)

39. a. douse   (b. relish)   c. adhere   (d. loathe)

40. (a. wither)   b. acquit   (c. thrive)   d. amble

Supplying Words in Context

In each of the following sentences, write on the line provided the most appropriate word chosen from the given list.

Group A

| refute | immense | prevail | gainful |
| delude | vow | maze | debut |

41. His arguments were so soundly based and so well presented that no one could _____refute_____ them.

42. The _____immense_____ distances between stars are measured in light-years.

43. Now that the two candidates have finished their long, hard campaigns, it is up to the voters to say which one will _____prevail_____ .

44. Let us _____vow_____ to do the very best we can to carry out our duties honestly, efficiently, and humanely.

45. You are just _____deluding_____ yourself if you think you can do well in school without regular, systematic study.

Group B

| keepsake | pantomime | misrepresent | unerring |
| sabotage | rendezvous | sleuth | eerie |

46. My long-awaited _____rendezvous_____ with Eileen turned out to be a terrible flop when she got sick and couldn't make it.

47. In the days of silent movies, actors and actresses had to express ideas and emotions by means of _____pantomime_____ .

48. We have learned by experience that she is so shrewd that her judgments of people are almost _____unerring_____ .

49. What a(n) _____eerie_____ feeling it gave us to listen to ghost stories as we sat around the flickering campfire!

50. I cannot believe that these repeated breakdowns of the machinery are no more than "accidents"; I suspect _____sabotage_____ !

Group C

| fray | epic | tally | subordinate |
| taskmaster | puncture | compact | allegiance |

51. In big-city apartment houses, where space is very valuable, kitchens are likely to be extremely _____compact_____ .

52. The story of the men who first climbed to the top of Mount Everest is a(n) _____ epic _____ of human courage and strength.

53. Coach Robinson is a strict _____ taskmaster _____, who expects instant obedience and 100% effort from all his players.

54. Only a tiny _____ puncture _____ in the skin showed where the doctor had made the injection.

55. I am grateful to my parents, who have always _____ subordinated _____ their own interests and desires to the well-being of their children.

Words That Are Unfavorable

*The words listed below are **unfavorable** or **negative**. Select the one that applies most suitably to each of the following short descriptive sentences or paragraphs. Write the word on the line provided.*

crotchety	bungle	self-seeking	cringe
libel	ingratitude	gloat	bigot
prevaricate	vandalism	hypocrite	uncouth

56. He is only interested in other people for what he can get out of them.

_____ self-seeking _____

57. In that book, the author made a statement which he knew to be untrue and which was intended to ruin a political career.

_____ libel _____

58. You can't depend on a word he says. He seems to tell lies for the sheer joy of lying.

_____ prevaricate _____

59. As my grandmother used to say, "Anyone with manners that bad must have been raised in a stable."

_____ uncouth _____

60. The mechanic did such a bad job of repairing our car that he actually caused us additional trouble and expense.

_____ bungle _____

61. She sat there with a big smile on her face, obviously enjoying the fact that I was in the most painful situation of my life.

_____ gloat _____

62. For no good reason, someone had tipped over the statue of Washington in the park and had tried to hammer it into pieces.

_____ vandalism _____

63. What do you think of people who have strong prejudices against anyone who differs from them in race, religion, or social background?

_____ bigot _____

64. No one can get along with him. You never know what is going to make him fly off the handle. He can get impossibly cranky fifty times a day.

_____ crotchety _____

65. Some children are not thankful for all that their parents have done for them and are always demanding more.

_____ ingratitude _____

Words That Are Favorable

The words listed below are **favorable** or **positive**. Select the one that applies most suitably to each of the following short descriptive sentences or paragraphs. Write the word on the line provided.

sage	persevere	optimist	initiative
wholesome	disinterested	amiable	fidelity
discretion	acute	strapping	fluent

66. He is a naturally friendly young man, who can get along pleasantly with almost anyone.

_____ amiable _____

67. We greatly admire the sharpness of her mind. She sees right through to the heart of a problem without being misled by secondary matters.

_____ acute _____

68. She takes a positive and upbeat attitude toward life. She believes that most problems can be solved and that things usually work out for the best.

_____ optimist _____

69. We admire her because she can get things started on her own, without being supported or guided by other people.

_____ initiative _____

70. He is faithful to his family and friends, true to his religion, and loyal to his community and his country.

_____ fidelity _____

71. Once he starts something, he keeps at it with all his energy. He won't let himself get discouraged, even when things go wrong.

_____ persevere _____

72. When the judge hears a case, she has only one concern— to arrive at a just and fair decision.

_____ disinterested _____

73. Professor Hahn has had a wide range of experience and has thought deeply about the problems of life. He has much wisdom to give to his students.

_____ sage _____

74. He is a big, husky fellow, with the strength and the stamina of a professional athlete.

_____ strapping _____

75. The reason she is so attractive is that she gives the impression of radiant health, not only physically but also mentally and morally.

_____ wholesome _____

*In each of the following, circle the word or expression that best completes the meaning of the sentence or answers the question, with particular reference to the meaning of the word in **boldface** type.*

76. A habit that is deeply **ingrained** is
a. a bad one
b. hard to change
c. easy to get rid of
d. of no great importance

77. Which of the following would be a **chastening** experience?
a. winning a scholarship
b. going to a party
c. spending the day at the beach
d. doing poorly on this exam

78. a school course dealing with **vocations** will help you
a. plan for a career
b. become a good dancer
c. become a "math shark"
d. develop your speaking ability

79. For what purpose might you join a **queue**?
a. to make new friends
b. to see a hit movie
c. to speak at a school assembly
d. to enjoy a beautiful day

80. A person who **reminisces** a great deal might be criticized for
a. living in the past
b. insulting other people
c. using foul language
d. borrowing money

81. A crisis is said to be **global** if it applies to
a. only one nation
b. almost all the nations of the world
c. big business
d. transportation

82. A basketball player who lacks **stamina** would be likely to
a. miss foul shots
b. tire quickly
c. argue with the referee
d. show a lack of team spirit

83. You would seek **sanctuary** if you were
a. hungry
b. being pursued
c. in the dark
d. rich

84. The word **martial** comes from the name of the Roman god Mars. We can guess from this that Mars was the god of
a. love
b. war
c. good health
d. farming

85. If you were **ravenous**, you might head for a
a. hospital
b. restaurant
c. library
d. skating rink

86. A person who has carried out an **abduction** will probably
a. receive a prize
b. be arrested for kidnapping
c. get a ticket for illegal parking
d. go to the hospital

87. For performing a **valiant** deed, a soldier would probably be
a. transferred
b. given a medal
c. called a coward
d. given a new uniform

88. A person who is generally considered to be an **oracle** should be
a. kept in a closed room
b. put on a diet
c. listened to carefully
d. turned over to the police

89. Which of the following would have **facets**?
   a. a planet
   b. an umbrella
   c. a diamond
   d. a chair

90. If you are in a debating contest and you want to be **logical**, you should
   a. smile a great deal
   b. speak in a loud voice
   c. make fun of your opponents
   d. try to reason accurately

91. Which of the following might be a suitable nickname for a person who is **glum** most of the time?
   a. "Deadeye Dick"
   b. "Waltzing Matilda"
   c. "Dapper Dan"
   d. "Weeping Willie"

92. A **pessimist** is a person who
   a. is sure everything will turn out for the worst
   b. expects the best but is prepared for bad luck
   c. refuses to worry about what the future may bring
   d. depends on fortune-tellers for guidance

93. a student who is lost in a **reverie**
   a. has taken a wrong turn
   b. has a toothache
   c. is daydreaming
   d. is well prepared for final exams

94. If you receive news that is **disquieting** you will probably be
   a. delighted
   b. serene
   c. pleasantly surprised
   d. upset

95. Which of the following are typical of **contemporary** life?
   a. hoopskirts and sun bonnets
   b. TV and computers
   c. colonies in outer space
   d. log cabins

96. A ballplayer would be most likely to receive an **ovation** for
   a. winning a game with a home run
   b. losing a game by striking out
   c. arguing with the umpire
   d. not playing because of an injury

97. Which of the following might best be described by **saunter**?
   a. a 50-yard run for a touchdown
   b. a stroll in the park
   c. a mad dash to catch a bus
   d. a forced march

98. A person who is wearing **manacles** is probably a
   a. prisoner
   b. model
   c. judge
   d. teacher

99. A study program might properly be called **intensive** if it
   a. is a lot of fun
   b. is open to everyone
   c. calls for hours of hard work
   d. will help you get a summer job

100. You will **affirm** your mastery of the words taught in this book if you
   a. spell them incorrectly
   b. forget what they mean
   c. never use them in class
   d. score 100% on this Final Test

The following tabulation lists all the basic words taught in the various units of this workbook, as well as those introduced in the *Vocabulary of Vocabulary, Working with Analogies, Building with Classical Roots,* and *Enriching Your Vocabulary* sections. Words taught in the units are printed in **boldface** type. The number following each entry indicates the page on which the word is first introduced. Exercises and review materials in which the word also appears are not cited.